Physical Basis

FOR

ELECTRICAL ENGINEERING

PRENTICE-HALL ELECTRICAL ENGINEERING SERIES

W. L. EVERITT, Ph.D., *Editor*

Physical Basis

FOR

ELECTRICAL ENGINEERING

by

THOMAS L. MARTIN Jr.

Professor of Electrical Engineering and
Head of Department, University of Arizona

Prentice-Hall, Inc., Englewood Cliffs, N. J.

Library of Congress Catalog Card Number: 57-7634

First printing . . . .*January, 1957*
Second printing . . . .*July, 1958*

PREFACE

THE PURPOSE of this book is to acquaint the reader with the general physical concepts and phenomena forming the basis for electrical engineering. Both the microscopic and macroscopic viewpoints are presented.

The book was written for engineers, and the viewpoint is that of the engineer. Physics is not engineering, but in electrical engineering the demarcation lines are often so blurred as to be meaningless. In such cases, the *material* presented to engineers and physicists may cover the same ground, but the reasons for doing so and the approaches followed are often quite different. I do not presume to speak for the physicists. However, the engineer studies physical phenomena and theories, not as ends in themselves, but with a view toward how he might apply them later to the ordinary purposes of life. He is less concerned with the historical and experimental development of an idea or theory than he is in how it may eventually be used by mankind. As a result, it is generally quite difficult to present physics in a form agreeable to both engineers and physicists. My efforts here are directed toward engineers.

The material presented in this book is a simplified presentation of well known phenomena and theories originally contributed and published by others. The purpose here is to show the broad physical basis supporting the phenomena associated with electrical engineering, to show the position of each subject in its general relation to other subjects. *Theory* and *concept* are stressed; little emphasis is placed on experimental or analytical methods. I feel that these latter aspects of the subject are presented more properly to the advanced reader.

The book can be used in a number of different ways, depending on the institution and local circumstances. There is little point in making detailed suggestions. However, for electrical engineering departments the book is suitable for either of two courses, as follows:

(1) the first course in electrical engineering;
(2) the first course in electronics.

v

Choice of chapters covered in each case will be somewhat different, of course.

Eventually, in the not so distant future, it is my belief that a course of this type, coupled with additional work in fields and circuits, will be required of *all* engineering students. To be perfectly candid, I feel that the present service course in electrical engineering, as generally constituted, is no longer in harmony with engineering curricular objectives. It is inconceivable to me that any present-day engineer could call his education complete without some exposure to material of the type contained in this book.

Professor Gilbert Mills of the Physics Department of Phoenix College kindly acted in concert with the University in first offering this course; his cooperation is gratefully acknowledged. Professors Charles R. Hausenbauer, Robert A. Manhart, and James C. Kemp of the Electrical Engineering Department of the University of Arizona taught the course with me. Their many helpful suggestions are largely responsible for the improvement over earlier mimeographed editions.

The administration of the University of Arizona has a constructive policy that encourages curricular experimentation. This book would almost certainly never have been published were it not for the liberal attitudes of John C. Park, Dean of the College of Engineering, and Dr. Richard A. Harvill, President of the University.

This work progressed through a number of different phases over a period of nearly five years before it emerged in its present form. I want to acknowledge the patience and encouragement of Dr. W. L. Everitt, Dean of the College of Engineering, University of Illinois. Finally, the tedious task of checking the manuscript for accuracy was performed by two nameless physicists. I cannot find appropriate words to express my thanks to them.

THOMAS L. MARTIN Jr.

Tucson, Arizona

CONTENTS

1

ELECTROSTATIC FIELDS
IN VACUUM

In this chapter we shall undertake a brief introductory study of the properties of electric fields in vacuum. The material presented enters into virtually every discussion of subject matter relevant to electricity and electrical engineering; it is almost impossible to over-emphasize its importance. The presentation is far from complete, however, because it is assumed that all students majoring in electrical engineering or physics will take more advanced and detailed courses in field theory later in their student careers. Other readers will find the introduction here adequate for most needs and more than adequate for the needs of later chapters.

The large scale, or *macroscopic*, viewpoint is adopted in this chapter. Later, in other chapters, we shall adopt the small scale, or *microscopic*, viewpoint. Both viewpoints are essential to a proper understanding of the characteristics of electrostatic fields and their interactions with matter in its various states. This is a departure from the classical course in field theory which largely neglects the microscopic view.

Only problems involving stationary, or *static*, charges are treated here. The case of moving charges is covered in chapter 2.

1.1. Concepts and models

According to an ancient Hindu myth[1], the earth rests upon the back of an elephant which stands upon the back of a tortoise. The

---

[1] Familiar to the author from Edward Bennett and H. M. Crothers, *Introductory Electrodynamics for Engineers*, New York: McGraw-Hill Book Co., Inc., 1926, p. 5.

1

explanation ceases at this point and no account is given concerning the support for the tortoise.

While the foregoing idea may be ridiculous, the end result is not. Any inquiry along a given path in the physical sciences ultimately concludes with a purely descriptive statement of a fact of nature. The *why* of this fact cannot be explained for want of greater information and knowledge. Clearly, the *tortoise* of the explanation has been attained. Every text book contains *tortoises* and often *elephants*, and this book is certainly no exception. However, in common with other writers, the author believes his *tortoises* are justified. There is simply not enough space to pursue every stated physical fact to the ultimate limit of human knowledge.

Much of the first four chapters uses the results of some of the higher sciences, such as quantum mechanics, and the derivation of these results could not be successfully included in this book. In such cases these results are simply given as matters susceptible to proof or justification, but otherwise taken to be necessary *tortoises* in developing the main theme of the book.

Of course, the *tortoises* of engineering and science are called *models*, *concepts*, or *theories*. These are useful schemes for organizing vast amounts of data and for explaining what happens without delving too deeply into *why* it happens. This is primarily the childhood game of *let's pretend* in which a simplified, theoretical, and physically unreal model is used to describe a reality. Some danger is involved because reality and model may become confused. For example, some people undergo strenuous emotional ordeals while watching moving pictures, projecting themselves into the flickering shadows and losing identity with their true physical reality. The engineer and scientist cannot afford this error; *the model must not be mistaken for the thing it represents.*

An engineer is mainly concerned with what things *do* and models, however flimsy, are very important to him. Sometimes the model points the way to new discoveries, while the results of new experiments may contradict the model. This is the never ending, day-to-day story of scientific progress, the testing of theories or models against the ever widening array of observed phenomena. *Tortoises* are not always welcome, but they are often necessary.

It is extremely important to understand that the data remains unchanged in most cases while the theories and models seem to be constantly changing. In other words, concentrate on the phenomena and recognize that the theory or model presented, though widely accepted now, may have to be completely revised later when new experimental evidence appears. Do not attach undue reality to word pictures.

1.2. Vectors and scalars

The various quantities encountered in physics and engineering are subdivided into two fundamentally different classes. One group of factors are called *scalars*, while the other quantities are called *vectors*. These two terms are defined as follows:

Scalar—A quantity that can be completely described by a magnitude and algebraic sign is called a *scalar*. Typical examples of scalar quantities include work, mass, time, temperature, electric charge, and so on. In written material scalars are denoted by ordinary letters such as A, B, C, or a, b, c.

Vector—A quantity is a *vector* if it requires that both *magnitude and direction* be specified. Examples of vectors include such quantities as force, displacement, velocity, acceleration, and electric field intensity. In written material vectors are denoted by bold face type as $\boldsymbol{A}$, $\boldsymbol{B}$, $\boldsymbol{C}$, or $\boldsymbol{a}$, $\boldsymbol{b}$, $\boldsymbol{c}$. A vector is represented pictorially by an arrow pointing in the proper direction and having a length proportional to the magnitude of the vector quantity. This is illustrated in figure 1.1.

Vectors and scalars appear throughout this book, so it is important that you thoroughly understand the distinctions between them.

Vectors are represented as shown in figure 1.1. This specification is complete and sufficient for many applications of vectors including the fundamental operations of vector analysis. However, in other instances it is desirable to relate the vector to some known or arbitrarily chosen reference system. In other words, it is often convenient to orient a vector in space with respect to some system of *directions* known to us.

Figure 1.1. Pictorial representation of a vector.

For example, if I say, "I moved 125 miles away," you know very little about what happened. Where did I move? What was the geographical direction of travel? However, if I say "I moved 125 miles due north of Tucson, Arizona," my position can be fixed with some degree of certainty. I have specified my starting point, or *origin*. My distance of travel (vector magnitude) and the direction in terms of the well known geographical frame of reference are both specified.

Thus, it is often helpful to express a vector in terms of *coordinates;* in such cases we describe the vector with respect to some frame of reference, or *coordinate system*, together with the *origin of coordinates*.

There are many different coordinate systems. For simplicity, our attention will be confined to *rectangular*, or *Cartesian*, coordinates.

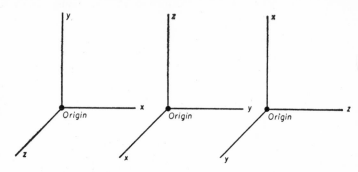

Figure 1.2. Right-handed sets of Cartesian coordinates.

Three sets of such coordinates are shown in figure 1.2. These coordinate systems divide all space into three directions parallel to one of the three coordinate axes. The common point where the axes originate is called the *origin* of coordinates.

The axes in figure 1.2 form a *right-handed set*. By this we mean that a right-hand threaded screw will advance in the positive z direction when twisted in a direction from x to y. The right-handed set is almost universally used in engineering.

Directions within the frames of reference shown in figure 1.2 are specified by *unit vectors*. There are three unit vectors, i_x, i_y, and i_z for a set of Cartesian coordinates. They are defined as vectors of unit length pointing in the x, y, and z directions as shown in figure 1.3. With these three unit vectors and our frame of reference, we can now completely specify a vector in magnitude and direction.

For example, consider the case of a vector A oriented with respect to some system of coordinates as shown in figure 1.4. The projection of the vector A onto any one of the three coordinate axes is called

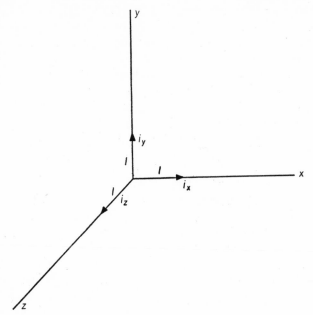

Figure 1.3. Definition of the three unit vectors i_x, i_y, i_z.

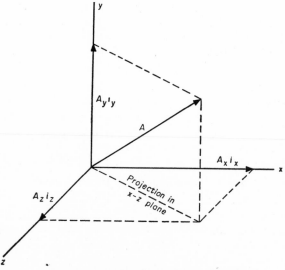

Figure 1.4. Components of the vector A.

the *component* of the vector in the direction of the axis. Hence, the projection of A on the x axis is the x component of A. It has a magnitude A_x and a direction i_x. The total description of the x component is then $A_x i_x$. The y and z components are obtained in the same way as shown in figure 1.4. Hence, the complete description of the vector A is the sum of its three components, or

$$A = A_x i_x + A_y i_y + A_z i_z \tag{1.1}$$

You should be able to prove the truth of this equation. It is a simple exercise in geometry to show that the vector magnitude is related to the magnitudes of the components by the following equation:

$$A = \sqrt{A_x^2 + A_y^2 + A_z^2} \tag{1.2}$$

The methods of manipulating vectors in some of the simpler operations are presented in the next section. It is assumed that you are already familiar with the algebraic manipulation of scalars using ordinary algebra.

1.3. Vector algebra

Naturally it is important to know what a vector is and how it is described. The information is useless, however, unless we know how to perform the simple operations of vector addition, subtraction, and multiplication.

Suppose that we want to add two vectors A and B located in space as shown in figure 1.5a. To simplify the problem it is assumed that

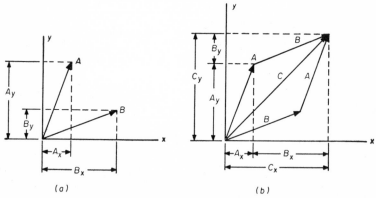

Figure 1.5. Addition of two vectors A and B to obtain the resultant sum C: (a) two vectors in space; (b) addition of two vectors.

both vectors are confined to the x–y plane so that they do not have z components. In other words,

$$A = A_x i_x + A_y i_y$$
$$B = B_x i_x + B_y i_y$$

We want to add the two vectors to obtain the *resultant* C. That is

$$C = A + B$$

This is easily done by simply joining the vectors head to tail as shown in figure 1.5b. The resultant C is the same regardless of whether we compute $A + B$ or $B + A$. Hence,

$$C = A + B = B + A \tag{1.3}$$

Moreover, it is also clear from figure 1.5b that the components of the resultant vector are

$$C_x = A_x + B_x$$
$$C_y = A_y + B_y$$

The complete description of the result is clearly

$$C = C_x i_x + C_y i_y$$
$$= (A_x + B_x)i_x + (A_y + B_y)i_y$$

If the two vectors had possessed all three components it is easily shown that

$$C = (A_x + B_x)i_x + (A_y + B_y)i_y + (A_z + B_z)i_z \tag{1.4}$$

By exactly the same procedure you can show that the resultant of *vector subtraction* is

$$C = A - B = (A_x - B_x)i_x + (A_y - B_y)i_y + (A_z - B_z)i_z \tag{1.5}$$

These two operations are fairly easily understood and fairly familiar in form and operation.

Vector multiplication is somewhat more involved. There are three types of vector multiplication, but we will consider only two types here. The two types to be covered are

(1) *scalar* or *dot product*, which is written as

$$C = A \cdot B$$

(2) *vector* or *cross product* which is written as

$$C = A \times B$$

Consider the *scalar* or *dot product* first. Two vectors A and B are shown in figure 1.6. The dot product is *defined* as the scalar quantity equal to the product of the magnitude of the vector B and the component of the vector A in the direction of B. In other words,

$$C = A \cdot B \triangleq (A\cos\theta)B = AB\cos\theta \qquad (1.6)$$

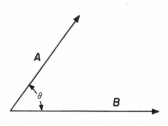

Figure 1.6. Terms involved in the product.

where A = magnitude of the vector A, B = magnitude of the vector B, θ = angle between A and B, $\triangleq$ signifies *equal by definition*.

Suppose that the two vectors can be described in the following way:

$$A = A_x i_x + A_y i_y$$
$$B = B_x i_x + B_y i_y$$

Now calculate the dot product.

$$A \cdot B = (A_x i_x + A_y i_y) \cdot (B_x i_x + B_y i_y)$$

Expand this and we obtain

$$A \cdot B = (A_x B_x)(i_x \cdot i_x) + (A_y B_y)(i_y \cdot i_y)$$
$$+ (A_x B_y)(i_x \cdot i_y) + (A_y B_x)(i_y \cdot i_x)$$

Observe that the dot product of the unit vectors i_x and i_y occurs in various different combinations. From the definition of the unit vectors it is apparent that $\theta = 90°$ between i_x and i_y, whereas it is $0°$ between i_x and i_x, or i_y and i_y. Hence,

$$i_x \cdot i_x = (1)(1)\cos 0° = 1$$
$$i_y \cdot i_y = (1)(1)\cos 0° = 1$$
$$i_x \cdot i_y = (1)(1)\cos 90° = 0$$
$$i_y \cdot i_x = (1)(1)\cos 90° = 0$$

Substitute these relationships into the preceding equation and the result is

$$C = A \cdot B = A_x B_x + A_y B_y$$

If the two vectors have three components apiece, you can use the same method to show that

$$C = A \cdot B = A_x B_x + A_y B_y + A_z B_z \qquad (1.7)$$

Equations (1.6) and (1.7) are used to calculate the scalar or dot product of two vectors.

The *vector* or *cross product* is defined somewhat differently and has an entirely different meaning. The *cross product* is *defined* as a *vector* having a magnitude equal to the area of the parallelogram formed by **A** and **B** as sides and directed perpendicular to the plane of **A** and **B** in accordance with the definition of a right hand set. So, the direc-

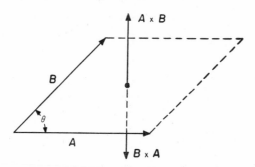

Figure 1.7. Illustration of the cross product.

tion of the product is the direction of advance of a right-hand threaded screw when turned from **A** into **B**. This definition is illustrated in figure 1.7. Please note that

$$A \times B = -B \times A \tag{1.8}$$

The area of the parallelogram, which is the magnitude of the vector product, is

$$C = AB \sin \theta \tag{1.9}$$

It is useful to apply the definition of the vector product to the various products possible between the unit vectors. In every case of dissimilar unit vectors, θ is either 90° or 270°. Hence, the following identities are easily established:

$$i_x \times i_y = (1)(1)i_z \sin\ 90° = +i_z \tag{1.10}$$
$$i_y \times i_x = (1)(1)i_z \sin 270° = -i_z \tag{1.11}$$
$$i_x \times i_z = (1)(1)i_y \sin 270° = -i_y \tag{1.12}$$
$$i_z \times i_x = (1)(1)i_y \sin\ 90° = +i_y \tag{1.13}$$
$$i_y \times i_z = (1)(1)i_x \sin\ 90° = +i_x \tag{1.14}$$
$$i_z \times i_y = (1)(1)i_x \sin 270° = -i_x \tag{1.15}$$
$$i_x \times i_x = i_y \times i_y = i_z \times i_z = (1)(1) \sin 0° = 0 \tag{1.16}$$

You should go over these relationships very carefully so that you fully understand the character of the cross product.

Suppose that the two vectors to be multiplied each have two components in the x and y directions. This gives

$$C = A \times B = (A_x i_x + A_y i_y) \times (B_x i_x + B_y i_y)$$

Expand the right-hand side of this equation to obtain

$$C = (A_x B_x)(i_x \times i_x) + (A_y B_y)(i_y \times i_y)$$
$$+ (A_x B_y)(i_x \times i_y) + (A_y B_x)(i_y \times i_x)$$

The values for the cross products of the unit vectors are available in equations (1.10) through (1.16). Substitute the proper values and the result is

$$C = (A_x B_y)i_z - (A_y B_x)i_z$$
$$= (A_x B_y - A_y B_x)i_z$$

If the two vectors each have three components, the same method can be used to show that

$$A \times B = (A_x B_y - A_y B_x)i_z + (A_z B_x - A_x B_z)i_y$$
$$+ (A_y B_z - A_z B_y)i_x \tag{1.17}$$

Equation (1.17) is very helpful. However, for most of our purposes the most important thing is to understand the definition of the cross product.

This concludes the discussion of the mathematics required in this book. From this point on we deal primarily with physical concepts that, at times, require an understanding of vectors and vector algebra.

1.4. Electric charge

Suppose that a glass rod is rubbed with a piece of silk. When the rod is passed near light bodies such as lint, hair, or bits of tissue, these small bodies are attracted to the rod, cling to it for a moment, and then are repelled. This phenomenon was observed with amber as early as about 600 B.C. In about 1570, Gilbert coined the words *electrify* and *electrification* to describe the action and effect produced when a glass rod is rubbed with a silken cloth.

If two glass rods are rubbed with silk and then placed near one another, it is observed that there is a force between the two rods acting to push them apart. In a similar way, two rubber rods rubbed with wool will repel one another when placed close together. However, if a *glass* rod is brought close to a rubber rod after both have been electrified, a force appears acting to pull the rods together. *All* other electrified materials can be compared to the glass and rubber rods. From this it appears that there are only two kinds of electrification, or putting it another way, there are only two kinds of electricity. If there is a third kind of electricity, it has not yet been observed.

It was Benjamin Franklin in 1747 who introduced the idea of *positive* (+) and *negative* (−) electricity. The choice is perfectly arbitrary, simply providing a convenient way of distinguishing between the two types of electricity. Positive and negative electricity are defined in terms of the electrified glass and rubber rods as follows:

(1) Those electrified bodies that repel electrified glass rods are said to be charged with positive (+) electricity.

(2) Those electrified bodies that repel electrified rubber rods are said to be charged with negative (−) electricity.

As you can see, there is nothing significant about positive and negative electricity except that they are different. Years of usage has simply established this choice as the universal convention.

The *quantity of electricity* contained within an electrified or charged body is denoted by the symbol q. The engineering units of electrical charge are *coulombs*. That is,

$$q = \text{electrical charge in coulombs}$$

Electrical charge can be either positive or negative, but it is a scalar quantity because it does not require direction for its complete description.

1.5. Elementary charged particles

Thus far we have discussed electric charge as something acquired by various materials as a result of rubbing with some other material. This is a man-made state of electrification. Experiments reveal the existence of particles present in nature that carry their own electric charge. The term *particle* is used here for want of a better term. We shall see later that the true nature of these *particles* is not yet known.

One of the elementary charged particles is the negatively charged *electron*. It has the following constants:

$$e = \text{electronic charge} = -1.602 \times 10^{-19} \text{ coulomb}$$
$$m = \text{electron mass} = 9.107 \times 10^{-31} \text{ kg}$$

The *positron* is another such particle. It has the same mass and charge as an electron, except that the charge is positive. A rather different particle is the *proton*. It carries a positive charge numerically equal to the electron charge, but it has a mass that is about 1836 times the mass of the electron.

There are a number of other charged particles occurring in nature, either naturally or artificially, but the electron and proton are the most important to electrical engineers.

Within the limits of all observations made to date, it appears that all electric charge is an integral multiple of the charge on an electron; a fractional electronic charge has never been observed. Hence, the electron is taken to be a fundamental particle in the study of electrical engineering and its physical basis.

1.6. Coulomb's experiments

Coulomb made extensive studies of the forces between charged bodies. Although his work was done in 1785, it has been confirmed to very high precision by measurements in recent years. Coulomb found that when the distances between charged bodies are very much larger than the sizes of the charged bodies, the following observations are true:

(1) Charges of the same sign experience a force of repulsion; charges of opposite sign experience a force of attraction.

(2) The magnitude of the force is directly proportional to the product of the electric charges.

(3) The magnitude of the force is inversely proportional to the square of the distance between charges.

(4) The direction of the force is along a straight line joining the two charges.

The terms involved in these observations are shown in figure 1.8.

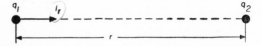

Figure 1.8. Terms involved in Coulomb's Law.

These observations can be stated mathematically as follows:

$$F \sim \frac{q_1 q_2}{r^2} \, i_r$$

The proportionality can be changed to an equation by introducing a constant of proportionality. This constant depends upon the system of units to be used and upon the properties of the medium separating the two charges. We shall assume the medium is vacuum. We shall follow engineering practice and use *rationalized MKSC* units. Hence,

$$F = \frac{q_1 q_2}{4\pi \epsilon_0 r^2} \, i_r \tag{1.18}$$

This is called *Coulomb's Law*. Terms in this equation are defined as follows: F = vector force in newtons, q_1 = charge in coulombs on one body, q_2 = charge in coulombs on the other body, r = distance between charges in meters, ϵ_0 = proportionality constant = 8.854×10^{-12} farad/meter for vacuum. The ϵ_0 factor is defined as the *dielectric constant* of vacuum. Its unit, *farad/meter*, will be explained in more detail in a later chapter.

Coulomb's Law is of tremendous importance to engineers and physicists. It tells *what* happens without providing any explanation of *why* it happens. In section 1.8 a theory is postulated to explain how and why electrical charges exert forces on one another.

1.7. The electric dipole

The case of two equal charges of opposite sign is important enough by itself to warrant special consideration. At the same time it illustrates the method used to calculate the total net force on some charge produced by several other charges.

An *electric dipole* consists of two equal charges of opposite sign separated by a distance d. This is shown in figure 1.9. We are going to calculate the total force produced by this dipole on a *test* charge q_2. For convenience we will assume the test charge to be located on the extended axis of the dipole as shown in figure 1.9.

The positive charge, $+q_1$, will exert a force on the test charge, q_2, that can be calculated from Coulomb's Law. If the test charge is assumed to be positive, this force will be directed to the right in figure 1.9. Hence, this force is

$$F_2 = \frac{q_1 q_2}{4\pi\epsilon_0 (r + d/2)^2} \, i_r$$

The negative charge, $-q_1$, also exerts a force on q_2, but this is directed to the left, or in the negative i_r direction. Hence,

$$F_1 = -\frac{q_1 q_2}{4\pi\epsilon_0 (r - d/2)^2} \, i_r$$

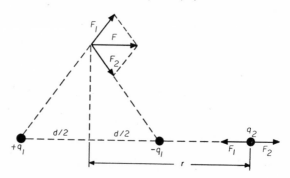

Figure 1.9. Force exerted on a test charge at either of two points by an electric dipole.

The total force on the test charge is the vector sum of the individual forces, or

$$F = F_1 + F_2$$

This yields

$$F = \frac{q_1 q_2}{4\pi\epsilon_0} \left[\frac{1}{(r + d/2)^2} - \frac{1}{(r - d/2)^2} \right] i_r$$

Use ordinary algebra to simplify this equation. Obtain the common denominator; expand the resulting numerator and cancel appropriate terms. The result is

$$F = -\frac{q_1 q_2}{4\pi\epsilon_0} \left[\frac{2rd}{(r^2 - d^2/4)^2} \right] i_r$$

Now *assume* that the distance d between the dipole charges is very small compared to the distance r to the test charge. This makes $d/2$ negligibly small compared to r and the force on the test charge reduces to

$$F \doteq -\frac{q_2}{4\pi\epsilon_0} \left[\frac{2q_1 d}{r^3} \right] i_r$$

The equal sign with the dot over it signifies *approximate equality.*

The product of the dipole charge and the distance between the dipole charges is *defined* as the *electric moment p* of the dipole. That is,

$$p \stackrel{\Delta}{=} q_1 d = q_1 d i_r \qquad (1.19)$$

Hence, the force exerted by the dipole on the test charge in the specified position is

$$F \doteq -\frac{q_2}{4\pi\epsilon_0}\left(\frac{2p}{r^3}\right) i_r$$

The same technique can be used to calculate the force on a test charge at any other point in the neighborhood of the dipole. The method is unchanged, but the details of the calculation become more involved because the forces on the test charge are no longer in direct alignment. Thus, the calculation of the total force requires a true vector addition of the two forces. For example, the force relationships when the test charge is on a line midway between the dipole charges is shown in figure 1.9. This sketch indicates the character of the problem involved. In this particular case you can prove that

$$F \doteq \left(\frac{q_2}{4\pi\epsilon_0}\right)\frac{p}{r^3} i_x \qquad (1.20)$$

where i_x = unit vector along the dipole axis. This derivation can be systematized by defining a coordinate system with q_2 at the origin, the x axis parallel to the dipole axis and the y coordinate perpendicular to the dipole axis.

1.8. The concept of flux

Coulomb's experiments clearly established the existence of forces between charged bodies. These forces exist even when there is no material connection between the charges. No one knows *why* this is so—it is so and we accept it as a fundamental fact of nature.

A single charged body is shown in figure 1.10. Assume that it carries a positive charge of q_1 coulombs. Suppose we place a second charge q_2 at various points in the region surrounding q_1. The force exerted on this second charge by the source charge q_1 can be calculated from Coulomb's Law. In all cases, the force vectors are along outward-directed radial lines, assuming q_2 is a positive charge.

For the moment, suppose that we are interested only in the *direction* of the force exerted on q_2 by q_1. We are not concerned with the magnitude. If the source charge is positive, the directions associated with forces on a positive test charge would be as shown in figure 1.10. Of course, we could draw an infinite number of these lines, but the general problem of indicating force direction is solved by using some definite number of lines as shown in figure 1.10. For convenience, let the number of lines drawn be proportional to the source charge q_1. Hence, if we double q_1, we double the number of lines drawn.

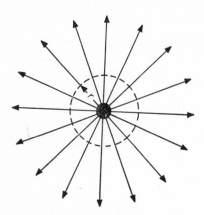

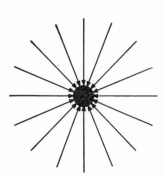

Figure 1.10. Electric flux about a positive charge q_1.

Figure 1.11. Flux lines about a negative charge.

These lines, which represent the direction of force on a positive test charge, are called *lines of flux*, or *flux lines*. Each line represents a certain amount of flux and the total amount of flux is equal to the charge q_1. That is, let

$$\psi_1 = \text{electric flux of } q_1$$

then $$\psi_1 = q_1 \qquad (1.21)$$

Now return to the question of the force *magnitude*. Suppose a test charge q_2 is located r meters from q_1. In the region of q_2 we assume that there are D lines of flux per square meter. That is,

$$D = \text{electric flux density}$$

If we double q_1, the number of flux lines in any region doubles, thereby doubling D. The force on q_2 also doubles. It appears that the force on the test charge is proportional to the density of the flux lines in the region of q_2.

We can test the validity of this last assertion. Draw a spherical surface of radius r about q_1. The area of this surface is

$$A = 4\pi r^2$$

The total flux associated with q_1 is

$$\psi_1 = q_1$$

Hence, the flux density at any point on the surface of the sphere is

$$D = \frac{\psi_1}{A} = \frac{q_1}{4\pi r^2} \tag{1.22}$$

If the force is proportional to the flux density, then

$$F \sim D$$

or

$$F \sim \frac{q_1}{4\pi r^2} \tag{1.23}$$

This last proportionality is indeed true as a comparison with Coulomb's Law will reveal.

It now becomes convenient to assign a synthetic *reality* to the flux lines. Although they are a creation of the mind only and do not exist physically, it is convenient to assume that flux lines do exist and to use them to describe the regions about charged bodies. Thus, we assume the following statements are true:

(1) Charged bodies are the sources of lines of electric flux. (a) Flux lines emanate from bodies carrying positive charge. (b) Flux lines terminate on bodies carrying negative charge as in figure 1.11.

(2) The flux lines are directed parallel to the force exerted on a positive test charge.

(3) The total number of flux lines associated with a charged body is proportional to the charge.

(4) The force exerted on a test charge is proportional to the flux density and the test charge.

The flux lines are used to represent systematically the flux about a charged body. The flux and the charge are really just two different ways of describing the same phenomenon. The charge q describes the properties at a point. The flux and flux density describe the properties some distance away from the point occupied by q. Thus, ψ and q are just different manifestations of the same physical quantity, so $\psi = q$. In vector notation we have[2]

---

[2] Area is a vector. The vector direction is perpendicular to the plane of area.

$$\psi = \boldsymbol{D} \cdot \boldsymbol{A} = q \qquad (1.24)$$

or $\qquad \psi = DA \cos \theta$

$\qquad \theta = $ angle between $\boldsymbol{D}$ and $\boldsymbol{A}$

1.9. Gauss's Law

A more sophisticated analysis can be used to obtain equation (1.24)

Figure 1.12. An irregular surface enclosing a charge q.

in a more elegant form. Consider the case shown in figure 1.12. Here we have some charge contained within a closed surface of perfectly arbitrary size and shape. The charge q contained emanates flux lines that cross this surface. The total flux is denoted by ψ.

Now consider a very small area **da** as shown in figure 1.12. A certain number of flux lines cross this small area producing a flux density

$\boldsymbol{D}$. Hence, from equation (1.24) we can write

$$\boldsymbol{D} \cdot \boldsymbol{da} = d\psi$$

To compute the total flux emanating from the charges enclosed by the surface, it is necessary to sum up the fluxes crossing every little elementary area **da** on the surface. That is,

$$\Sigma \, \boldsymbol{D} \cdot \boldsymbol{da} = \psi \text{ (over whole surface)}$$

In the limit, as **da** becomes differentially small, the summation becomes an integration over the entire closed surface. That is,

$$\oint_s \boldsymbol{D} \cdot \boldsymbol{da} = \psi \qquad (1.25)$$

The circled integral sign with a subscript s denotes *surface integration over a closed surface*. The flux and charge are numerically equal so that

$$\psi = q$$

and so $\qquad \oint_s \boldsymbol{D} \cdot \boldsymbol{da} = q \qquad (1.26)$

where $q = $ total charge contained within the closed surface. This equation, which is the desired result, shows that the integral of the perpendicular component of the flux density over any closed surface is equal to the charge contained within that surface. In scalar form we can write

$$\oint_s D \cos \theta \, da = q$$

where θ = angle between D and da.

This can be extended to an even more general case. Suppose that the charge enclosed by the surface is distributed throughout the enclosed volume. Let

ρ = charge density within the enclosing surface

Hence,

$$q = \int_{\text{vol.}} \rho \, dv \tag{1.27}$$

In other words, the total charge in the volume is equal to the volume integral of the charge density. Now combine equations (1.26) and (1.27) and the result is

$$\oint_s D \cdot da = \int_{\text{vol.}} \rho \, dv \tag{1.28}$$

Equations (1.26) and (1.28) are frequently called Gauss's Law. According to Gauss's Law, the surface integral of the flux density over a closed surface is equal to the volume integral of the charge density contained within that surface. This is, of course, a more general and elegant way of saying that $\psi = q$.

1.10. Coulomb's Law and field intensity

In the basic assumption in which electric flux was defined, it was stated that the flux exerts a force on any other charge; the force is proportional to the flux density and to the test charge. That is,

$$F \sim q_2 D$$

where F = force in newtons, q_2 = charge in coulombs on the test charge, D = electric flux density in coulombs per square meter. This proportionality is converted into an equality by inserting a function of proportionality. Let

$$\frac{1}{\epsilon_0} = \text{function of proportionality}$$

so that the equation for the force on the test charge is

$$F = \frac{q_2 D}{\epsilon_0} \qquad (1.29)$$

We can use equation (1.29) to compute the force exerted on q_2 when the flux density D originates from another small charged body q_1. The flux density at any point about a small charged body was derived previously and given in equation (1.22) as

$$D = \frac{q_1}{4\pi r^2} i_r$$

where the unit vector i_r has been inserted to show that the direction of the flux density is radially outward from the assumed positive source charge. Substitute this into equation (1.29) and the equation for the force on q_2 is

$$F = \frac{q_1 q_2}{4\pi \epsilon_0 r^2} i_r$$

This is exactly the same as Coulomb's Law. Coulomb obtained this result by experiment. We derived it from the assumed character of the flux. Thus, our theory provides calculated results that agree with experiments and we conclude that it is a satisfactory theory, for the present anyway.

The general form of Coulomb's Law is actually that given in equation (1.29) as

$$F = \frac{q_2 D}{\epsilon_0}$$

Divide both sides through by q_2, the magnitude of the test charge. Hence,

$$\frac{F}{q_2} = \frac{D}{\epsilon_0}$$

The factor on the left, which is the *force per unit positive test charge*, is defined as the *electric field intensity* E. That is,

$$E = \text{electric field intensity} = \frac{F}{q_2} \qquad (1.30)$$

This is a vector having the same direction as the force exerted by the flux on a positive charge.

Now substitute equation (1.30) into the preceding equation and the result is

$$E = \frac{D}{\epsilon_0} \tag{1.31}$$

or

$$D = \epsilon_0 E \tag{1.32}$$

This is a very compact expression of Coulomb's Law.

The units associated with electric field intensity are easily determined from equation (1.30) to be *newtons/coulomb*. A more common unit is defined in a later section.

Gauss's Law can be rewritten now in a more common form. According to equation (1.26)

$$\oint_s D \cdot da = q = \int_{\text{vol.}} \rho \, dv$$

Substitute equation (1.32) and we have

$$\oint_s E \cdot da = \frac{q}{\epsilon_0} = \int_{\text{vol.}} \frac{\rho}{\epsilon_0} \, dv \tag{1.33}$$

1.11. Calculation of field intensity

Electric field intensity was defined in the preceding section as the force per unit positive test charge. Thus, the field intensity is easily calculated for a few special cases.

Consider the case of a source charge q_1 exerting a force on a positive test charge q_2. According to Coulomb's Law the force is

$$F = \frac{q_1 q_2}{4\pi\epsilon_0 r^2} i_r$$

Therefore, the electric field intensity produced by q_1 at the point occupied by q_2 is

$$E = \frac{F}{q_2} = \frac{q_1}{4\pi\epsilon_0 r^2} i_r \tag{1.34}$$

The field intensity has the same direction as the force on the *positive* test charge q_2. The electric flux density at this same point is readily obtained because

$$D = \epsilon_0 E = \frac{q_1}{4\pi r^2} i_r \tag{1.35}$$

Similar calculations can be made for the case of the electric dipole. It was shown in section 1.7 that an electric dipole exerts a force on a positive test charge q_2 located on the extended axis of the dipole.

This force was shown to be approximately, for the case in figure 1.9,

$$F \doteq -\frac{q_2}{4\pi\epsilon_0}\left(\frac{2p}{r^3}\right)i_r \qquad (1.36)$$

where $p = q_1 d$ = electric moment of the dipole. Hence, the electric field intensity at the point occupied by the test charge q_2 is

$$E = \frac{F}{q_2} \doteq \frac{2p}{4\pi\epsilon_0 r^3}i_r \qquad (1.37)$$

and the flux density at this same point is

$$D \doteq \frac{2p}{4\pi r^3}i_r \qquad (1.38)$$

Similar cases are computed in the same way.

1.12. Application of Gauss's Law

One method of calculating electric field intensity was illustrated in the preceding section. It is a perfectly satisfactory way to calculate field intensity for cases involving various geometric arrangements of point charges. Such cases do occur in practice, but they are less common than those problems involving continuous distributions of charge. In these cases it is more convenient to use Gauss's Law.

Gauss's Law from equation (1.33) is

$$\oint_s E \cdot da = \frac{q}{\epsilon_0}$$

or

$$\oint_s D \cdot da = q$$

We will now apply this equation to a particular problem to illustrate its use.

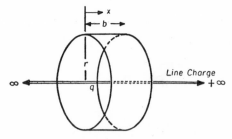

Figure 1.13. Calculation of field intensity using Gauss's Law.

Suppose we have a continuous *line* of charge extending to infinity in both directions as shown in figure 1.13. Let q = charge per unit length. The lines of flux from the charge on a unit length emanate radially outward from the line charge. The problem is to calculate the electric field intensity created by this flux r meters radially out from the line charge.

At a distance r meters out from the line charge construct a surface concentric about the line charge as shown in figure 1.13. The flux lines emanating from the line charge intersect this surface at right angles. Therefore,

$$da = (2\pi r)\, dx\, i_r$$

The charge on a length dx is

$$dq' = q\, dx$$

Over a length b the charge is

$$q' = qb$$

Hence, using Gauss's Law,

$$\oint_s \boldsymbol{D} \cdot \boldsymbol{da} = \int_0^b D(2\pi r)\, dx = qb$$

or

$$2\pi r D = q$$

and therefore,

$$D = \frac{q}{2\pi r} \tag{1.39}$$

Hence, the magnitude of the electric field intensity is

$$E = \frac{q}{2\pi \epsilon_0 r} \tag{1.40}$$

This indicates, in a general, the use of Gauss's Law. It is ideally suited to calculations where geometric symmetry of continuous charge distributions is involved.

1.13. Electric potential

The flux emanating from a positive source charge q_1 extends to infinity in all directions as shown in figure 1.14. Through the action of this flux, q_1 exerts a force on any other test charge q_2 located in space. For the sake of discussion, assume the test charge is positive.

If the test charge q_2 is located at infinity the force exerted by q_1 is zero. As q_2 moves in closer to q_1, work must be done on q_2 to move it against the force of repulsion that develops at all points except

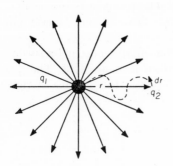

infinity. The total work done in moving the test charge from infinity to any point r meters distant from q_1 is the *potential energy* of q_2 in the flux of q_1.

In moving q_2 a differential distance dr, a differential amount of work is done against the Coulomb force of repulsion F. That is,

$$dW = -F \cdot dr \text{ newton-meters} \quad (1.41)$$

Figure 1.14. Calculation of electric potential.

Work, W, or energy, is a scalar quantity while force and displacement are vectors. In the rationalized MKSC system of units, force is expressed in *newtons* and displacement is in *meters*. The unit of work or energy is the *newton-meter*. *Newton-meter* is dignified by the name *joule*. That is,

$$1 \text{ newton-meter} = 1 \text{ joule}$$

The minus sign in equation (1.41) arises from the assumption that q_2 is moved from a point quite distant from q_1 to another point less distant. However, the positive direction associated with the distance r is *from* q_1, outward; q_2 is assumed to move *toward* q_1, inward. Therefore, dr is negative because q_2 is moved in the negative r direction. The *dot product* arises from the fact that work is done only when the displacement has a component in the direction of the force.

The potential energy of q_2 at any point r is readily determined from equation (1.41). Simply integrate the equation from

$$r = \infty \quad \text{where} \quad W = 0$$
$$r = r \quad \text{where} \quad W = W$$

Hence,

$$\int_0^W dW = -\int_\infty^r F \cdot dr \quad (1.42)$$

or

$$W = -\int_\infty^r F \cdot dr \quad (1.43)$$

This is the general equation for potential energy in a field of force of the type produced by electric charges.

Now divide both sides of equation (1.43) through by the charge q_2 to obtain

$$\frac{W}{q_2} = -\int_\infty^r \frac{F}{q_2} \cdot dr$$

However, the force per unit positive test charge was defined earlier as the electric field intensity E. That is,

$$E = \frac{F}{q_2}$$

Moreover, we now *define* the work per unit positive charge as the *electric potential* V. Hence,

$$V \triangleq \frac{W}{q_2} \triangleq \text{electric potential} \qquad (1.44)$$

Equation 1.43 can now be written as

$$V = -\int_\infty^r E \cdot dr \quad \text{joules/coulomb} \qquad (1.45)$$

The units of electric potential are *joules/coulomb*. A new unit is defined for electric potential as follows:

$$1 \text{ joule/coulomb} = 1 \text{ volt} \qquad (1.46)$$

It is particularly important to observe that both the electric potential V and potential energy W are completely independent of the path followed by the test charge in moving from infinity to the point r. This is clear because of the presence of the dot product.

The relationships here are readily illustrated by a simple example. We shall calculate the electric potential and potential energy a distance r from a point charge q_1. Let q_2 denote the test charge. The force between charges is

$$F = \frac{q_1 q_2}{4\pi\epsilon_0 r^2} i_r$$

Hence, the potential energy of q_2 is

$$W = -\int_\infty^r \left(\frac{q_1 q_2}{4\pi\epsilon_0 r^2}\right) i_r \cdot dr$$

However, i_r and dr are in the same direction so

$$i_r \cdot dr = (1)dr \cos 0° = dr$$

and the equation for the potential energy is

$$W = -\int_\infty^r \frac{q_1 q_2}{4\pi\epsilon_0 r^2} dr$$

Integrate, substitute limits, and the result is

$$W = \frac{q_1 q_2}{4\pi\epsilon_0 r} \quad \text{joules} \tag{1.47}$$

This is the potential energy of q_2 in the flux of the point charge q_1. The electric potential at the point occupied by q_2 is

$$V = \frac{W}{q_2} = \frac{q_1}{4\pi\epsilon_0 r} \quad \text{volts} \tag{1.48}$$

According to this equation the potential has the same value at every point on the surface of a sphere of radius r drawn about the source charge. This is called an *equipotential surface*. Of course, the point charge is a very special case, but equipotential surfaces or lines are always produced, even though they become quite involved in many cases.

The idea of *potential difference* is extremely important. For example, suppose that the potentials at two different points in space are computed from equation (1.45). Let V_a = potential at point a in volts, V_b = potential at point b in volts. The *difference in potential* between points a and b is then $(V_a - V_b)$ volts. This is exactly equal to the work done in moving a unit positive test charge from b to a, or

$$V_{ab} = V_a - V_b = -\int_b^a E \cdot d\mathbf{r} = -\int_b^a \frac{F}{q_2} \cdot d\mathbf{r} \tag{1.49}$$

If it is necessary to supply energy to a positive test charge to move it from b to a, the potential of point a is *positive with respect to* the potential of point b. Conversely, the potential at point b is *negative with respect to* the potential at point a. When this condition exists, V_{ab} is a *voltage rise* while V_{ba} is a *voltage drop*. This is shown in figure 1.15.

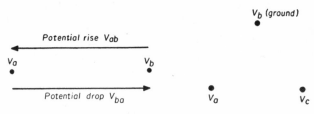

Figure 1.15. Potential difference; $V_a > V_b$.

Figure 1.16. Potential difference.

When electrical engineers speak of *voltage* they nearly always mean *potential difference*. The use of the words *positive* and *negative voltage* implies that the potential of the point in question is positive or negative *with respect to* some reference potential called *ground*. For example, consider the three points shown in figure 1.16. All three points have potentials designated as V_a, V_b, and V_c with respect to infinity. However, infinity is hard to reach and in most engineering problems interest centers mainly upon the relative potentials, or potential differences between points. In this case we arbitrarily decide to measure all potentials relative to the potential of point b. Thus, b is called the *ground*, where this simply means *reference point*. Thus, the potential of point a with respect to b is $(V_a - V_b)$. The potential of c with respect to b is $(V_c - V_b)$. It should be clear that these potential differences could be either positive or negative depending upon the relative values of V_a, V_b, and V_c. Thus, the *voltage difference* could be either positive or negative.

1.14. Potential gradient

A *gradient* is the rate of change of some scalar quantity in some direction. The gradient is, therefore, the directional derivative of the scalar; gradient is a vector. A simple example should clarify this idea.

A small hill or mountain is shown diagrammatically in figure 1.17. Lines of equal height appearing on the side view are the *contour* lines used to describe the hill in the top view. The contour lines are merely

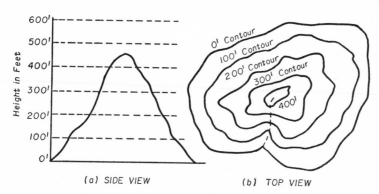

Figure 1.17. Representation of a hill by contour lines. The contour lines all represent lines of constant height.

lines representing equal height. At every point on any one contour, the height above the base of the hill is the same. Height is a scalar quantity.

Now suppose that a round ball is released at the very top of the hill. It will roll down the side of the hill in the direction of the steepest slope as shown by the dotted lines in figure 1.17b. The path will always be perpendicular to the contour lines. The steepest slope is the *gradient* of the height of the hill at any particular point.

Now consider the case of an electric potential field. Like the height of the hill, electric potential is a scalar. A representative electric field is shown in figure 1.18 by means of a series of equipotential lines.

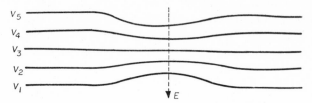

Figure 1.18. Equipotential lines of an electric field.

These correspond to the contour lines in figure 1.17. The gradient is the directional derivative of the electric potential. Hence, in rectangular coordinates,

$$\text{gradient } V \triangleq i_x \frac{\partial V}{\partial x} + i_y \frac{\partial V}{\partial y} + i_z \frac{\partial V}{\partial z} \tag{1.50}$$

where i_x, i_y, and i_z are unit vectors in the x, y, and z directions. It is clear from equation 1.50 that the gradient is a vector quantity.

Equation (1.50) can be written in a more sophisticated form more suitable to vector analysis. We simply define a new term called *del*, the *differential vector operator*. That is, let

$$\nabla \triangleq \text{del} \triangleq i_x \frac{\partial}{\partial x} + i_y \frac{\partial}{\partial y} + i_z \frac{\partial}{\partial z} \tag{1.51}$$

Consequently, equation (1.50) can be written in short hand form as

$$\text{gradient } V = \nabla V \tag{1.52}$$

Any differentially short distance dr located in the scalar potential field of figure 1.18 can be expressed in terms of unit vectors as follows:

$$dr = i_x \, dx + i_y \, dy + i_z \, dz \tag{1.53}$$

Now take the dot product of this vector and the gradient of the potential. This yields

(gradient V) $\cdot$ dr

$$= \left(i_x \frac{\partial V}{\partial x} + i_y \frac{\partial V}{\partial y} + i_z \frac{\partial V}{\partial z} \right) \cdot (i_x\, dx + i_y\, dy + i_z\, dz)$$

Hence,

$$\text{(gradient } V) \cdot dr = \frac{\partial V}{\partial x}\, dx + \frac{\partial V}{\partial y}\, dy + \frac{\partial V}{\partial z}\, dz \qquad (1.54)$$

The factor on the right-hand side of equation (1.54) is the total differential of the potential. That is,

$$\text{(gradient } V) \cdot dr = dV \qquad (1.55)$$

According to equation (1.41), a differential amount of work dW is done in moving a charge a distance dr against a force F. Hence,

$$dW = -F \cdot dr$$

Divide both sides through by the charge q. This yields

$$dV = -E \cdot dr \qquad (1.56)$$

Now set equation (1.56) equal to (1.55) and we have

$$E = -(\text{gradient } V) = -\nabla V \qquad (1.57)$$

In Cartesian coordinates this equation appears as

$$E = -\left(i_x \frac{\partial V}{\partial x} + i_y \frac{\partial V}{\partial y} + i_z \frac{\partial V}{\partial z} \right) \qquad (1.58)$$

This states that the electric field intensity is the negative gradient of the scalar electric potential. This is the desired result.

Because the potential V is expressed in volts and x, y, and z are in meters, the units for electric field intensity are *volts/meter*.

The lines of electric field intensity are always perpendicular to the equipotential lines as shown in figure 1.18.

Equation (1.57) is useful because it permits the electric field intensity to be calculated by differentiating the scalar electric potential. This is often much easier than using vector integration and Gauss's Law. For example, the potential at any point r about a point charge q_1 was given in equation (1.48) as

$$V = \frac{q_1}{4\pi\epsilon_0 r}$$

Hence, the electric field intensity at this point is

$$E = -i_r \frac{dV}{dr} = -i_r \frac{d}{dr}\left(\frac{q_1}{4\pi\epsilon_0 r}\right)$$

or
$$E = \frac{q_1}{4\pi\epsilon_0 r^2} i_r$$

This agrees with the results calculated by other methods.

1.15. Divergence theorem

Consider some region in space containing free electric charge. Suppose that we use some method to establish an electric flux of density D in this region. Now consider a very small cubical volume located at some point in this region. This is illustrated in figure 1.19.

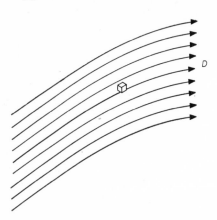

The cube is shown in an enlarged view in figure 1.20. It is assumed that the volume enclosed by the cube is so small that the density of charge, ρ, is constant throughout the volume. The total charge enclosed by this differentially small volume is

Figure 1.19. Electric flux in a region containing electric charge.

$$dq = \rho \text{ (differential volume)}$$
$$= \rho \, dx \, dy \, dz$$

The electric flux density vector D has been resolved into three components in figure 1.20. Each component is perpendicular to one of the cube faces and is in the positive x, y, or z direction.

The cubical volume contains electric charge. Hence, flux originates within this volume. This additional flux may add to that produced externally or it may subtract from it. At any rate, it will cause the flux leaving one face of the cube to be different from that entering the opposing face.

For example, consider the x component of the flux density. This is denoted as D_x in figure 1.20 and it is perpendicular to the left-hand $dy\,dz$ face of the cube. The flux in the x direction leaving the opposing right-hand cube face is

$$D'_x = D_x + \Delta D_x$$

where ΔD_x = change in the magnitude of the x component of the flux density caused by charges within the volume. If this flux density is changing at a rate dD_x/dx as it goes through the cube, then

$$\Delta D_x = \frac{dD_x}{dx}\,dx$$

and so $\quad D'_x = D_x + \dfrac{dD_x}{dx}\,dx$

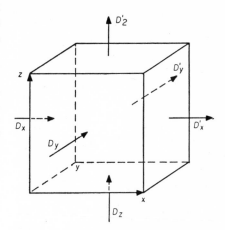

Figure 1.20. Enlargement of the cube shown in figure 1.19.

This is the x-directed component of the flux density leaving the right-hand face of the cube in figure 1.20. The flux in the x direction is the flux density times the area perpendicular to D_x and D'_x. Hence,

$$\psi_x = D_x\,dy\,dz$$

$$\psi'_x = \left(D_x + \frac{dD_x}{dx}\,dx \right) dy\,dz$$

The *net* flux in the x direction is the difference between ψ'_x and ψ_x, or

$$d\psi_x = \frac{dD_x}{dx}\,dx\,dy\,dz$$

The same technique can be applied to the other two components of flux density, yielding

$$d\psi_y = \frac{dD_y}{dy}\,dx\,dy\,dz$$

$$d\psi_z = \frac{dDz}{dz}\,dx\,dy\,dz$$

Thus, the total flux originating within the small cubical volume is

$$d\psi = d\psi_x + d\psi_y + d\psi_z$$

so
$$d\psi = \left(\frac{dD_x}{dx} + \frac{dD_y}{dy} + \frac{dD_z}{dz}\right)(dx\,dy\,dz)$$

However, the second bracketed term in the preceding equation is the volume of the small cube. That is, volume = $dx\,dy\,dz$. Also, the total charge contained within the cubical volume is equal to the flux originating from the cube. That is, $dq = d\psi$. The charge density within the small volume is the total charge divided by the volume. That is,

$$\rho = \frac{d\psi}{dx\,dy\,dz} = \frac{dq}{dx\,dy\,dz}$$

Substitute this relationship back into the equation for the differential flux emanating from the small volume and the result is

$$\frac{dD_x}{dx} + \frac{dD_y}{dy} + \frac{dD_z}{dz} = \rho \tag{1.59}$$

From the definitions of the del operator and the dot product given earlier, equation (1.59) can be rewritten as

$$\nabla \cdot D = \rho \tag{1.60}$$

The dot product of the del operator with any vector is called the *divergence* of that vector. Hence, $\nabla \cdot D$ is the divergence of the electric flux density and it is equal to the volume charge density ρ. Divergence is a scalar quantity.

From Gauss's Law we have

$$\oint_s D \cdot da = \int_v \rho\,dv$$

Substitute equation (1.60) for the charge density ρ and we have

$$\oint_s D \cdot da = \int_v \nabla \cdot D\,dv \tag{1.61}$$

This is called the *divergence theorem*. It shows that the integral of the flux density over a closed surface s is equal to the volume integral of the divergence of the flux density, with the integration over the volume enclosed by the surface. This theorem is immensely useful in electric field theory.

1.16. Poisson's and Laplace's equations

It was shown in the preceding section that the divergence of the electric flux density is equal to the volume charge density. That is,

$$\nabla \cdot D = \rho$$

The flux density and electric field intensity are related to one another by the dielectric constant of vacuum according to

$$D = \epsilon_0 E$$

so that

$$\nabla \cdot E = \frac{\rho}{\epsilon_0}$$

It has also been shown that the electric field intensity is the negative gradient of the scalar electric potential V. That is,

$$E = -\nabla V$$

Consequently, the final form for the divergence equation is

$$\nabla \cdot \nabla V = -\frac{\rho}{\epsilon_0}$$

Our problem now is to express this in a more familiar form.

It was shown previously that the del operator is defined as a differential vector operator of the form

$$\nabla \triangleq i_x \frac{\partial}{\partial x} + i_y \frac{\partial}{\partial y} + i_z \frac{\partial}{\partial z}$$

Thus, the gradient of the potential is

$$\nabla V = i_x \frac{\partial V}{\partial x} + i_y \frac{\partial V}{\partial y} + i_z \frac{\partial V}{\partial z}$$

Now follow the rules developed for the dot product of two vectors, taking the dot product of the two preceding equations. The result is

$$\nabla \cdot \nabla V = \frac{\partial^2 V}{\partial x^2} + \frac{\partial^2 V}{\partial y^2} + \frac{\partial^2 V}{\partial z^2} = -\frac{\rho}{\epsilon_0} \tag{1.62}$$

This is called *Poisson's equation*. It is an extremely useful relationship. It can be written in a more compact form as

$$\nabla^2 V = -\frac{\rho}{\epsilon_0} \tag{1.63}$$

where

$$\nabla^2 \triangleq \frac{\partial^2}{\partial x^2} + \frac{\partial^2}{\partial y^2} + \frac{\partial^2}{\partial z^2} \tag{1.64}$$

If a region has no free charge so that ρ is zero, Poisson's equation reduces to

$$\nabla^2 V = 0 \qquad (1.65)$$

This is called *Laplace's equation*.

PROBLEMS

1.1. Compute the force between two positive charges in vacuum if the charges are both 6.2×10^{-19} coulomb and are 10^{-6} cm apart.

1.2. Repeat problem 1.1 for a charge separation of 10^{-8} cm.

1.3. Compute the force between two electrons 10^{-8} cm apart in vacuum.

1.4. Derive equation (1.20).

1.5. A dipole, consisting of a proton and an electron 0.529×10^{-8} cm apart, exerts a force on another nearby electron. Assume the electron is 10^{-6} cm away from the center of the dipole along the axis of the dipole. Compute the electric moment and the force on the nearby electron.

1.6. Three protons are arranged on the points of an equilateral triangle in space. The triangle measures 2×10^{-8} cm on a side. Compute the net force on each charge and clearly specify its direction.

1.7. Repeat problem 1.6 with one proton replaced by an electron.

1.8. Calculate the electric field intensity at the point occupied by either charge in problem 1.1.

1.9. Calculate the electric field intensity at the point occupied by either charge in problem 1.2.

1.10. Calculate the electric field intensity at the point occupied by the electron in problem 1.5.

1.11. Calculate the electric field intensity at the point occupied by the electron in problem 1.7.

1.12. Calculate the potential of either charge in problem 1.1.

1.13. Calculate the potential at the point occupied by the electron in problem 1.5.

1.14. Calculate the potential at the point occupied by the electron in problem 1.7.

1.15. Derive the equation for the electric field intensity at the center of a circular ring of electric charge. Let q be the total charge distributed in a line over a circle of radius r. Calculate the field intensity d meters up from the center of the circle along the axis of the circle.

1.16. Assume a sphere with a uniform distribution of electric charge. Using Gauss's Law prove that the electric intensity at points outside this sphere is the same as if the charge were all concentrated at the center of the sphere.

✓ **1.17.** An electron is released at rest at a point of zero potential in an electric field. The point of highest potential is V volts. Compute the energy of the electron in falling through this potential difference. What is the maximum electron velocity?

1.18. The potential of a given electric field is described by the following function:

$$V = ax^2 + bx + c$$

Compute the electric field intensity. What is the direction of the field intensity?

1.19. The potentials of two different two-dimensional electric fields are described by the following functions:

(a) $V = ax^2 + \dfrac{b}{y^2}$ (b) $V = \dfrac{ax}{x^2 + y^2}$

Calculate the electric field intensity in each case.

1.20. Repeat problem 1.19 for a three-dimensional field for which

$$V = \frac{a}{x^2 + y} + \frac{b}{y^2 + z}$$

1.21. Use Laplace's equation to derive the equation for the electric field intensity between a pair of infinite, parallel, metal plates separated by vacuum and having a potential difference of V volts between plates. There is no free charge in the interelectrode space.

1.22. Assume a pair of parallel metal plates of infinite area separated by a distance d. The space between is filled with charge uniformly distributed with a charge density ρ. One plate is at zero potential, the other is held at V volts. Use Poisson's equation to calculate the electric potential in the interelectrode space.

PROBLEMS ON VECTOR ANALYSIS

1.23. Calculate the magnitudes of the following vectors:

(a) $A = 1i_x + 2i_y + 3i_z$

(b) $B = 3i_x + 2i_y + 1i_z$

(c) $C = 2i_x + 3i_y + 1i_z$

1.24. Add the vectors A and B.

1.25. Subtract vector C from vector A.

1.26. Calculate $A \cdot B$ and $B \cdot C$.

1.27. Calculate $A \times B$ and $B \times C$.

1.28. An area is enclosed between the following vectors:

$$x = 2i_x \qquad y = 3i_y$$

Calculate the area and specify its vector direction.

2

STATIC MAGNETIC FIELDS
IN VACUUM

Static electric fields produced by stationary electric charges were treated in the preceding chapter. In the present chapter we are concerned with the various physical effects produced when electric charges are in motion. It is shown that this is the origin of *magnetic* phenomena.

The discussion is restricted to effects produced in vacuum. The discussion of magnetic effects associated with matter is reserved for chapter 11. At that point the structure of matter will be more fully presented so that the effects of magnetic fields will be more easily understood in terms of contemporary theories.

2.1. Electric current

The time rate of change at which electric charge passes across a surface is *defined* as *electric current*. That is,

$$i \triangleq \frac{dq}{dt} \tag{2.1}$$

where i = electric current in coulombs/second, q = charge in coulombs, t = time in seconds. The surface involved in this definition is not specified here, but its function is apparent from the discussion in a succeeding paragraph. The units for electric current are coulombs per second. This is defined as the *ampere* so that

$$1 \text{ amp} \triangleq 1 \text{ coulomb per second}$$

Time rates of change of electric charge across surfaces occur in vacuum, gases, liquids, and solids. The charges may be associated with electrons or with grosser particles. A large part of the fundamental theory of electrical engineering has evolved from studies of electric current produced by various charged bodies in various media.

The factors involved in the production of electric current are explained by consideration of the case shown in figure 2.1. This represents a section of a very long piece of material that contains many free positive charges. Let n = number of charged particles per unit volume, e = charge in coulombs on each particle, A = cross sectional area. Now suppose that we somehow produce an electric field of intensity E inside the material and directed as shown in figure 2.1. This electric field exerts forces on the free positive charges causing them to move in the direction of E with a velocity v. In dt seconds of time a charge dq is transported across the surface A. Hence,

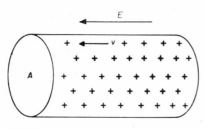

Figure 2.1. Section of a material containing free electric charges subject to an electric field.

$$dq = neA \cdot v \, dt \qquad (2.2)$$

Divide through by dt and replace dq/dt with i. Hence,

$$i = neA \cdot v \qquad (2.3)$$

In the particular case shown in figure 2.1, the vectors representing A and v are parallel so that $A \cdot v = Av$. Hence,

$$i = neAv \qquad (2.4)$$

Equation (2.3) shows that the electric current depends upon the charge density n, the charge on each particle e, the charge velocity v, and the component of area parallel to the charge velocity vector.

We can get some idea of the approximate orders of magnitude involved here by a simple numerical example. In a representative metal we might have

$$n = 8.5 \times 10^{22} \text{ charges/cc}$$
$$e = 1.6 \times 10^{-19} \text{ coulomb}$$
$$v = 0.02 \text{ cm/sec}$$
$$A = 1 \text{ cm}^2$$

Hence, $i = 272$ amp

The equation for the current can be changed slightly by rearranging terms as follows:

$$i = (nev) \cdot A \tag{2.5}$$

The bracketed factor is defined as the *current density* vector J. That is,

$$J \triangleq \text{current density} = nev \tag{2.6}$$

so that

$$i = J \cdot A \tag{2.7}$$

Electric current is a scalar quantity so it does not have direction. However, current density is a vector and is directed in the same sense as the velocity of the positive charges. This is the same as the direction of the electric field intensity. In other words, the electric field intensity E is directed from a point of high potential $+V$ to a point of low potential $-V$. The positive charges move from $+$ potential to $-$ potential producing a current density directed from $+$ to $-$. Thus, current density is taken to be from $+$ to $-$ in elements like that shown in figure 2.1.

This statement remains true even when the charge carriers are negative. This is so because the direction of the charge velocity reverses opposite to the direction of the electric field intensity. As a result, v is negative when e is negative and we have

$$J = n(-e)(-v) = nev$$

This is exactly the same equation as that given for current density produced by moving positive charges. Hence, the direction of the current density vector remains the same, from $+$ to $-$.

This may bother you a bit at first because negative charges are more commonly involved in the production of electric current than are positive charges and they actually move from $-$ to $+$ in producing a current density directed from $+$ to $-$. However, convention has established that the current density is directed from $+$ to $-$, the direction that positive charges would move if they were actually present.

While on the subject of electric current we can derive one more equation. It is not important by itself; we merely need it later as a substitution in a derivation. This seems to be the most convenient point to work it out.

Multiply both sides of equation (2.3) through by dx, where dx = differential displacement in the direction of v. Hence,

$$i\, dx = (neA \cdot v)\, dx = (neA \cdot dx)v$$

Integrate both sides of the equation over the length L of the material.

$$\int_0^L i\, dx = (neAL)v$$

However, AL = volume of material, n = number of charged particles per unit volume, e = charge on each particle. Hence,

$neAL$ = total charge contained within the volume
of material = q

Therefore,

$$\int_0^L i\, dx = qv \tag{2.8}$$

This is the desired result and is used later in the development of the *magnetic field* equation.

2.2. Some magnetic phenomena

The sudden introduction of *magnetic* phenomena into the discussion may seem like a sudden change of subject. However, toward the end of the chapter we will see that magnetic phenomena have their origins in the very factors discussed in chapter 1 and in the preceding section. In the meantime we will summarize some of the well known magnetic phenomena.

Permanent magnets are familiar to you. You probably also remember that an elementary compass consists of a thin *magnetized* steel rod suspended so that it can swing freely about a vertical axis. One end of the steel rod points approximately north while the other end points approximately south. The end pointing north is called the *north*, or *north seeking*, *pole* of the magnet. The end pointing south is called the *south*, or *south seeking*, *pole* of the magnet. All magnets have *both* north and south poles. Isolated north or south poles have never been observed; magnetic poles are always found paired together.

It is a well known experimental fact that if we bring two north poles close together they exert a force of repulsion. Two south poles behave in the same way. However, a north pole and a south pole in the same neighborhood attract one another with a measurable force.

In our study of electric charges in chapter 1 we observed that one charge exerts a force on any other charge in the same general region. This led us to the idea of imagining that lines of electric flux emanate from positive charges and terminate on negative charges. We then assumed that the force exerted on a test charge was proportional to the density of electric flux and the amount of charge on the test particle.

In the same way, the fact that magnets exert forces on other magnets in the same vicinity suggests that we visualize the presence of *magnetic flux*. This magnetic flux is assumed to emanate from north poles and terminate on south poles. This idea is explored in more detail later.

In 1819, Oersted observed that a magnetic flux exists about a wire carrying an electric current. Because electric current can be produced by moving electric charges, Oersted's work demonstrated that *moving electric charges produce magnetic fields of flux*. This is one of the two fundamental experimental facts associated with magnetic phenomena.

The second fundamental experimental fact is the converse of the first. That is, a magnetic field exerts a force on a charge *moving* with a velocity component perpendicular to the magnetic field. These two effects provide the basic experimental support for the balance of our work in this chapter. They are fundamental to the study of magnetics in the same way that Coulomb's Law is fundamental to the study of static electric fields.

Later, in chapter 11, we will find that *all* static magnetic fields are produced by moving electric charges. This is true even in the case of permanent magnets as we shall see in chapter 11.

2.3. Defining equations for magnetic phenomena

The theory of electrostatics presented in chapter 1 is supported by a single experimental observation. This is Coulomb's Law for the force between charged bodies. We find that two such fundamental experimental laws are required to support the study of static magnetic fields. This is so because we must have one experiment to define how a magnetic field is produced. Then we need a second experimental law showing how such fields exert forces on electric charges. Thus, we need two experimentally determined relationships to tell us the following:

(1) What factors are involved in the production of a magnetic field by *moving* source charges?

(2) What factors control the force exerted by a magnetic field on a *moving* test charge?

Note the emphasis on the word *moving*. It requires a moving source charge to produce a magnetic field and a moving test charge to detect the presence of a magnetic field.

Oersted's work demonstrated that electric currents, or moving charges, produce magnetic fields. Careful experimental studies express this fact in the following form:

$$B = \frac{v_1 \times E_1}{c^2} \tag{2.9}$$

where B = magnetic flux density at a point r meters from q_1, q_1 = moving source charge, v_1 = velocity of q_1 with respect to some observer, E_1 = electric field intensity produced by q_1 at a point r meters from q_1, c = velocity of light. All quantities are expressed in rationalized MKSC units. The units for magnetic flux density are derived later.

The equation for the electric field intensity E at any point about a source charge was given in chapter 1 as

$$E = \frac{q_1}{4\pi\epsilon_0 r^2} i_r \tag{2.10}$$

Hence, the equation for the magnetic flux density produced by q_1 is

$$B = \frac{q_1}{4\pi r^2 \epsilon_0 c^2} v_1 \times i_r \tag{2.11}$$

Now, define a new constant as follows:

$$\mu_0 = \frac{1}{\epsilon_0 c^2} = 4\pi \times 10^{-7} \tag{2.12}$$

$$= \text{permeability of vacuum}$$

The units associated with the permeability are derived later.

Substitute equation (2.12) into (2.11) and we get

$$\frac{B}{\mu_0} = \frac{q_1}{4\pi r^2} v_1 \times i_r \tag{2.13}$$

Now define one more new term as follows:

$$H = \frac{B}{\mu_0} = \text{magnetic field intensity} \qquad (2.14)$$

Hence, equation (2.13) can be written as

$$H = \frac{q_1}{4\pi r^2} \, v_1 \times i_r \qquad (2.15)$$

Suppose we have a whole succession of source charges q_1 moving with a velocity v_1. This constitutes an electric current i. According to equation (2.8) derived earlier we can then write

$$\int i \, dx = q_1 \, v_1 \qquad (2.16)$$

where dx = vector displacement in the direction of v_1. Substitute equation (2.16) into (2.15) and the result is

$$H = \int \frac{i}{4\pi r^2} \, dx \times i_r \qquad (2.17)$$

This is the practical form of the basic experimental law derived from Oersted's observations. It is often called the *Biot-Savart Law*. This equation permits the calculation of the magnetic field intensity H or flux density B produced by a wire carrying current. A typical example illustrating the use of this equation is presented in the next section.

Figure 2.2 shows the relative spatial orientations of the vectors in equation (2.17). For example, the equation shows that the magnetic field vector is always perpendicular to the plane formed by the vectors $i \, dx$ and i_r. This is also evident for the case shown in figure 2.2.

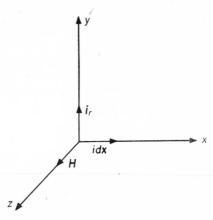

Figure 2.2. Directional relationships between the magnetic field and the current producing it. (See equation 2.17).

Equation (2.17) is the first of the two experimentally determined equations required to describe the properties and origins of magnetic fields. The second such equation gives the expression for the force produced by the magnetic field on a moving test charge. This equation is

$$F = q_2 v_2 \times B \qquad (2.18)$$

where F = force on q_2 in newtons, v_2 = velocity of q_2, q_2 = test charge in coulombs, B = flux density of the magnetic field.

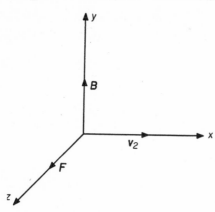

It is important to note that the force on the test charge is directed perpendicular to the plane formed by the vectors representing the velocity of the test charge and the magnetic flux density. This is illustrated in figure 2.3 for one possible arrangement of v_2 and B.

You should also note that the force exists only when the test charge q_2 has a velocity v_2 with some component at right angles to the magnetic flux density vector B.

Figure 2.3. Directional relationships in equation 2.18.

You will recall from chapter 1 that the concept of *electric flux* was introduced to provide a method for explaining why one charge exerts a force on another charge. We obtained such an explanation by endowing the hypothetical flux with the following properties:

(1) it exerts a force proportional to the flux density;
(2) the force is proportional to the amount of charge on the test particle.

It is clear from equation (2.18) that magnetic flux has similar assumed properties. Like electric flux, it is a hypothetical invention of the mind used to "explain" how magnetic forces arise. Like electric flux it produces a force on the test charge that is proportional to the flux density and the amount of charge on the test particle. However, unlike the situation in the electric field, the force of the magnetic field appears only when the test charge is in motion.

Equations (2.17) and (2.18) are the starting points for all further derivations in this chapter. Equation (2.17) provides the basic principle controlling the operation of practical devices called *inductors* and *coils*. Equation (2.18) provides the essential principle controlling the operation of electric motors, generators, and meters.

2.4. Magnetic field of a circular current

In this section we will give a practical example of the use of the Biot-Savart Law stated in equation (2.17).

Consider the case shown in figure 2.4. Here we have a circular wire carrying electric current. We will use equation (2.17) to calculate the magnetic field intensity at the center of the circle. The equation for the magnetic field intensity at any point r meters away from a wire carrying current is

$$H = \int \frac{i}{4\pi r^2}\, dx \times i_r$$

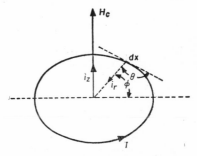

Figure 2.4. Magnetic field intensity at the center of a circular current carrying wire.

where i_r = unit vector along a line drawn from the current element $i\,dx$ to the point in question, r = distance from $i\,dx$ to the point in question.

For the case of the circular current shown in figure 2.4, the differential current element is a very short section of the circle as shown. The distance from this current element to the center of the circle is obviously equal to the radius r of the circle. The unit vector i_r is directed along this line toward the center of the circle. It is very clear from the known properties of circles and from the figure that a radial line is perpendicular to a tangent line. Hence,

$$i\,dx \times i_r = (i\,dx \sin 90°)\, i_z = i\,dx\, i_z$$

where i_z = unit vector perpendicular to the plane of the page. Hence, the equation for the magnetic field intensity at the center of the circle is

$$H_c = i_z \int \frac{i\,dx}{4\pi r^2}$$

The length of a differential arc on the perimeter of the circle is

$$dx = r\,d\phi$$

where r = radius of the circle, $d\phi$ = differential angle enclosed by radial lines drawn to the end points of the arc. Therefore, the magnetic field intensity is

$$H_c = i_z \int \frac{i}{4\pi r^2} r \, d\phi = i_z \int \frac{i}{4\pi r} \, d\phi$$

In a complete traverse around the circle, ϕ varies from 0 to 2π, while i and r are constant. If there are N turns of wire we must integrate around the circle N different times. As a result, ϕ varies from 0 to $2\pi N$ so that the magnetic field intensity is

$$H_c = \left(\frac{i}{4\pi r}\right) i_z \int_0^{2\pi N} d\phi$$

Integrate and substitute limits. The result is

$$H_c = \left(\frac{2\pi N i}{4\pi r}\right) i_z$$

or
$$H_c = \left(\frac{iN}{2r}\right) i_z \qquad\qquad (2.19)$$

This is the desired result. From this equation it is clear that the units of magnetic field intensity H are *ampere-turns per meter*. The corresponding magnetic flux density is

$$B_c = \mu_0 H_c = \left(\frac{\mu_0 i N}{2r}\right) i_z \qquad\qquad (2.20)$$

Other cases can be analyzed in the same general manner, but the simplicity of this example seldom occurs in practical cases.

2.5. Magnetic symbols, concepts, and units

Before plunging deeper into the study of magnetic phenomena, it is wise to pause for a moment and re-emphasize some important ideas and also to define magnetic units.

The notation and terminology used to describe the properties of the magnetic field closely parallel the notation and terminology used for the electric field. This is a rather natural consequence of the assumption that the properties of each can be described by fields of flux, electric or magnetic as the case may be. In spite of the similarity of terms it is important to remember that:

(1) Static electric fields are produced by stationary source charges.

(2) Static magnetic fields are produced by moving source charges.

We visualize the properties of an electric field in terms of the electric flux density D. The force exerted on a stationary test charge is proportional to D.

In a similar way, the properties of a magnetic field are visualized in terms of the magnetic flux density B. The force exerted on a moving test charge is proportional to B.

The total flux of an electric field crossing some surface of area A is

$$\psi = D \cdot A$$

In the same way, the total magnetic flux crossing a surface of area A is

$$\phi = B \cdot A \tag{2.21}$$

The electric field intensity E in vacuum is directly proportional to the electric flux density D, according to the equation

$$D = \epsilon_0 E$$

where ϵ_0 = dielectric constant of vacuum. Similarly, the magnetic field intensity H is directly proportional to the magnetic flux density according to the equation

$$B = \mu_0 H$$

where μ_0 = permeability of vacuum.

Thus, the following terms associated with magnetic phenomena have been defined:

ϕ = magnetic flux

B = magnetic flux density

H = magnetic field intensity

μ_0 = permeability of vacuum

Each of these terms is the analog of a corresponding term used in the description of the electric field. Now we will determine the units associated with these magnetic factors.

The fundamental equation for the force on a moving test charge was given earlier as

$$F = q_2 v_2 \times B$$

The magnitude of the force when the charge velocity and magnetic field are at right angles is

$$F = q_2 v_2 B$$

and the magnetic flux density is

$$B = \frac{F}{q_2 v_2}$$

Substitute proper units for the force, charge, and velocity.

$$B = \left(\frac{\text{newton}}{\text{coulomb}}\right)\left(\frac{\text{second}}{\text{meter}}\right)$$

However, in chapter 1 it was shown that

$$\text{newton/coulomb} = \text{volt/meter}$$

Hence,

$$B = \frac{\text{volt}}{\text{meter}}\frac{\text{second}}{\text{meter}} = \frac{\text{volt-second}}{\text{meter}^2}$$

We now define a new unit as follows:

$$1 \text{ volt-second} = 1 \text{ weber} \qquad (2.22)$$

so that the units of magnetic flux density are clearly

$$B = \text{webers/meter}^2$$

Therefore, it is also clear that the units associated with magnetic flux are

$$\phi = \text{webers} = BA$$

The permeability of vacuum was defined earlier by the equation

$$\mu_0 = \frac{B}{H} \qquad (2.23)$$

The units of magnetic field intensity were given earlier as ampere-turns per meter, or just as amperes per meter. Substitute units in equation (2.23) and we have

$$\mu_0 = \frac{\text{weber}}{\text{meter}^2}\frac{\text{meter}}{\text{ampere}} = \frac{\text{webers}}{\text{ampere}}\frac{1}{\text{meter}}$$

We now define the last new unit as follows:

$$1 \text{ weber/ampere} = 1 \text{ henry} \qquad (2.24)$$

Hence, the units of permeability are

$$\mu_0 = \text{henries/meter}$$

Thus, to summarize, the MKSC system of units for magnetic phenomena are as follows:

(1) weber = volt-second

(2) henry = weber/ampere
(3) flux = webers
(4) flux density = webers/meter^2
(5) field intensity = AT/meter
(6) permeability = henries/meter

2.6. Force on a current-carrying conductor

The fundamental equation for the force exerted by a magnetic field on a moving charge was given previously as

$$F = q_2 v_2 \times B \qquad (2.25)$$

From a consideration of this equation you quickly conclude that a magnetic field should also exert a force on a wire carrying an electric current. This should be so because the current results from the motion of electric charge. We can easily prove that such a force is produced.

According to equation (2.8) derived in section 2.1,

$$\int_0^L i \, dx = q_2 v_2 \qquad (2.26)$$

where i = current in a wire, dx = differential length of wire, L = total length of wire, q_2 = charge contained within the wire, v_2 = velocity of the charges in the wire. Carry out the integration in equation (2.26) and we have

$$iL = q_2 v_2 \qquad (2.27)$$

Substitute this into equation (2.25) and the resulting force equation is

$$F = iL \times B \qquad (2.28)$$

This is the desired result.

Equation (2.28) shows that a force F is exerted on a wire of length L in a magnetic field if

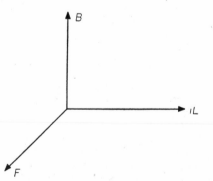

Figure 2.5. Vector relationships in equation (2.28).

the wire has a direction component at right angles to B. The force is zero when the wire and field are parallel or when the current is zero. The force produced is always at right angles to the plane formed by the field and the current element vectors. This is illustrated for one case in figure 2.5.

Equation (2.28) is basic to the study of electrical engineering because it expresses a direct relationship for *coupling* between an electrical system, represented by iL, and a mechanical system, represented by F. This is the basic principle governing the operation of electric motors. Equation (2.28) is sometimes called the *motor principle*.

2.7. Electromotive force (emf)

The ideas of electric potential V, and potential difference $(V_b - V_a)$ were discussed in some detail in chapter 1. It was shown there in the case of *stationary* electric charges and *static* electric fields that the potential V of a point in space is independent of the path followed in reaching that point. Under these conditions the line integral of the electric field intensity around a closed path is zero. That is,

$$\oint E \cdot dr = 0$$

As long as this is true no work is required to move an electric charge around any *closed* path in an electric field, regardless of the path followed. Such fields are called *conservative* fields and the electric field intensity in such fields is the negative gradient of the electric potential V. That is,

$$E = -\nabla V \tag{2.29}$$

or
$$E = -\left(\frac{\partial V}{\partial x} i_x + \frac{\partial V}{\partial y} i_y + \frac{\partial V}{\partial z} i_z\right) \tag{2.30}$$

or
$$E = -(E_x i_x + E_y i_y + E_z i_z) \tag{2.31}$$

where
$$E_x = \frac{\partial V}{\partial x} \qquad E_y = \frac{\partial V}{\partial y} \qquad E_z = \frac{\partial V}{\partial z} \tag{2.32}$$

A simple mathematical test can be applied to determine if an electric field is conservative or not. Take the cross product of the del operator ∇ and the electric field intensity E. That is, calculate $\nabla \times E$, where E is given by equation (2.31) for a conservative field. Carry out this operation and you get

$$-\nabla \times E = \left(\frac{\partial E_z}{\partial y} - \frac{\partial E_y}{\partial z}\right) i_x + \left(\frac{\partial E_x}{\partial z} - \frac{\partial E_z}{\partial x}\right) i_y + \left(\frac{\partial E_y}{\partial x} - \frac{\partial E_x}{\partial y}\right) i_z \tag{2.33}$$

Now substitute equations (2.32) for the components of the electric field intensity and we have

$$-\nabla \times E = \left(\frac{\partial^2 V}{\partial y \partial z} - \frac{\partial^2 V}{\partial y \partial z}\right) i_x + \left(\frac{\partial^2 V}{\partial x \partial z} - \frac{\partial^2 V}{\partial x \partial z}\right) i_y + \left(\frac{\partial^2 V}{\partial x \partial y} - \frac{\partial^2 V}{\partial x \partial y}\right) i_z$$

$$(2.34)$$

Each component of this equation is zero. Hence, for conservative fields

$$\nabla \times E = 0 \qquad (2.35)$$

Whenever $\nabla \times E = 0$, the electric field intensity is the negative gradient of the electric potential. Moreover, the potential difference between two points is

$$V_b - V_a = -\int_a^b E \cdot dr \qquad (2.36)$$

The foregoing discussion applies only to stationary electric fields. Actually, our present interest in this chapter centers about charges moving in magnetic fields. The force on such a charge is

$$F = q_2 v_2 \times B$$

The dynamic electric field intensity at the point occupied by the moving test charge is

$$E_d = \frac{F}{q_2} = v_2 \times B \qquad (2.37)$$

This is a *dynamic* electric field intensity in the sense that it exists only under the dynamic conditions of charge motion. When the charge is stationary and the situation is static, E_d is reduced to zero.

In electric fields of this type we find that $\nabla \times E_d$ is *not* equal to zero. Such fields are said to be *nonconservative*. The dynamic electric field intensity E_d *cannot* be derived from the negative gradient of the electric potential. Moreover, in nonconservative fields, the line integral of the electric field intensity around a closed path is *not* zero. That is,

$$\oint E \cdot dr \neq 0 \quad \text{(nonconservative)}$$

Also, the value obtained for the integral depends upon the path followed. This contrasts directly with conditions obtained for the static electric field.

Because of the very clear cut differences between static and dynamic electric fields, it is important to distinguish between the line integral of the electric field intensities in the two cases. For the *static* electric field we defined

$$V_b - V_a = \text{potential difference}$$

$$= -\int_a^b \boldsymbol{E} \cdot d\boldsymbol{r} \quad \text{(any path)}$$

For the nonconservative *dynamic* field we introduce a new term called the *electromotive force* (emf). This is defined as follows:

$$\text{emf} = \int_a^b \boldsymbol{E}_d \cdot d\boldsymbol{r} \quad \text{(specific path)} \tag{2.38}$$

The units of potential difference are *volts*. *Emf* also has the units of *volts*. Despite the use of identical units, different names are required for *emf* and potential difference so that we can identify their origins as from conservative or nonconservative fields.

There are other important differences between conservative and nonconservative fields. The lines of electric flux representing stationary conservative fields originate on positive charges and terminate on negative charges. Lines of flux representing nonconservative fields are closed, endless lines; they neither originate nor terminate on charges.

2.8. The generator principle

We will now combine the basic force equation with the definition of electromotive force. In this way we will derive the fundamental equation governing the operation of electrical generators.

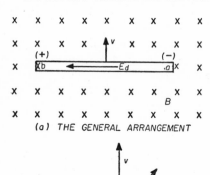

(a) THE GENERAL ARRANGEMENT

(b) VECTOR RELATIONSHIPS.

Figure 2.6

Assume the physical situation shown in figure 2.6. Here we have a magnetic field of flux density $\boldsymbol{B}$ directed into the paper in the z direction. A conductor L meters long is aligned along the x direction and is given a velocity v in the y direction. As a result of this velocity, a dynamic electric field is produced according to equation (2.37), which is

$$E_d = v_2 \times B$$

This dynamic field is in the x direction along the wire as shown in figure 2.6a.

The electromotive force (emf) developed across the ends of the conductor is computed from

$$\text{emf} = \int_a^b E_d \cdot dx = \int_0^L v_2 \times B \cdot dx \tag{2.39}$$

or, after integration

$$\text{emf} = (v_2 \times B) \cdot L \tag{2.40}$$

The *emf* calculated from this equation has the polarity sense shown in figure 2.6a. The end marked b is positive with respect to the end marked a. The dynamic electric field intensity is directed from the $(-)$ end to the $(+)$ end, opposite to the direction associated with the field intensity in the static case.

The relative spatial orientations of the vectors in equation (2.40) are shown in figure 2.6b.

One other important observation remains. Figure 2.7 shows the electric flux lines produced when the conductor moves in a magnetic

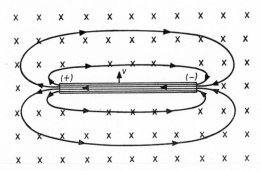

Figure 2.7. Electric flux lines produced by a conductor moving in a magnetic field.

field. Observe that the electric flux representing the dynamic field in the conductor is directed from $(-)$ to $(+)$. The external electric flux lines leave the $(+)$ end and enter the $(-)$ end in the same sense as that associated with static fields. The electric flux lines are considered completely closed lines.

2.9. Law of magnetic induction

In the preceding section it was shown that an electromotive force is developed across the ends of a conductor moving at right angles to a magnetic field. In this section a more general equation is derived to describe this and an associated phenomenon of great engineering importance.

The vector relationships used in deriving the generator principle are reproduced in figure 2.8. This shows a conductor L directed along the negative x axis. The conductor has a velocity v along the y axis

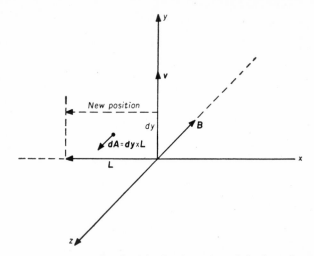

Figure 2.8. Factors involved in the dernation of the law of magnetic induction.

and the magnetic field is directed along the negative z axis. This should be compared to figure 2.6 used in deriving the generator principle. Although we have shown one arrangement of conductor and field, the result is general and applies to any configuration.

After a short instant of time, the conductor L moves vertically up, sweeping over an area given by

$$dA = dy \times L \qquad (2.41)$$

The time rate of change of area is

$$\frac{dA}{dt} = \frac{dy}{dt} \times L \qquad (2.42)$$

L is a constant independent of time and dy/dt is the conductor velocity v. Hence,

$$\frac{dA}{dt} = v \times L \tag{2.43}$$

The total flux passing through an area A is

$$\phi = B \cdot A$$

where B = magnetic flux density. The time derivative of the flux is

$$\frac{d\phi}{dt} = B \cdot \frac{dA}{dt} + A \cdot \frac{dB}{dt}$$

If the flux density is independent of time its derivative is zero and

$$\frac{d\phi}{dt} = B \cdot \frac{dA}{dt} \tag{2.44}$$

Now substitute equation (2.43) into (2.44) and we have

$$\frac{d\phi}{dt} = B \cdot (v \times L) \tag{2.45}$$

It should be a fairly simple exercise in vector analysis for you to use figure 2.8 to show that

$$B \cdot (v \times L) = -(v \times B) \cdot L \tag{2.46}$$

so that the time rate of change of flux is

$$\frac{d\phi}{dt} = -(v \times B) \cdot L \tag{2.47}$$

However, in the derivation of the generator principle we obtained equation (2.40) which showed that

$$\text{emf} = (v \times B) \cdot L$$

Hence, the time rate of change of flux is

$$\text{emf} = -\frac{d\phi}{dt} \tag{2.48}$$

If there had been N turns of wire stacked one on top of the other, we would get

$$\text{emf} = -N\frac{d\phi}{dt} \tag{2.49}$$

This is called *Faraday's Law* or the *Law of Magnetic Induction*.

Faraday's Law states that the *emf* produced across the terminals of a conductor is the negative time rate of change of flux cut by the conductor. At first thought this merely seems to be a restatement of the generator principle. Something deeper is involved, however, because Faraday's Law does *not* stipulate mechanical motion of the conductor. Although mechanical motion can be used to produce the required $d\phi/dt$, and we did use it in the discussion, it is not necessary. A time variation in flux could be produced by a magnetic field in which the flux density varies as a function of time. This is, in fact, the physical principle controlling the operation of such practical devices as *transformers* and *self inductors*.

Faraday's Law gives the equation for the *rise* in voltage from one end of a conductor to the other under the conditions specified. When electrical engineers write the equations describing the operation of coils and inductors they more generally use *voltage drops*. If we let the voltage drop be denoted by V (drop), then

$$V \text{ (drop)} = -\text{emf} = N \frac{d\phi}{dt} \qquad (2.50)$$

A simple application of Faraday's Law of magnetic induction is given in the next section.

2.10. An elementary alternator

The essential elements required in the operation of an electrical generator are shown in figure 2.9a. This figure shows a rectangular coil having N turns rotating in a magnetic field of flux density B. The coil is rotated about an axis that is perpendicular to the magnetic field. The two ends of the coil are connected to two *slip rings* that are concentric with the axis of the coil and rotate with the coil. The slip rings are insulated from one another; each is connected to the load by stationary *brushes* that make continuous contact with the slip rings. We shall now derive the equation for the generator voltage appearing across the load.

At any instant of time the coil is oriented at some arbitrary angle θ with respect to the magnetic field. The area A of the coil perpendicular to the lines of magnetic flux is

$$A = \text{(area of coil)} \cos \beta$$

or
$$A = A_c \cos \beta = A_c \sin \theta \qquad (2.51)$$

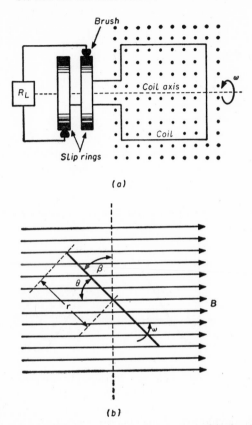

Figure 2.9. An elementary electrical generator with the electrical power dissipated in the load resistance R_L: (a) side view with the arrows representing the magnetic field coming out of the paper; (b) view seen from the slip ring end, showing the orientation of the coil.

If we assume that the coil is driven counterclockwise with a constant angular velocity ω, the area of the coil perpendicular to the direction of the flux lines varies with time. The time rate of change of the perpendicular projection of the coil area is

$$\frac{dA}{dt} = A_c \cos \theta \, \frac{d\theta}{dt} \tag{2.52}$$

but

$$\omega = \frac{d\theta}{dt} \quad \text{and} \quad \theta = \omega t \tag{2.53}$$

Hence, $$\frac{dA}{dt} = \omega A_c \cos \theta = \omega A_c \cos \omega t \qquad (2.54)$$

The amount of flux linking each turn of the coil is equal to the product of the flux density and the area A perpendicular to the flux. The time rate of change of flux is then

$$\frac{d\phi}{dt} = B \frac{dA}{dt} = \omega A_c B \cos \omega t \qquad (2.55)$$

The voltage induced in the coil is N times the time rate of change of flux. Hence, the generator voltage appearing across the load is

$$\text{emf} = -\omega N A_c B \cos \omega t \qquad (2.56)$$

This voltage varies with time according to a cosine function as shown in figure 2.10.

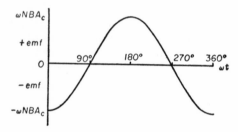

Figure 2.10. Cosinusoidal emf developed by the generator in Figure 2.9.

The voltage developed by the generator is alternately positive and negative. This is called an *alternating* voltage. When an alternating voltage is impressed across an electrical load it produces an *alternating current*. The alternating current generator is called an *alternator;* the rotating coil type is the simplest form assumed by practical alternators.

2.11. The d-c generator

The d-c generator shown in figure 2.11 is fundamentally the same machine as the alternator discussed in the preceding section. Precisely the same operating principles are involved. The only difference lies in the different method of delivering electrical energy to the load.

Slip rings are used in the alternator to couple the load to the coils.

of the generator. In the d-c generator a *commutator* is used. This is a split ring as shown in figure 2.11. One end of the coil is connected to one segment of the ring and the other end is connected to the other segment. The brushes are precisely positioned so that the brush con-

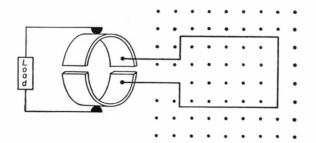

Figure 2.11. Elementary direct current generator.

tacts change segments just as the coil voltage starts to reverse. This has the effect of reversing the connection of the coil to the load. Thus, the reversal of coil voltage is exactly offset by the commutator which reverses the connection of the coil to the load. As a result, the

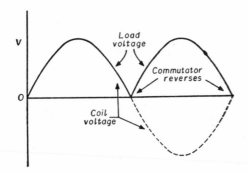

Figure 2.12. Load voltage for the d-c generator showing the action of the commutator.

voltage across the load does *not* reverse or alternate; it pulsates so that the voltage is always of one polarity. This produces a current through the load that pulsates, but has only one direction. This is shown in figure 2.12.

In practical d-c generators more than one coil is used and a separate pair of commutator segments is used for each coil. If we had 10 coils there would be 20 commutator segments, and so on. The pulsation of the d-c is less pronounced as more coils and commutator segments are used. You can see that this is so by comparing the voltage shown

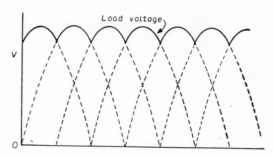

Figure 2.13. Load voltage in a 6-coil d-c generator; note reduction of pulsation.

in figure 2.13 for a 6-coil machine with that of the 1-coil machine in figure 2.12.

When the load current becomes unidirectional and essentially constant, as in figure 2.13, it is called direct current, or d-c.

2.12. Electro-mechanical coupling

In discussing the *motor* principle it was shown in equation (2.28) that

$$F_m = iL \times B \tag{2.57}$$

If iL and B are perpendicular we can write

$$F_m = BLi \tag{2.58}$$

This equation states that when an *electrical* current is supplied to a conductor in a magnetic field, a *mechanical* force appears on the conductor. Evidently, the magnetic field acts as a coupling system between an electrical system and a mechanical system. This is called *electro-mechanical coupling*.

In the discussion of the *generator* principle it was shown that

$$\text{emf} = (v \times B) \cdot L \tag{2.59}$$

If **L**, **B**, and **v** are mutually perpendicular we obtain the scalar relationship

$$\text{emf} = BLv \qquad (2.60)$$

This equation shows that when a *mechanical* velocity is imparted to a conductor in a magnetic field, an electromotive force appears across the ends of the conductor. As before, the magnetic field apparently serves as the coupling agency, producing *electro-mechanical coupling*.

Solve equations (2.58) and (2.60) for the product *BL*. This yields

$$BL = \frac{\text{emf}}{v} = \frac{F_m}{i}$$

Hence, $$(\text{emf})\, i = F_m v \qquad (2.61)$$

From equation (2.61) it is apparent that

$$(\text{emf})\, i = \text{electrical power} = P \text{ (electrical)}$$
$$F_m v = \text{mechanical power} = P \text{ (mechanical)}$$

Therefore,

$$P \text{ (electrical)} = P \text{ (mechanical)} \qquad (2.62)$$

In essence, this last equation states that the electrical and mechanical power are equal, neglecting losses arising in actual systems. In other words, if we supply a certain amount of mechanical power to a generator, the electrical power output is equal to the mechanical power input. Conversely, if we operate the device as a motor, the mechanical power output will be equal to the electrical power input. This is the fundamental process involved in the more common electro-mechanical energy conversion devices.

Of course, some electrical and mechanical losses are always present. They can be reduced to very small values in many cases, however, so that electrical machines quite generally operate very close to the ideal relationship given in equation (2.62).

2.13. The Michelson-Morley experiment

The experimental observations and later derivations presented in the preceding sections clearly point to *moving charges* as the key factors in the production and measurement of magnetic phenomena. The entire presentation proceeded from the two experimental laws

given at the beginning of the chapter. As a result, we are confronted
with the existence of two apparently different types of fields:

(1) an electric field produced by stationary charges, and

(2) a magnetic field produced by moving electric charges.

The question must surely arise in your mind—are these two fields
truly different and both fundamental? Is it possible that one might
be derived from the other?

There is a theory that permits us to derive the basic laws of magnetics from Coulomb's Law and we will cover it briefly here. It will
be shown that the two basic equations describing magnetic phenomena, which are

$$F = q_2 v_2 \times B$$

$$H = v_1 \times D$$

can be derived from Coulomb's Law.

Before these derivations can be understood, we must establish
certain assumptions fundamental to the theory. We are particularly
interested in the effects produced by electric charges having trans-
lational velocity. Therefore it is important to determine if there is
such a thing as *absolute velocity*, or does velocity have meaning only
when compared to some reference system? This question was an-
swered by one of the classic experiments supporting modern physics.
This is the famous Michelson-Morley experiment.

The purpose of this experiment was to measure the *absolute* velocity
of the earth as it moved through space, by comparing it with the
absolute velocity of light. The essential form of the experimental
setup is shown schematically in figure 2.14a. This shows an arrangement of three mirrors and a source of light. One mirror, M_1, is
silvered over only half the surface. Thus, it reflects from the top part
and transmits light through the bottom part.

Assume that the system of mirrors has an *absolute* velocity that is
zero. Under these conditions, one ray of light passes through M_1 and
on to M_3 where it is reflected back to M_1. The light travels this entire
distance $2y_0$ with an *absolute* velocity c.

The other ray of light is reflected from M_1 to M_2 and then back
to M_1. The total distance travelled is $2y_0$ and the velocity of travel
is c. Because both rays of light travel the same distance at the same
speed, the two rays of light arrive back at M_1 so that they reinforce
one another.

Now suppose that the system of mirrors is given an *absolute* velocity v directed to the right as shown in figure 2.14b. The *absolute* velocity of light is still taken to be c as before. The physical situation assumed in the Michelson-Morley experiment is described in the balance of this section.

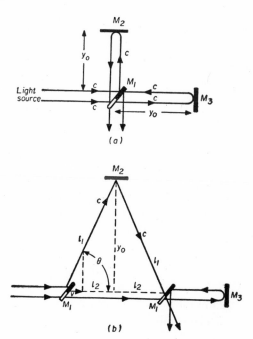

Figure 2.14. Michelson-Morley experiment: (a) mirrors stationary; (b) mirrors have velocity v directed to the right.

One ray of light passes through M_1 and heads toward M_3 with an *absolute* velocity c. However, M_3 is moving away with an *absolute* velocity v. Hence, the light is assumed to have a velocity, relative to the mirrors, of $(c - v)$. The distance between mirrors is y_0. Hence, the light will reach M_3 after t_1 seconds of travel, where

$$t_1 = \frac{y_0}{(c - v)} \tag{2.63}$$

When the light is reflected back toward M_1, the velocity of the light relative to the mirrors is taken to be $(c + v)$. Hence, the time required to travel y_0 meters is

$$t_2 = \frac{y_0}{(c + v)} \qquad (2.64)$$

Hence, the total time required for the round trip between this system of mirrors is

$$t = t_1 + t_2 = \frac{y_0}{c - v} + \frac{y_0}{c + v}$$

or

$$t = \frac{1}{c} \frac{2y_0}{1 - v^2/c^2} \qquad (2.65)$$

The *absolute* distance travelled by the light is the *absolute* velocity times the travel time. So

$$y_t = ct = \frac{2y_0}{1 - v^2/c^2} \qquad (2.66)$$

The *other* ray of light is reflected from M_1 toward M_2 with a velocity c. Because the system of mirrors has a velocity v, a *stationary observer* would see the effect shown in figure 2.14b. The light *apparently* moves along the path y_1 with a velocity c. The mirrors move a distance y_2 to the right in the time required for the light to move from M_1 to M_2. Hence, in figure 2.14b,

$$\cos \theta = \frac{v}{c} = \frac{y_2}{y_1} \qquad (2.67)$$

and

$$y_1^2 = y_0^2 + y_2^2 \qquad (2.68)$$

Solve equation (2.67) for y_2 and substitute this into equation (2.68). Then solve for y_1. The result is

$$y_1 = \frac{y_0}{\sqrt{1 - v^2/c^2}} \qquad (2.69)$$

The total distance of travel is $2y_1$, or

$$2y_1 = \frac{2y_0}{\sqrt{1 - v^2/c^2}} \qquad (2.70)$$

Compare the distance travelled by this ray of light to that travelled by the other as given in equation (2.66). The results differ by a factor $\sqrt{1 - v^2/c^2}$. Hence, the two light rays arrive back at M_1 in such a way that they interfere with one another. At least, under the assumptions used in deriving these equations, interference should result.

When the experiment was actually performed, interference between light rays did *not* occur. The experiment was apparently a failure.

As a result of the outcome of the Michelson-Morley experiment and other data then available, Einstein postulated that *there is no meaning in absolute motion of translation.* In other words, the Michelson-Morley experiment failed because it was designed to measure something that is meaningless, the *absolute* velocity of the earth through space. Thus, figure 2.14b has no meaning because it was drawn by assuming that the system of mirrors had an *absolute* velocity v. In short, the situation depicted in figure 2.14b never occurs. Instead, figure 2.14a always applies and interference does not result.

This can be stated in another way. The velocity of the light travelling between mirrors is always c so that figure 2.14a always results. This is independent of any motion of the system of mirrors. Thus, the *velocity of light is the same in any reference system;* it does not change when there is any relative motion of translation between systems.

This last conclusion is generally inconsistent with Newton's Laws which predicted a figure of the form shown in 2.14b. However, this *apparent* inconsistency can be resolved if we *redefine* the length of a line as follows:

$$y = y_0 \sqrt{1 - v^2/c^2} \qquad (2.71)$$

where y_0 = length of line at rest in a frame of reference, y = length of line when in motion, v = velocity with respect to frame of reference, c = velocity of light. This is called the *Lorentz transformation* of the space coordinate.

This transformation causes the length of the line to be reduced along the direction of its motion. Hence, in figure 2.14b, the distance y_t is reduced by this factor so that the *new* value for y_t is

$$y_t = \frac{2y_0}{\sqrt{1 - v^2/c^2}} \qquad (2.72)$$

As you can see, this distance is now exactly equal to that calculated for the other light ray in equation (2.70). Hence, interference does *not* result as confirmed by experiment. Thus, by redefining the length of a line, Newton's Laws are still found to be adequate.

2.14. The Lorentz transformations

It was shown in the preceding section that the space coordinate is defined by the following equation:

$$y = y_0\sqrt{1 - v_y^2/c^2}$$

where y_0 = space coordinate at rest with respect to the frame of reference of the observer, v_y = velocity of the coordinate system in the y_0 direction relative to the frame of reference of the observer, c = velocity of light, y = space coordinate as it appears to the observer in his frame of reference. As the velocity of a line, relative to an observer, approaches the velocity of light, the length of the line in the direction of the velocity appears to be reduced as viewed by an observer. The apparent length becomes zero when the velocity equals the velocity of light.

Similar transformations can be worked out for force, electric field intensity, and so on. However, it is *postulated* that electric charge is unchanged in the Lorentz transformation so that

$$q = q_0 \tag{2.73}$$

In other words, a charge moving with any velocity relative to the frame of reference of the observer, always has the same charge.

The *mass transformation* is similar to the space transformation. That is,

$$m = \frac{m_0}{\sqrt{1 - v^2/c^2}} \tag{2.74}$$

where m_0 = mass of a body at rest with respect to the frame of reference of the observer = *rest mass*, m = mass of the body as it appears to the observer, v = velocity of the mass relative to the frame of reference of the observer. This equation shows that the mass apparent to the observer becomes infinite when the velocity equals the velocity of light.

Another immensely useful equation can be derived by expanding equation (2.74) in a power series as

$$m = m_0\left(1 + \frac{1}{2}\frac{v^2}{c^2} + \frac{3}{8}\frac{v^2}{[c^2]^2} + \cdots\right) \tag{2.75}$$

Multiply through by c^2. The result is

$$mc^2 = m_0c^2 + \frac{1}{2}m_0v^2\left(1 + \frac{3}{4}\frac{v^2}{c^2} + \cdots\right) \tag{2.76}$$

The first term on the right-hand side of this equation is

$$m_0 c^2 = \text{energy of constitution} \qquad (2.77)$$

The second term is the total kinetic energy of the mass. That is

$$\text{kinetic energy} = \frac{1}{2}\, m_0 v^2 \left(1 + \frac{3}{4}\frac{v^2}{c^2} + \ldots \right) \qquad (2.78)$$

This reduces to the familiar $\frac{1}{2}m_0 v^2$ form when the velocity v is small compared to the velocity of light. Hence, the total energy of the system is the sum of these two terms, or

$$W = mc^2 \qquad (2.79)$$

This is Einstein's famous equation for the equivalence of mass and energy. This equation plays an important part in our discussion of the nucleus presented in chapter 4.

We shall now use the Lorentz transformations to determine the effects produced when electric charges are in motion. This is undertaken in the next section.

2.15. Origin of the magnetic effect

Consider the case of a *stationary source charge* q_1 located at the origin of a stationary system of rectangular coordinates as shown in figure 2.15. A second *stationary test charge* q_2 is assumed to be located

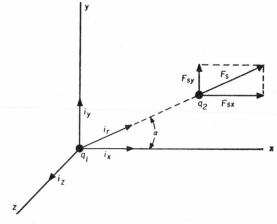

Figure 2.15. Force between two stationary electric charges.

in the x-y plane of the coordinate system. The charges are assumed stationary with respect to the observer.

The total force exerted on the test charge q_2 is F_s and is along a radial line as shown in figure 2.15. The force is calculated from Coulomb's law to be

$$F_s = \frac{q_1 q_2}{4\pi\epsilon_0 r^2} i_r$$

This force can be resolved into x and y components as shown in figure 2.15. There is no z component because the test charge q_2 was assumed to be in the x-y plane. The x and y components of the force are

$$F_{sx} = \left(\frac{q_1 q_2}{4\pi\epsilon_0 r^2} \cos \alpha \right) i_x \tag{2.80}$$

$$F_{sy} = \left(\frac{q_1 q_2}{4\pi\epsilon_0 r^2} \sin \alpha \right) i_y \tag{2.81}$$

Now suppose the *source* charge q_1 is given a velocity v_1 relative to the system of stationary coordinates. It is assumed that this velocity is directed along the x axis. It is also assumed that the test charge q_2 remains stationary.

By using the Lorentz transformation, trigonometry, and algebra, it can be shown[1] that the x component of the force on the test charge is not affected by the motion of the source charge. That is,

$$F_{dx} = F_{sx} = \left(\frac{q_1 q_2}{4\pi\epsilon_0 r^2} \cos \alpha \right) i_x \tag{2.82}$$

The subscript d refers to the word *dynamic* while the subscript s signifies *static*, or stationary.

The same analysis shows that the y component of the force is increased as shown in figure 2.16 when the source charge is in motion. As a result, the total force is no longer along a radial line, but is more nearly aligned to the y axis. The *new* value for the y component of the force has a value

$$F_{dy} = \left(\frac{q_1 q_2}{4\pi\epsilon_0 r^2} \sin \alpha \right) \left(\frac{1}{1 - v_1^2/c^2} \right)^{1/2} i_y \tag{2.83}$$

where v_1 = velocity of the source charge, c = velocity of light. This

[1] Paul C. Shedd, *Fundamentals of Electromagnetic Waves* Englewood Cliffs, N. J.: Prentice-Hall, Inc., 1954, pp. 93-106.

reduces to the value computed from Coulomb's law when q_1 is stationary because this makes v_1 zero.

Equation (2.83) shows that the component of force perpendicular to the direction of charge velocity is modified by the Lorentz transformation. The component of force in the direction of charge motion is *not* affected.

It is also clear from equation (2.83) that the increase in force in the y direction will be quite small until the charge velocity approaches the velocity of light.

Now we will carry the discussion one step further and assume that the test charge q_2 is given a velocity v_2 along the x axis and relative to the frame of reference of the observer. This is shown in figure 2.17.

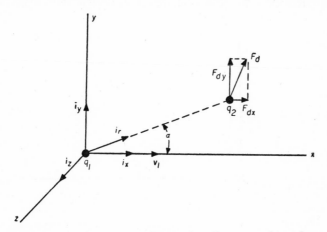

Figure 2.16. Force on a test charge when the source charge has a velocity v_1.

As before, application of the Lorentz transformation, algebra, and trigonometry makes it possible to prove[2] that the x component of force is still unchanged. However, it is found that the y component of the force is *again* changed through the effect of the moving test charge. This time the y component of the force is reduced by an amount

$$\Delta F_{dy} = -\left(\frac{q_1 q_2}{4\pi\epsilon_0 r^2}\right)\frac{(\sin \alpha)\, v_1 v_2}{c^2(1 - v_1^2/c^2)^{1/2}}\, i_y \qquad (2.84)$$

[2] *Ibid.*

It is clear from this equation that the change in force is reduced to zero when the test charge is stationary because this makes v_2 zero. Thus, ΔF_{dy} is a *force that appears only when the test charge is in motion.* This is the origin of magnetic effects as we shall soon see.

Assume that the velocity v_1 of the source charge is small compared to the velocity of light. This reduces equation (2.84) to

$$\Delta F_{dy} = -\frac{q_1 q_2}{4\pi\epsilon_0 r^2} \frac{v_1 \sin \alpha v_2}{c^2} i_y \qquad (2.85)$$

Under these conditions the Lorentz correction is so small that it is neglected. Consequently, the force on the test charge when it is stationary is given by Coulomb's law even if the source charge is in motion. However, if the test charge moves while the source charge

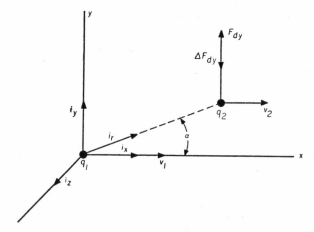

Figure 2.17. Change in force when the test charge q_2 moves with a velocity v_2.

is in motion, a new force appears equal to that given by equation (2.85). This is *defined as the force exerted by the magnetic field,* with the term *magnetic field* yet to be defined.

Equation (2.85) can be expressed in a more general form by a short exercise in vector analysis. From figure 2.17 you can show that

$$v_2 i_y = -v_2 \times i_z \qquad (2.86)$$

and
$$(v_1 \sin \alpha)i_z = v_1 \times i_r \qquad (2.87)$$

Thus, the general form for equation (2.85) becomes

$$\Delta F_{dy} = \left(\frac{q_1 q_2}{4\pi\epsilon_0 r^2} \right) \frac{v_2 \times (v_1 \times i_r)}{c^2} \tag{2.88}$$

This is *the* basic equation from which all laws of magnetic fields are derived. These definitions are presented in the next section.

2.16. Basic laws of magnetics

It was shown in the preceding section that a test charge q_2 moving in the electric field of a moving source charge q_1 experiences a force ΔF_{dy} above and beyond the normal Coulomb force. It was stated that this is defined as the force of the magnetic field. Hence, let

$$F_m \overset{\Delta}{=} \Delta F_{dy} \overset{\Delta}{=} \text{force of the magnetic field}$$

Then, according to equation (2.88),

$$F_m = \left(\frac{q_1 q_2}{4\pi\epsilon_0 r^2} \right) \frac{v_2 \times (v_1 \times i_r)}{c^2} \tag{2.89}$$

where q_1 = source charge in coulombs, q_2 = test charge in coulombs, v_2 = velocity of the test charge in meters/sec with respect to some frame of reference, v_1 = velocity of the source charge in meters/sec with respect to the same frame of reference, r = distance between charges in meters, i_r = radial unit vector, c = velocity of light, ϵ_0 = dielectric constant of vacuum. First define a new constant of the system. Let

$$\mu_0 \overset{\Delta}{=} \frac{1}{\epsilon_0 c^2} \overset{\Delta}{=} \text{permeability of vacuum} \tag{2.90}$$

This reduces equation (2.89) to the following form:

$$F_m = \left(\frac{\mu_0 q_1 q_2}{4\pi r^2} \right) v_2 \times (v_1 \times i_r) \tag{2.91}$$

In chapter 1, equation (1.25), it was shown that the electric flux density D about a point source charge q_1 was

$$D = \frac{q_1}{4\pi r^2} i_r \tag{2.92}$$

Therefore, the equation for the force of the magnetic field becomes

$$F_m = \mu_0 q_2 v_2 \times (v_1 \times D) \tag{2.93}$$

We now define the *magnetic field intensity* H as

$$H = v_1 \times D \qquad (2.94)$$

This is the first of the two equations given as experimental facts at the beginning of the chapter.

The equation for the force of the magnetic field is

$$F_m = q_2 v_2 \times (\mu_0 H) \qquad (2.95)$$

The bracketed term is clearly the magnetic flux density B. Hence,

$$B = \mu_0 H \qquad (2.96)$$

Thus, the final form of the magnetic force equation is

$$F_m v = q_2 v_2 \times B \qquad (2.97)$$

This is the same as the second of the two experimental laws given at the beginning of the chapter.

Hence, we have derived the two basic laws of magnetics and find them to be identical with the laws established by experiment.

2.17. Plane waves

It probably seems that we are wandering far afield to suddenly bring in the subject of *waves*. We have discussed stationary electric

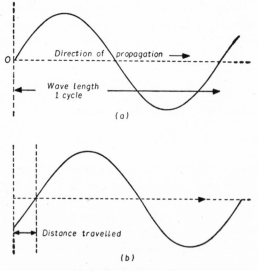

Figure 2.18. Water wave in cross section.

and magnetic fields so far. These are static fields. When we consider the dynamic case the subject is then called *electromagnetic wave* theory. This subject is not covered here, except for some very general characteristics of plane waves.

The most familiar wave to most of us is the *water wave*. If, at some instant of time, we could look at these waves from the side, in cross section, they would have the idealized form shown in figure 2.18a. This is called a travelling wave because it travels in space as a function of time. Thus, if we were to observe the wave a few moments after the first observation, it would appear as shown in figure 2.18b. The wave has moved.

The *wave length*, λ, of a plane wave is the distance between identical points on the wave as shown in figure 2.18a. The *period, T*, of the

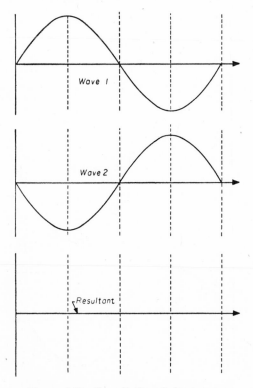

Figure 2.19. Cancellation of plane waves.

wave is the time required for it to travel one wave length. If the
wave velocity is v, then

$$\lambda = vT \tag{2.98}$$

and

$$T = \frac{\lambda}{v} \tag{2.99}$$

The wave undergoes one complete *cycle* in one period. Hence, the
frequency, f, of the wave is the reciprocal of the period; that is,

$$f = \frac{1}{T} \quad \text{and} \quad f\lambda = v \tag{2.100}$$

When two or more waves occur at the same place in the medium
at the same time, they may interfere with one another. An extreme
and interesting case is shown in figure 2.19. This shows two plane
waves of the same wave length and having the same crest values

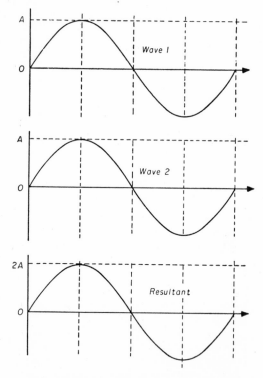

Figure 2.20. Reinforcement of plane waves.

travelling in the same direction. One wave is displaced a half wave length ahead of the other. Now, if these two waves are produced simultaneously and at the same place, they cancel one another completely.

Another special case results when two identical waves are propagated in the same space in a medium as shown in figure 2.20. In this case the two waves reinforce one another as shown.

Any intermediate condition of cancellation or reinforcement can occur depending upon the crest values of the waves and their relative timing. This is a rather oversimplified explanation, but it illustrates the general idea sufficiently well for the purposes of this book.

The properties and behavior of *light*, or *electromagnetic energy*, are partly explained by the *wave theory*. According to Maxwell, a plane electromagnetic wave consists of transverse, or mutually perpendicular, electric and magnetic fields which vary as functions of time. The electric field is perpendicular to the magnetic field and both are perpendicular to the direction of propagation of the wave. This is shown in figure 2.21.

Figure 2.21 shows the wavelike properties of both the electric and magnetic field intensities.

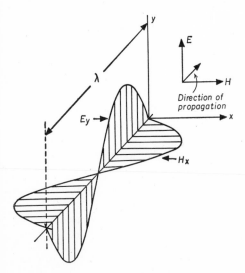

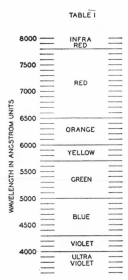

Figure 2.21. One wave length of a plane electromagnetic wave such as light.

The velocity of light is denoted by c and has a value of approximately 3×10^8 meters/sec. Therefore, equation (2.100) can be written as

$$f\lambda = c \qquad (2.101)$$

for plane electromagnetic waves. The wave in figure 2.21 is called an *electromagnetic* wave because both the electric and magnetic fields exist simultaneously whenever the wave propagates.

A detailed treatment of fields and waves cannot be pursued further here. It is an extremely interesting subject and has been thoroughly developed in a number of standard text and reference books[3].

The *color* of observed light depends upon its wave length. The colors associated with the various wave lengths of visible light are given in Table 1.

PROBLEMS

2.1. A certain wire has a cross-sectional area of 0.01 sq in. There are 5×10^{22} electrons per cubic centimeter of material moving with a velocity of 1500 cm/sec. Compute the electric current in the wire.

2.2. From equation (2.74) calculate and plot m/m_0 as a function of v/c.

2.3. From equation (2.71) calculate and plot y/y_0 as a function of v/c.

2.4. Calculate the magnetic force between two electrons 1×10^{-8} cm apart moving with velocities of 1×10^3 cm/sec and 3×10^3 cm/sec with respect to a stationary frame of reference. Assume the electrons are moving parallel to one another.

2.5. Repeat problem 2.4 assuming the electrons are moving along paths forming an angle of 45°.

2.6. Calculate the magnetic field intensity at the point occupied by either electron in problem 2.4.

2.7. Calculate the magnetic flux density at the point occupied by either electron in problem 2.4.

2.8. Calculate the force on an electron as it enters a magnetic field of flux density 6 webers/meter². The electron velocity is 2.5×10^6

---

[3] See, for example, H. H. Skilling, *Fundamentals of Electric Waves*, 2nd Ed., New York: John Wiley & Sons, 1948; Paul C. Shedd, *Fundamentals of Electromagnetic Waves*, Englewood Cliffs, N. J.: Prentice-Hall, Inc., 1954.

meter/sec and the angle between the electron velocity and magnetic field is 45°.

2.9. Compute the gravitational force on an electron. How does this compare with the magnetic force calculated in problem 2.8?

2.10. Calculate the force on a wire 25 cm long, carrying a current of 5 amperes in a magnetic field of 0.72 weber/meter². Assume the wire is at an angle of 90° with respect to the magnetic field.

2.11. Repeat problem 2.10 for angles of 0°, 30°, 45°, and 60°.

2.12. Calculate the magnetic field intensity at the center of a circular coil having 50 turns of radius 2.5 cm and carrying a current of 0.03 ampere.

2.13. Derive the equation for the magnetic field intensity at the center of a square coil of wire having N turns.

2.14. A wire 10 cm long moves with a velocity of 250 cm/sec at right angles to a magnetic field of 0.8 weber/meter². Calculate the voltage generated across the ends of the wire.

2.15. Assume that a current of 5 amperes exists in the wire of problem 2.14. How much power is required to move the wire with the specified velocity? How much work is done in moving the wire for a period of time of 1 minute?

2.16. Two radio broadcast stations operate at frequencies of 780×10^3 cycles/sec and 1460×10^3 cycles/sec. Calculate the wave length of each station.

2.17. Radar stations may operate at wave lengths of 3 cm or 10 cm. Calculate the corresponding frequencies of operation.

3

EXTRANUCLEAR ATOMIC
STRUCTURE

Presumably the reader is acquainted with the idea of the divisibility
of all matter into constituent atoms of the 100 or more presently
known *elements*. That the atoms are themselves composed of about
a half dozen different kinds of particle-like quantities should be another familiar idea. However, because of its importance to the material that follows, some general aspects of atomic structure are
reviewed here.

All atoms are composed of a heavy nucleus, which is positively
charged, surrounded by a dynamic array of negatively charged electrons. In the normal state of the atom, the total charge embodied
in the electrons is exactly equal to the total positive charge in the
nucleus.

In the past, the structure of the nucleus was a matter of some
indifference to engineers. With the advent of nuclear power this is
no longer true and all engineers should plan to study nuclear physics
at some point in their careers.

For the purposes of this chapter we can largely neglect the nucleus
and concentrate upon the surrounding electronic array. Thus, at this
point we are interested primarily in the extra-nuclear structure of the
atom.

Present concepts of the structure of matter have been derived from
a subject called *quantum mechanics*. The model of the atom thus
constructed is supported by extensive experimental evidence.

The picture presented in this chapter is largely that developed from
the older quantum theory associated with the work of Bohr, Sommer-

feld, DeBroglie, and others. We use this rather than the newer work of Schrödinger's *Wave Mechanics* and Heisenberg's *Uncertainty Principle* because it is the simplest basis for an intuitive and more familiar picture of atomic structure. However, you must bear in mind that the purpose of a theory is not so much to provide an ultimate explanation of experimental facts, but to specify the relations between these facts. Thus, you must not attach too great a sense of reality to the atomic picture presented.

3.1. Wave particle duality

The discussion in this chapter is concerned with the dynamic array of electrons surrounding the nucleus of an atom. Because electrons will be discussed at length it is important for us to have a definite understanding of present knowledge of electrons.

In many cases electrons *act* like charged particles of a certain mass. This concept of the character of electrons is based upon observations of the motion of electrons in electric and magnetic fields. For example, suppose that an electron e is located in an electric field of intensity E. The force on the electron is

$$F = -eE$$

This force causes the electron to be accelerated according to the equation

$$F = ma$$

where m = electron mass, a = acceleration. Through the use of these two equations and the general laws of mechanics, it is found that electrons follow the laws of particle dynamics.

In a corresponding case, assume an electron enters a magnetic field of flux density B with a velocity v. The field exerts a force on the electron according to the equation

$$F = -ev \times B = ma$$

As before, accurate predictions of the behavior of the electron is secured through the use of particle dynamics.

In both of the foregoing cases the electron is treated as though it had the properties of a *particle* of mass m and electric charge $-e$.

When a stream of electrons is focused upon a grating, where the grating is of atomic dimensions, the electrons exhibit *diffraction pat-*

terns. This action is characteristically associated with *waves.* Thus, under certain sets of experimental conditions an electron exhibits the properties of a wave. This apparently dual nature of electrons is called *wave-particle* duality.

Please note that it has *not* been said that an electron is a wave or a particle or anything else. It is simply stated that it *acts like* a particle at times and like a wave at other times. The true nature of an electron is unknown even though it is generally possible to describe its behavior under certain sets of experimental conditions.

A somewhat similar situation of duality exists in the case of light, which is electromagnetic energy. Most electrical engineering work with electromagnetic energy has led to extensive treatments of transmission lines, wave guides, antennas, and radio propagation. In these cases the wave theory provides satisfactory explanations of observed behavior. However, in experiments with the photoelectric emission (see chapter 5) of electrons from various metals, the wave theory fails to explain the effect. If electromagnetic energy is postulated to travel in discrete bundles, or particles, of energy called *photons,* a satisfactory explanation of the photoelectric effect is secured.

The energy of a *photon* is given by

$$W = hf = \text{photon energy in joules} \tag{3.1}$$

where h = Planck's constant = 6.624×10^{-34} joule-sec, $\qquad$ (3.2)

f = frequency of the wave in cycles/sec. Because a photon acts like a particle, it is apparent that duality is also exhibited by electromagnetic energy.

It was postulated by L. DeBroglie[1] that the wave-particle dual character should not be confined just to electrons and photons, but should be characteristic of all fundamental particles such as protons, atoms, and molecules.

We can establish DeBroglie's hypothesis by considering the photon. As previously noted, a photon has an energy given by

$$W = hf$$

You will also recall from chapter 2 that

$$f\lambda = c \quad \text{or that} \quad f = \frac{c}{\lambda} \tag{3.3}$$

---

[1] L. DeBroglie, Thesis, Paris, 1924; *Ann. de Phys.,* Vol. 10, No. 3, 1925, p. 22.

Hence, the photon energy is

$$W = \frac{hc}{\lambda} = \text{wave energy} \tag{3.4}$$

According to the Special Theory of Relativity noted in chapter 2, a mass m is equivalent to a certain amount of energy given by

$$W = mc^2 = \text{particle energy} \tag{3.5}$$

Equate the two expressions for the photon energy given in equations (3.4) and (3.5). This gives

$$mc^2 = \frac{hc}{\lambda}$$

Cancel one c on both sides to obtain

$$mc = \frac{h}{\lambda} \tag{3.6}$$

However, the momentum p of a particle is the particle mass times the particle velocity, or

$$p = mc \tag{3.7}$$

Hence,

$$p = \frac{h}{\lambda} \tag{3.8}$$

DeBroglie extended this to include any particle such that if m = particle mass, v = particle velocity, $p = mv$ = momentum, then the wavelength associated with this moving particle is

$$\lambda = \frac{h}{p} \tag{3.9}$$

The existence of waves associated with moving electrons was experimentally verified by Davisson and Germer and later by G. P. Thomson. The same effect was observed with atoms and molecules by Stearn and T. H. Johnson.

With this apparently contradictory picture of the electron we are now ready to begin the discussion of atomic structure.

3.2. Necessary assumptions

Hydrogen is the simplest of all atoms because it consists of a heavy nucleus of a single proton and a single electron relatively quite distant from the nucleus. The atom is electrically neutral because the positive charge of the proton is exactly offset by the negative charge of the electron.

The forces inside an atom have never been measured directly. Practically all of our knowledge of forces is based upon observations of rather large scale phenomena. When the dimensions become as small as those associated with an atom, we really do not know definitely whether forces on this scale act the same way as for large scale phenomena or whether they act differently. Thus, we must make some assumptions regarding the nature of the forces present at the submicroscopic level. Actually, we have very little choice other than to assume that

(1) Coulomb's Law for the force between charged particles applies, and that

(2) Newton's Laws also apply.

These assumptions are not necessary in the more elegant derivations of wave mechanics, but they are necessary for us.

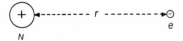

Figure 3.1. First representation of a hydrogen atom.

As a result of these assumptions, the electrostatic force of the nucleus on the electron in the hydrogen atom of figure 3.1 is

$$F = \frac{(+e)(-e)}{4\pi\epsilon_0 r^2} \tag{3.10}$$

or

$$F = -\frac{e^2}{4\pi\epsilon_0 r^2} \tag{3.11}$$

where e = electronic charge, r = distance of the electron from the nucleus. If this electrostatic force of attraction is not offset by some other force, the electron will be drawn to the proton and the total electric charge will be annihilated. This does not occur. Therefore, it is *assumed* that the electron revolves about the nucleus in a circular orbit as shown in figure 3.2. This is not a necessary assumption in wave mechanics.

From Newton's second law of motion, the mechanical force on the electron is

$$F = ma \qquad (3.12)$$

where a = centripetal acceleration = $-v^2/r$.
Hence, the mechanical force on the electron is

$$F = -\frac{mv^2}{r} \qquad (3.13)$$

Equate the electrical and mechanical forces. Cancel a common r and the result is

$$mv^2 = \frac{e^2}{4\pi\epsilon_0 r} \qquad (3.14)$$

We will use this equation in calculating the energy of the electron in the hydrogen atom in section 3.4.

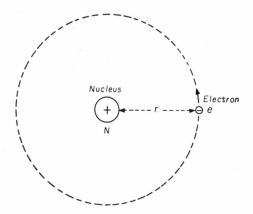

Figure 3.2. Second representation of a hydrogen atom.

3.3. Quantizing the orbit

Up to this point we have thought of the electron as a charged *particle* whirling about the nucleus in a circular orbit. Now we must consider its other aspect as represented by its properties as a wave. According to DeBroglie's hypothesis, a wavelength λ should be associated with an electron moving with a velocity v. That is,

$$\lambda = \frac{h}{p} = \frac{h}{mv} \qquad (3.15)$$

The distance around the orbit, which is the circumference of the circular path, must be an integral number of these electron wavelengths. If this were not so the electron waves would tend to cancel one another by interference. Hence,

$$2\pi r = n\lambda \tag{3.16}$$

where n = any integer = 1, 2, 3, . . . , ∞.

The general idea embodied in the last statement is illustrated by the very crude sketches in figure 3.3. Please do *not* interpret these figures as pictures of the electrons about the nucleus. They are used only to show the reason that the circumference of the orbit must be an integral multiple of λ.

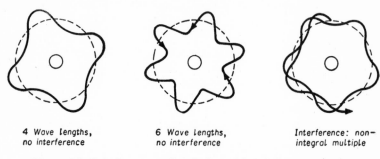

4 Wave lengths,   6 Wave lengths,   Interference: non-
no interference   no interference   integral multiple

Figure 3.3. Interference produced when orbital circumference is not an integral multiple of the wave length.

According to equation (3.16) the distance around the orbit must be a whole multiple of the electron wave length. This is called the *quantizing of the orbit*, because the orbital circumference has been restricted to certain very particular values. Substitute equation (3.15) for λ into equation (3.16).

$$2\pi r = \frac{nh}{mv}$$

Rearrange terms and solve for the magnitude of the orbital momentum of the electron. The result is

$$p = mvr = \frac{nh^*}{2\pi} \tag{3.17}$$

This equation states that the only possible orbits for the electron are those for which the magnitude of the orbital momentum is an

---

$* P = Iw = (mr^2)\, v/r.$

integral multiple of $(h/2\pi)$. n is called the *principal quantum number* and can have any value from 1 to infinity.

The radii of these permissible orbits can be calculated by solving for the velocity v from equation (3.17). That is,

$$v = \frac{nh}{m2\pi r} \tag{3.18}$$

Now substitute this into equation (3.14) to obtain

$$m\left(\frac{nh}{m2\pi r}\right)^2 = \frac{e^2}{4\pi\epsilon_0 r} \tag{3.19}$$

Solve for the radius r in this equation. The result is

$$r_n = n^2 \frac{\epsilon_0 h^2}{\pi m e^2} \tag{3.20}$$

where r_n = radius for any value of n. When $n = 1$, the radius works out to be

$$r_1 = 0.529 \times 10^{-10} \text{ meter} \tag{3.21}$$

Thus, the radius of any other orbit is

$$r_n = n^2 r_1 \tag{3.22}$$

According to equation (3.22) the radii of permissible orbits increases as the square of the principal quantum number. We can now show a picture of the hydrogen atom in two dimensions, as illustrated in figure 3.4. This shows a few of the permissible orbits.

It is obvious that the one electron in a hydrogen atom can only be in one orbit at a time. Under normal conditions the electron reverts to the lowest energy state possible. Thus, we must now determine which orbit corresponds to the lowest energy level. To do this we must calculate the electronic energy in any orbit. This derivation is carried through in the next section.

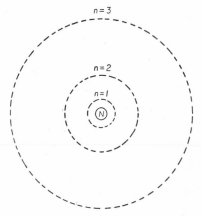

Figure 3.4. Some permissible orbits in the hydrogen atom.

3.4. Principal energy levels

The electron in an orbit in a hydrogen atom has potential energy by virtue of its position in the electric field of the nucleus. This energy is

$$W_p = \text{(electric potential)(electronic charge)}$$

$$= -\frac{e^2}{4\pi\epsilon_0 r_n} \qquad (3.23)$$

The electron also has kinetic energy because of its orbital rotation. Hence, from equation (3.14),

$$W_k = \tfrac{1}{2}mv^2 = \frac{e^2}{8\pi\epsilon_0 r_n} \qquad (3.24)$$

Thus, the total energy of the electron in any orbit is

$$W_n = W_p + W_k = -\frac{e^2}{8\pi\epsilon_0 r_n} \qquad (3.25)$$

Substitute for r_n from equation (3.20).

$$W_n = -\frac{me^4}{8\epsilon_0^2 n^2 h^2} \qquad (3.26)$$

Equation (3.25) shows that the electron energy is zero when the orbital radius, r_n, is infinite. The minus sign shows that the electron energy decreases as the orbital radius decreases. Thus, the lowest energy state for an electron corresponds to the orbit closest to the nucleus.

The same conclusion is equally evident from equation (3.26). This shows that the electron energy is zero when the principal quantum number n is infinite. The energy decreases, becoming progressively more negative as the principal quantum number is assigned progressively smaller values. Thus, the lowest energy state of an electron coincides with the least value for n, which is $n = 1$. This corresponds to the orbit nearest the nucleus.

The assumed motion of the electron in a plane, circular orbit is a very simple case. The electron has only one degree of freedom under these conditions so it is necessary to specify only one constant of this motion to achieve a complete description. The electron energy is selected as the constant of motion to be described. This energy is then quantized by the principal quantum number n. So, only a single quantum condition is required to describe the state of an electron traversing a circular orbit in a hydrogen atom.

A very important fact that has emerged from this discussion is given by equation (3.26). This shows that the electron can exist only in those particular energy levels computed for values of the principal quantum number 1, 2, 3, and so on. Intermediate energy levels are not possible at this stage of our analysis.

Equation (3.26) can be used to construct an energy level diagram for the electron in circular orbits in hydrogen. This is shown in figure

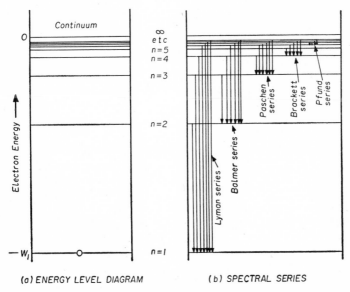

Figure 3.5. Schematic diagrams showing the energy levels permitted in a hydrogen atom and the electron transitions giving rise to the various spectral series.

3.5. Electronic energy is plotted vertically. The horizontal lines represent *permitted* energy levels corresponding to integral values of the principal quantum number n. As n becomes larger, the spacing between successive permitted levels becomes less and less until a *continuum* of energy levels is produced for $n = \infty$. The normal position of the electron, corresponding to the lowest permitted energy level, is shown by the small circle on the $n = 1$ level.

In closing, it seems appropriate to point out that the preceding discussion assumed a stationary nucleus. The nucleus would be stationary only if the mass of the nucleus were infinite. Because the nuclear mass is not infinite, both the nucleus and the electron rotate

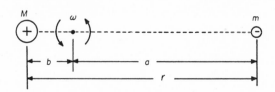

Figure 3.6. Rotation of the nucleus and the electron about a common axis.

about a common point as shown in figure 3.6. It is a straightforward exercise in classical mechanics to prove that

$$a = r \frac{M}{M + m}, \qquad b = r \frac{m}{M + m}$$

It can be shown that the energy of the atom is changed when the nuclear motion is included in the calculation. This fact permitted the spectroscopic determination of *deuterium*. However, the electron energies previously calculated remain unchanged.

3.5. Spectral series

Figure 3.5a shows an energy level diagram for a hydrogen atom. An electron in the atom can exist only at those energy levels denoted by the horizontal lines. If an electron is to change from one energy level to another, its energy must change by a whole quanta, hf. Energy must be added to the electron to make it move to higher energy levels. Photons of energy are released when an electron makes a transition downward from one permitted energy level to another.

Suppose then that an electron is located in some arbitrary orbit at some energy level corresponding to any value, except 1, of the principal quantum number n. In this state the electron energy is

$$W_n = -\frac{me^4}{8\epsilon_0^2 h^2 n^2}$$

Now suppose that the electron reverts to the energy level corresponding to $n = 1$. The electron energy is now

$$W_1 = -\frac{me^4}{8\epsilon_0^2 h^2}$$

W_1 is less than W_n so that the electron must release a photon of energy in the process of making the transition. The photon energy is

$$hf = W_n - W_1$$

Hence, the frequency of the photon is

$$f = \frac{W_n - W_1}{h}$$

or

$$f = \frac{me^4}{8\epsilon_0^2 h^3}\left(\frac{1}{1^2} - \frac{1}{n^2}\right) \tag{3.27}$$

where $n = 2, 3, 4, \ldots, \infty$.

This equation can be used to verify experimentally the correctness of the atomic theory proposed so far. This is done by measuring the photon frequencies associated with electronic transitions between the specified energy levels. Such experiments have been conducted and the results are in close agreement with theoretical predictions.

The series of frequencies associated with the transitions specified in equation (3.27) is called the *Lyman series*. All of these frequencies fall in the ultraviolet region.

Equation (3.27) can be expressed in a more common form. Multiply numerator and denominator by c, the velocity of light. This gives

$$f = c\left(\frac{me^4}{8c\epsilon_0^2 h^3}\right)\left(\frac{1}{1^2} - \frac{1}{n^2}\right)$$

The first bracketed factor is called the *Rydberg constant, R.* That is,

$$R = \frac{me^4}{8c\epsilon_0^2 h^3} = 10{,}967{,}758 \quad \text{per meter}$$

Hence, the equation for the Lyman series is

$$f = cR\left(\frac{1}{1^2} - \frac{1}{n^2}\right) \tag{3.28}$$

where $n = 2, 3, 4, \ldots, \infty$. The transitions involved in the production of the Lyman series are shown in figure 3.5b.

It is clear that another series of photon frequencies would be observed for electrons making jumps from any level n to the level corresponding to $n = 2$. This yields the *Balmer series* in the range of visible light and the frequencies are

$$f = cR \left(\frac{1}{2^2} - \frac{1}{n^2} \right)$$

where $n = 3, 4, 5, \ldots, \infty$. This is also illustrated in figure 3.5b together with some of the following series:

$$f \text{ (Paschen series)} \quad = cR \left(\frac{1}{3^2} - \frac{1}{n^2} \right) \qquad n = 4, 5, \ldots, \infty$$

$$f \text{ (Brackett series)} \quad = cR \left(\frac{1}{4^2} - \frac{1}{n^2} \right) \qquad n = 5, 6, \ldots, \infty$$

$$f \text{ (Pfund series)} \quad = cR \left(\frac{1}{5^2} - \frac{1}{n^2} \right) \qquad n = 6, 7, \ldots, \infty$$

$$f \text{ (Humphreys series)} = cR \left(\frac{1}{6^2} - \frac{1}{n^2} \right) \qquad n = 7, 8, \ldots, \infty$$

The first three of these series yield photons in the infrared region. The Humphreys series falls in the far infrared.

Each element in the periodic table can be described by an energy level diagram in which energy differences between allowed levels correspond to certain spectral series. However, none are as simple as that of the hydrogen atom.

3.6. Orbital quantum number

So far we have assumed that the electron in a hydrogen atom traverses one of an infinite number of circular orbits about the nu-

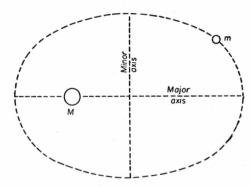

Figure 3.7. An elliptical orbit for the electron in a hydrogen atom.

cleus. However, *elliptical* orbits are distinctly possible in any motion under inverse square forces. Such an elliptical orbit will result with the nucleus at one of the foci. The orbit will be planar. The energy of the system depends only upon the major axis of the ellipse.

Sommerfeld introduced the idea of elliptical orbits into the model of the hydrogen atom. One such orbit for a hydrogen atom is shown schematically in figure 3.7.

A circle is a special case of an ellipse in which the two foci coincide, forming the center of the circle. Thus, the preceding discussion of circular orbits is just a special case of the generalized elliptical orbit. For the circular orbit there is only one component of momentum. Because the radius r is a constant as the angle ϕ varies during electron rotation, only angular momentum p_ϕ results. The one component of momentum leads to a single quantum condition in terms of both the energy and the momentum. The situation is somewhat different when the orbit is elliptical.

As ϕ varies in the case of the elliptical orbit, the radial distance r from the nucleus to the electron also varies. Over a complete revolution around the orbit, ϕ varies from 0 to 2π and r undergoes a cyclic variation from minimum to maximum. Thus, there are two components of momentum, the angular momentum p_ϕ and the radial momentum p_r. Sommerfeld assumed that each component of momentum must be quantized. As a result, the elliptical orbit requires two quantum numbers for its complete description.

The two quantum conditions can be defined in a number of different ways. The quantum numbers can be specified directly from the quantum conditions on each of the components of momentum. When defined this way the electron energy depends upon both quantum numbers, but is independent of the shape of the orbit. This is possible because the energy depends only upon the major axis of the ellipse; it does not depend upon the shape. However, the use of these two quantum numbers leads to some notational confusion when the quantum numbers of wave mechanics are introduced.

To avoid this confusion we will define our two quantum conditions so that one specifies the energy of the electron in its orbit and the other specifies the shape of the orbit. In this way the electron energy will depend only upon one of the two quantum numbers.

From these considerations we now define two quantum numbers as follows:

n = principal quantum number = 1, 2, 3, ... , ∞

l = orbital quantum number = 0, 1, 2, ... , $(n - 1)$

The principal quantum number specifies the major axis of the ellipse and thereby specifies the electron energy as the first of the two quantum conditions. This energy is

$$W_n = -\frac{me^4}{8e_0^2 n^2 h^2}$$
(3.29)

The orbital quantum number can have only the values specified. It is clearly determined by n. The orbital quantum number specifies the shape of the orbit by specifying the minor axis of the ellipse. Because it also depends upon the major axis of the ellipse, as shown by its dependence upon n, it is used to express the second quantum condition on the total angular momentum as

$$p_l = \frac{h}{2\pi} \sqrt{l(l + 1)}$$
(3.30)

The assignment of these two quantum numbers for the first three values of n is illustrated in table 2.

Table 2

ASSIGNMENT OF FIRST TWO QUANTUM NUMBERS

If n is	then l is	and the orbit is
1	0	elliptical
2	0	elliptical
2	1	circular
3	0	elliptical
3	1	elliptical
3.	2	circular

3.7. The relativity correction

The speed of the electron in its motion around its elliptical orbit is very great, so great that it is necessary to account for the change in mass derived from the Special Theory of Relativity. Sommerfeld worked out this correction and showed that the path of an electron is a rosette as shown in figure 3.8.

The effect of this relativistic mass correction is to introduce a correction factor in the equation for the energy of an electron. The corrected equation, as derived by Sommerfeld, for hydrogen is

$$W_n = -\frac{me^4}{8\epsilon_0^2 n^2 h^2}\left[1 + \frac{1}{137n}\left(\frac{n}{l+1} - \frac{3}{4}\right)\right] \qquad (3.31)$$

It is clear from this formula that the total electron energy is determined by both the principal and orbital quantum numbers. Thus, the various values assigned to l have the effect of splitting the main energy level determined by the principal quantum number into n separate energy levels very close to one another. This idea is illustrated by the approximate energy level diagram for a hydrogen atom shown in figure 3.9.

3.8. Electron spin

In spite of the success of the Sommerfeld relativity correction in accounting for a great many of the known properties of the atom, difficulties developed shortly thereafter as new evidence became available. It was

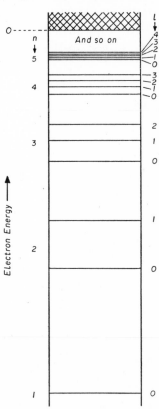

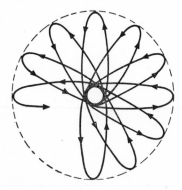

Figure 3.8. Rosette pattern of electronic orbit resulting from the relativity correction.

Figure 3.9. Energy levels in a hydrogen atom for various values of n and l.

shown by Uhlenbeck and Goudsmit in 1925 that these difficulties could be resolved by assuming that the electron has the properties of a charged body spinning about its axis like a top. Dirac put this theory on a very sound basis in 1928.

The angular momentum of the electron caused by its spin is *assigned* the value

$$p_s = \frac{h}{2\pi} \sqrt{s(s+1)} \qquad (3.32)$$

where s = spin quantum number = $\frac{1}{2}$.

The complexity of our physical picture of the atom has now increased to the point where we need three quantum numbers to describe the state of an electron in an atom. These three numbers are

n = principal quantum number = $1, 2, 3, \ldots, \infty$

l = orbital quantum number = $0, 1, 2, \ldots, (n-1)$

s = spin quantum number = $\frac{1}{2}$

Dirac's theory developed from his solution of the relativistic wave equation. It is interesting that the electron energy calculated by Dirac for the hydrogen atom, assuming electron spin, is exactly the same as that calculated by Sommerfeld, who neglected spin and considered only the relativistic mass correction. Thus, more recent theory ascribes the splitting of energy levels to electron spin rather than to the relativistic mass correction.

3.9. Vector representation of electronic momenta

An electron moving in its orbit about the nucleus has angular momentum. Angular momentum is a vector quantity and is represented by a vector along the axis of rotation and perpendicular to the plane of rotation in the sense shown in figure 3.10.

In our previous model of the atom the magnitude of the angular, or orbital, momentum was assigned a value controlled by the orbital quantum number l. That is,

$$p_l = \frac{h}{2\pi} \sqrt{l(l+1)}$$

where $l = 0, 1, 2, \ldots, (n-1)$. Now we want to express the orbital momentum as a vector. Define a vector quantum number l to have a value

$$\boldsymbol{l} = l\boldsymbol{i} \qquad (3.33)$$

where i = unit vector perpendicular to the plane of rotation as shown in figure 3.10. Therefore, the total orbital momentum in vector form is

$$p_l = \frac{h}{2\pi} \sqrt{\frac{l+1}{l}} \, l \quad (3.34)$$

This vector representation is a necessary step prior to the final quantizing operations described in section 3.10.

It is also desirable to express the spin momentum in vector form. Here we define a *spin vector* s as follows:

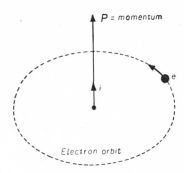

Figure 3.10. Vector representation of angular momentum.

$$s = si_s \quad (3.35)$$

where i_s = unit spin vector. Therefore, the vector spin momentum is

$$p_s = \frac{h}{2\pi} \sqrt{\frac{s+1}{s}} \, s \quad (3.36)$$

In an atom containing several electrons, the spin vectors s for the electrons can be either parallel or antiparallel as shown in figure 3.11. No intermediate orientations are normally possible. This is given

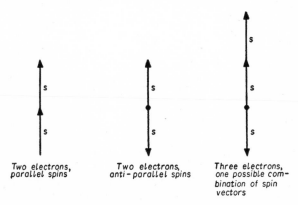

Two electrons, parallel spins

Two electrons, anti-parallel spins

Three electrons, one possible combination of spin vectors

Figure 3.11. Combination of spin vectors in atoms having more than one electron.

without proof, so you must accept it as an assumption that fits experimentally determined facts.

3.10. Magnetic quantum numbers

So far only electron motion in a single plane has been considered. In other words, a two-dimensional model of the hydrogen atom has been proposed. In reality, an atom is three-dimensional and the plane of the orbit can be inclined at any angle with respect to some system of coordinates. If such a system of coordinates is somehow specified, then one more quantum condition will be necessary to describe the state of an electron in an atom.

The three quantum conditions stipulated up to this point are necessary to describe the state of an electron in a two-dimensional model of an atom. The introduction of one more degree of freedom in the system requires the specification of one more quantum condition.

The determination of this final quantum condition resolves itself into a problem of relating the electron motion to some particular system of meaningful coordinates. Offhand it seems that we might just arbitrarily select some system of coordinates and then proceed with the final quantizing operation. This is not very helpful, however, because such a set of *arbitrary* coordinates has no meaning with respect to physical reality.

There is a way out of this apparent dilemma. It was shown in chapter 2 that a force $F = qv \times B$ is exerted on an electric charge q moving with a velocity v in a magnetic field B. When an electron is in rotational motion, as in an atom, this force is directed perpendicular to the plane of the orbit. This makes the force either parallel or antiparallel to the momentum vector. The effect of this force is to cause the electron orbit to take up definite positions in space with respect to the magnetic field vector. Any field, no matter how weak it may be, will provide space orientation for the electron orbit; this provides the mechanism for specifying the final quantum condition.

The vector representing the orbital momentum is l as defined in equation (3.33). The component of l in the direction of some applied magnetic field is called the *magnetic orbital quantum number*, m_l. Because l can have only particular values, there are only particular orientations in space for the vector l with respect to the magnetic field.

It can be shown from wave mechanics, but is not proved here, that the *only* possible values for the magnetic orbital quantum number are

$$m_l = 0, \pm 1, \pm 2, \pm 3, \ldots , \pm l \qquad (3.37)$$

Hence, there are $(2l + 1)$ possible values for m_l. These ideas are illustrated for the case where $l = 4$ in figure
3.12. Please note that the only orientations possible for l are those giving integral
values for the projection of l in the direction
of the magnetic field.

You should also consider the fact that
a *spinning* electron in a magnetic field
will experience a force. This force acts in
such a way that it causes the total spin
momentum vector to be either parallel or
antiparallel to the direction of the applied
magnetic field. The spin vector s is used to
represent the spin momentum. The projection of the spin vector s in the direction
of the magnetic field is called the *magnetic
spin quantum number*, m_s. This is illustrated for one case in figure 3.13.

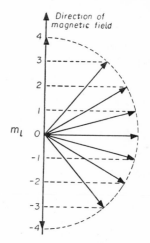

Figure 3.12. Values for m_l corresponding to various positions of the orbital momentum vector l.

We have introduced a total of five
quantum numbers so far, as follows:

$$
\begin{cases}
n &= \text{principal quantum number} = 1, 2, 3, \ldots , \infty \\
l &= \text{orbital quantum number} = 0, 1, 2, \ldots , (n-1) \\
m_l &= \text{magnetic orbital quantum number} = 0, \pm 1, \pm 2, \ldots , \pm l \\
m_s &= \text{magnetic spin quantum number} = \pm \tfrac{1}{2} \\
s &= \text{spin quantum number} = \tfrac{1}{2}
\end{cases}
$$

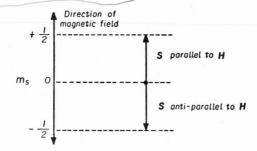

Figure 3.13. Values for m_s corresponding to various orientations of spin vector s. Only values possible for m_s are $\pm \tfrac{1}{2}$.

Only four of these five quantum numbers are required to specify the state of an electron in a three-dimensional model of an atom. The only unnecessary number is the spin quantum number s. Thus, from this point on, the complete state of an electron will be specified using the four quantum numbers n, l, m_l, and m_s.

3.11. Assignment of quantum numbers

The four quantum numbers to be used to describe the state of an electron in an atom were listed in the preceding section. In 1925, Pauli formulated the now famous *Exclusion Principle*. According to this principle, no two electrons in an atom can have the same set of four quantum numbers. This is stated as a rule, without proof. Results obtained following this rule are closely confirmed by experiment. The Pauli exclusion principle provides us with a convenient rule for assigning quantum numbers. It is necessary to remember the following characteristics of the quantum numbers:

(1) n = principal quantum number = $1, 2, 3, \ldots, \infty$. This specifies the main energy level, or *main shell*, of the electron by specifying the major axis of the elliptical orbit.

(2) l = orbital quantum number = $0, 1, 2, \ldots, (n-1)$. This subdivides the electrons in the main shell into n slightly different energy levels, or *subshells*. This quantizes the orbital momentum of the electron by specifying the minor axis of the elliptical orbit.

(3) m_l = magnetic orbital quantum number = $0, \pm 1, \pm 2, \ldots,$ $\pm l$. This completes the space quantizing of the electron orbit by specifying the particular orientations possible in space for the plane elliptical orbit. This does not affect the electron energy.

(4) m_s = magnetic spin quantum number = $\pm \frac{1}{2}$. This specifies the orientation of the electron spin vector in space with respect to the same frame of reference as that used in specifying m_l.

With all of this data on the possible values for the quantum numbers we can construct table 3 by using the exclusion principle. You should study this table very carefully. The remarks in the next paragraph should assist you in analyzing table 3.

When $n = 1$, the only possible value for l is 0. Because l is 0, the only possible value for m_l is 0. However, m_s can be either $+\frac{1}{2}$ or $-\frac{1}{2}$ so that there can be only two electrons in the first main shell.

When $n = 2$ there are two subshells corresponding to $l = 0$ and $l = 1$. In the subshell for $l = 0$, m_l can only be 0 and $m_s = \pm\frac{1}{2}$. Hence, there are, at most, two electrons in this subshell. For the $l = 1$ subshell, m_l can be -1, 0, and $+1$. For each of these three values of m_l the spin quantum number m_s can be either $+\frac{1}{2}$ or $-\frac{1}{2}$. Hence, a maximum of six electrons will fit into this subshell.

Table 3

ASSIGNMENT OF QUANTUM NUMBERS

n	l	m_l	m_s	Electrons in Subshell	Electrons in Main Shell
1	0	0	$+\frac{1}{2}$	2	2
1	0	0	$-\frac{1}{2}$		
2	0	0	$+\frac{1}{2}$	2	
2	0	0	$-\frac{1}{2}$		
2	1	0	$+\frac{1}{2}$		8
2	1	9	$-\frac{1}{2}$		
2	1	$+1$	$+\frac{1}{2}$	6	
2	1	$+1$	$-\frac{1}{2}$		
2	1	-1	$+\frac{1}{2}$		
2	1	-1	$-\frac{1}{2}$		
3	0	0	$+\frac{1}{2}$	2	
3	0	0	$-\frac{1}{2}$		
3	1	0	$+\frac{1}{2}$		
3	1	0	$-\frac{1}{2}$		
3	1	$+1$	$+\frac{1}{2}$	6	
3	1	$+1$	$-\frac{1}{2}$		
3	1	-1	$+\frac{1}{2}$		
3	1	-1	$-\frac{1}{2}$		
3	2	0	$+\frac{1}{2}$		18
3	2	0	$-\frac{1}{2}$		
3	2	$+1$	$+\frac{1}{2}$		
3	2	$+1$	$-\frac{1}{2}$		
3	2	-1	$+\frac{1}{2}$	10	
3	2	-1	$-\frac{1}{2}$		
3	2	$+2$	$+\frac{1}{2}$		
3	2	$+2$	$-\frac{1}{2}$		
3	2	-2	$+\frac{1}{2}$		
3	2	-2	$-\frac{1}{2}$		

The same process can be followed for any value of the principal quantum number n.

If you study table 3 very carefully you will see that the following statements are true:

(1) Maximum number of subshells in a main shell = n

(2) Maximum number of electrons in a subshell = $2(2l + 1)$

In other words, the principal quantum number n determines the main shell. The orbital quantum number l determines the subshell. The two magnetic quantum numbers, m_l and m_s, together with the exclusion principle, determine the number of electrons in each subshell. These ideas are applied to atomic structure in section 3.12.

3.12. Extranuclear atomic structure

The dynamic array of electrons about the positively charged nucleus follows the pattern established by the quantum number assignments given in the preceding section. In the *normal state* of an atom the electrons are in their lowest energy levels. Hence, the inner shells and subshells fill first. There are some *apparent* exceptions to this statement as we shall see shortly.

In the discussion that follows the symbol Z is used to denote the *atomic number* of the element. This is numerically equal to the number of nuclear protons or the number of orbital electrons.

Hydrogen is the simplest element with an atomic number $Z = 1$. Thus, the single electron associated with the hydrogen atom enters the lowest energy level corresponding to $n = 1$ and $l = 0$. Helium, with $Z = 2$, is next and the second electron fills the $n = 1$, $l = 0$ subshell. The two electrons have opposing spins so the net electronic spin of the atom is zero. The quantum numbers for the two electrons differ only in the value assigned to m_s.

For lithium, with $Z = 3$, two electrons fill the $n = 1$, $l = 0$ subshell, so the third electron must move up to the next higher energy level corresponding to $n = 2$, $l = 0$. This change in quantum number assignments is dictated by the exclusion principle and the requirement that the electrons enter the lowest possible energy level not already filled with electrons.

Beryllium, which has $Z = 4$, is next. The fourth electron completes the $n = 2$, $l = 0$ subshell with a spin opposite to that of the other electron in this subshell. Boron, $Z = 5$, has the same structure as beryllium, but the fifth electron enters the $n = 2, l = 1$ subshell. This is the next higher energy level.

The same general process can be followed through successive electron additions to fix the electron assignments for all of the atoms. Table 4 shows the assignments for the first 46 elements.

An apparent discrepancy appears for the first time with potassium, which is the 19th element. In this case a quantum level is skipped. The 18th electron fills the $n = 3, l = 1$ subshell. Normally, we would expect the 19th electron to move to the next subshell corresponding to $n = 3, l = 2$. However, contrary to expectations, the 19th electron

Table 4
DISTRIBUTION OF ELECTRONS IN VARIOUS ELEMENTS

Value of n		1	2		3			4			
Value of l		0	0	1	0	1	2	0	1	2	3
Z	Name										
1	H	1									
2	He	2									
3	Li	2	1								
4	Be	2	2								
5	B	2	2	1							
6	C	2	2	2							
7	N	2	2	3							
8	O	2	2	4							
9	F	2	2	5							
10	Ne	2	2	6							
11	Na				1						
12	Mg				2						
13	Al				2	1					
14	Si	10-electron			2	2					
15	P	core			2	3					
16	S				2	4					
17	Cl				2	5					
18	A				2	6					
19	K							1			
20	Ca		18-electron					2			
21	Sc		core				1	2			

Table 4 (Cont'd.)

DISTRIBUTION OF ELECTRONS IN VARIOUS ELEMENTS (Cont'd.)

Value of n	1	2		3			4				5		
Value of l	0	0	1	0	1	2	0	1	2	3	0	1	2
Z — Name													
22 Ti						2	2						
23 V						3	2						
24 Cr						5	1						
25 Mn						5	2						
26 Fe		18-electron	core			6	2						
27 Co						7	2						
28 Ni						8	2						
29 Cu						10	1						
30 Zn						10	2						
31 Ga						10	2	1					
32 Ge						10	2	2					
33 As						10	2	3					
34 Se						10	2	4					
35 Br						10	2	5					
36 Kr						10	2	6					
37 Rb											1		
38 Sr											2		
39 Y									1		2		
40 Zr			36-electron		core				2		2		
41 Cb									4		1		
42 Mo									5		1		
43 Ma									6		1		
44 Ru									7		1		
45 Rh									8		1		
46 Pd									10				

appears in the *next* higher level at $n = 4$, $l = 0$, leaving $n = 3$, $l = 2$ empty. A similar situation arises with rubidium ($Z = 37$), silver ($Z = 47$), caesium ($Z = 55$), and gold ($Z = 79$).

The discrepancy is more apparent than real. You must remember that the equation derived for the electron energy was correct only for the very simple case of a single electron and proton. It seems fairly clear that slightly different energy levels will be obtained when the atom has many electrons and protons. This is the cause of the

apparent inconsistency. The electrons *are* in their lowest possible
energy levels in all atoms in the normal state. The skipping of quantum levels as noted is evidence that the many-electron atoms differ

at times from the single electron atom
in the calculation of energy levels.
This problem is explored in a little
more detail in the next section.

3.13. Many electron atoms

It was shown in the preceding section that the simple energy level diagram obtained using hydrogen as a
model fails at various points for many-
electron atoms. If we actually calculated the energy levels for many-electron
atoms we would find that the spacing
between main energy levels eventually
becomes so small that the subshells
overlap from one main energy level to
the next.

A careful study of this effect reveals
that the energy levels follow the
sequence shown schematically in figure 3.14 for some materials. Slightly
different arrangements are obtained
for other materials. Two examples are
shown in chapter 5 in figures 5.6 and
5.7.

Figure 3.14 shows the approximate
relative positions of the various energy
levels for one class of many-electron
atoms. The white circles are used to
represent electrons. The total number
of white circles represents the maximum number of electrons permitted in
each energy level.

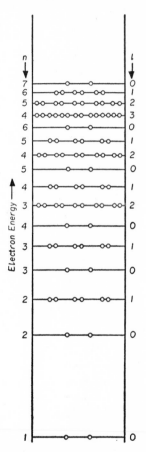

Figure 3.14. Electron energy
level diagram for a many-electron atom; shows maximum
number of electrons allowed in
each level.

This diagram differs from the hydrogen diagram. The difference
appears in the overlapping of the energy levels commencing with

$n = 3$ and 4 and continuing thereafter. This is the diagram that should be used in constructing certain parts of table 4. This shows why the 19th electron occupies the $n = 4$, $l = 0$ level rather than the $n = 3$, $l = 2$ as predicted from the hydrogen atom model. According to figure 3.14, $n = 4$, $l = 0$ corresponds to a lower energy level than $n = 3$, $l = 2$. Hence, the electron falls to the lowest unfilled energy level.

You should check figure 3.14 against the data in table 4. When you come up against a discrepancy it signifies that some other arrangement of energy levels is required, such as those shown in figures 5.6 and 5.7. The first such discrepancy occurs with element 29. The diagram in figure 5.7 applies to this case.

3.14. Valence, excitation, and ionization

Under normal conditions the number of extranuclear electrons is exactly equal to the number of protons in the nucleus. The atom is electrically neutral. The atom is said to be in the *normal state* when these electrons are in the lowest possible energy levels; these energy levels correspond to the orbits nearest the nucleus.

The outermost electrons in the dynamic array are called the *valence* electrons. These are the electrons that take part in electrical conduction as we shall see in chapter 5.

In the energy level diagrams previously shown and discussed, it was evident that electrons could exist only at certain particular levels. The regions between these permitted levels are forbidden so that electrons can have only the particular specified energies. These permitted energy levels in an atom are always separated by *discrete* energy differences.

If any one electron in an atom is raised to a permitted energy level higher than the one occupied in the normal state, the atom is said to be *excited;* the valence electrons are the ones most susceptible to excitation. This is so because the next higher permitted energy levels are empty. In addition, the energy difference between the valence level and the next higher level is small compared to the energy differences between lower energy levels. An *inner* electron is difficult to excite because there are no empty spaces in the next higher energy level. Hence, an inner electron would have to be excited into a valence level, at least, if it is not completely filled.

This requires more energy than is needed to excite a valence electron.

The energy required to excite an electron may come from some externally supplied energetic particle such as an electron or photon. Excitation is possible only if the electron in an atom receives a discrete amount of energy equal to the energy difference between its energy level and the excitation level. In short, the electron in an atom must receive a very specific amount of energy to accomplish excitation.

Photons are the most convenient sources of discrete amounts of energy. They have an energy $W = hf$ that is linearly dependent upon the frequency of the light. Thus, by changing the frequency of the light the photon can be made to have virtually any energy. In this way we can supply energy in just the right amount to produce the desired excitation.

A stream of photons is aimed at an atom. The photon energy is carefully set equal to the excitation energy. Eventually a photon collides with a valence electron in the atom. When this occurs the photon releases its energy to the electron and disappears. This increment in energy excites the electron to some higher permitted energy level.

A brief moment later the electron may revert back to its original normal state. To do this it must release an amount of energy exactly equal to the amount absorbed from the photon. As a result, when the electron reverts back to its normal state it ejects a photon with an energy equal to that of the original photon. A large part of the supporting experimental evidence for atomic theory was derived from studies of the frequencies of photons ejected following excitation of atoms.

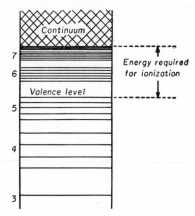

Figure 3.15. Minimum energy required to ionize a particular atom.

In an extreme case of excitation a valence electron can be completely separated from its parent atom. This occurs when an electron acquires sufficient energy to reach the zero energy level shown in figure 3.15. The atom is then *ionized*. It is a *positive ion* because there is one positive nuclear charge that is not offset by an orbital electron. The ion is said to be *singly charged* because its net charge is that of one proton. Some atoms can form doubly charged, or even triply charged ions.

Another possibility is also evident. Instead of removing electrons from atoms and making positive ions, it should be possible in some atoms to *add* extra orbital electrons. In such a case the atom acquires a net negative charge equal to that of the excess electrons. The atom is then a *negative ion*.

3.15. Splitting of energy levels

Up to this point we have considered the energy level diagrams for single atoms only. The situation is somewhat more involved when there are many atoms present because interactions develop between the electrons and nuclei of adjacent atoms. The extent of the interactions would be expected to increase as the distance between atoms decreases.

We can illustrate this general idea by the hypothetical case shown in figure 3.16. Here we have a row, or line, of five hydrogen atoms

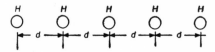

Figure 3.16. Five equally spaced hydrogen atoms arranged in a line.

all equally spaced along the row. As the spacing between the atoms decreases, the extent of the electronic interactions increases and a number of apparently new energy levels are created. This is shown by the energy level diagram of figure 3.17. In this figure electronic energy is plotted vertically and the spacing between atoms is shown horizontally. Only the first two quantum states are shown.

From figure 3.17 it is clear that the energy level diagram is essentially that of an isolated hydrogen atom when the atoms are rather remote from one another. This corresponds to the right-hand side of the figure. As the spacing between atoms decreases toward the left of figure 3.17, interactions result and five apparently new energy levels are created for each quantum state. No new levels are actually created. The existing levels which had the same energy now have different energies.

This is an admitted simplification of a rather complicated problem. However, you can probably see that when this reasoning is carried to a consideration of gases, where many atoms are present, many more new energy levels are created. It is also clear that the spacing and precise values for the energy levels of the gas will depend upon the gas pressure, which controls the atomic spacing, and the type of atoms.

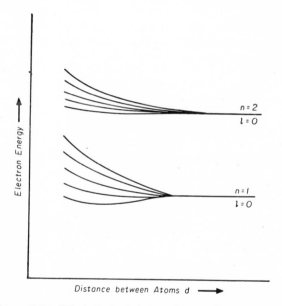

Figure 3.17. Effect of atomic interactions on the energy level diagram.

If the atoms are further compressed so that the gas becomes a liquid, the interatomic forces are greatly increased and this causes a large number of intermediate energy levels to be created. This again reduces the energy difference between successive permitted energy levels. Further reductions in spacing would occur if the liquid were compressed to a solid.

A word of caution should be injected at this point. Our discussion here has primarily centered about hydrogen atoms. Actually, most of the atoms of primary interest to us are more complicated and involve many more electrons. Because of the larger number of electrons in the outer orbits, and because the radii of these orbits increase as the square of the principal quantum number, interactions between the outer electrons of heavier atoms occur at larger atomic separations than is the case for hydrogen. Such materials usually solidify before there are extensive interpenetrations of electrons from one atom into the orbits about other atoms.

The most important conclusion we draw from this is that liquefaction and solidification of the heavier elements will not cause appreciable splitting of the lower energy levels of the atoms. The most important splitting of energy levels occurs at the levels of the valence electrons.

We shall see in chapters 5 and 6 that this has important practical consequences. As it develops, the interactions of valence energy levels of metallic atoms are so great that a nearly continuous distribution of allowed energy levels is created for the valence electrons. This contrasts with the very *discrete* character of the allowed energy levels for electrons in single atoms. Actually the distribution of allowed energies for valence electrons is never really continuous; it is always discrete. However, the difference in energy of the various levels becomes very, very small.

PROBLEMS

3.1. Compute the values for the radii permitted electrons in a hydrogen atom corresponding to the first five values for the principal quantum number.

3.2. Compute the values for the lowest five main energy levels in a hydrogen atom. Plot these to scale on an energy level diagram.

3.3. For each of the first five values of the principal quantum number, compute the energy levels corresponding to each permitted value of the orbital quantum number. Plot your results to scale.

3.4. Make up a table assigning values for the various quantum numbers corresponding to a value of 4 for the principal quantum number.

3.5. From the data computed in problem 3.2, determine the first ionization potential of the hydrogen atom.

3.6. From the data calculated in problem 3.3, calculate the first five excitation potentials of hydrogen.

3.7. Calculate the wave length of the photon ejected when an ionized hydrogen atom reverts back to its normal state.

3.8. Compute the photon wave lengths associated with the excited electrons in problem 3.6.

3.9. Calculate the first ionization potential of lithium, sodium, and potassium from the diagram plotted in problem 3.3.

4

NUCLEAR STRUCTURE

In the light of recent history it would be forcing the obvious to stress the practical engineering importance attached to the structure of atomic nuclei. While the subject is immensely important, this chapter is not a prerequisite to succeeding chapters and may be by-passed for the moment if desirable.

It was shown in chapter 3 that all atoms are composed of a dynamic array of electrons surrounding a very dense, positive nucleus. Chapter 3 was concerned with the extranuclear array of electrons. In this chapter attention is confined to the nucleus and the various nuclear reactions most frequently encountered.

At present there is only the beginning of a complete nuclear theory. The subject is still the object of very considerable research activity. Because we have no model, like that used in chapter 3, this chapter merely sets forth the barest essentials of what is currently believed to be the properties and structure of atomic nuclei.

4.1. Nucleons

Hydrogen is the simplest of all atoms. The essential elements of its structure are set forth in figure 4.1 in a schematic manner. The hydrogen atom consists of a single orbital electron revolving about a positively charged *nucleus*. The atom is electrically neutral. Therefore, the nuclear charge must be equal and opposite to the electronic charge.

The mass m of the electron has been measured in various different ways. Its most commonly accepted value is

$$m = 9.107 \times 10^{-31} \quad \text{kg} \qquad (4.1)$$

The mass M_H of the hydrogen atom has been accurately measured and is generally taken to be

$$M_\mathrm{H} = 1837.13m \qquad (4.2)$$

You should now recall the Einstein mass-energy equation $W = mc^2$. According to this, mass and energy are different manifestations of the same physical phenomenon. Thus, the energy binding the electron to the nucleus is equivalent to a certain amount of mass Δm. This makes the total measured mass M_H of the hydrogen atom equal to the sum of the masses of the constituent parts less the equivalent mass representing the electronic binding energy. That is,

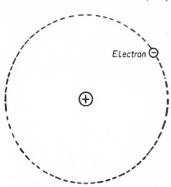

Figure 4.1. Schematic representation of a hydrogen atom.

$$M_\mathrm{H} = M_p + m - \Delta m \qquad (4.3)$$

where M_p = mass of the nucleus of the atom. In other words,

$$M_\mathrm{H} = \left(\begin{array}{c}\text{nuclear}\\\text{mass}\end{array}\right) + \left(\begin{array}{c}\text{electron}\\\text{mass}\end{array}\right) - \left(\begin{array}{c}\text{mass equivalent of}\\\text{electron binding energy}\end{array}\right)$$

Hence, the mass of the nucleus, M_p, is

$$M_p = M_\mathrm{H} + \Delta m - m \qquad (4.4)$$

The mass of the electron is equivalent to an energy of about 500,000 *electron-volts*[1]. The atomic mass is nearly 2000 times larger than this. However, the electronic binding energy, which is only about 13 or 14 electron-volts, is entirely negligible and can be neglected. Hence, the mass of the nucleus of the hydrogen atom is

$$M_p = M_\mathrm{H} - m = 1837.13m - m \qquad (4.5)$$

or $\qquad\qquad M_p = 1836.13m \qquad\qquad\qquad\qquad (4.6)$

This hydrogen nucleus is called a *proton*. It has the mass given by equation (4.6). The proton charge is equal and opposite to the charge

---

[1] 1 electron-volt = 1 eV = energy gained by an electron in falling through a potential difference of 1 volt.

on an electron. About 99.98 per cent of all naturally occurring hydrogen has the structure just discussed.

About 0.02 per cent of the naturally occurring hydrogen has a mass nearly twice that of ordinary hydrogen. More specifically, the mass of this heavy hydrogen, or *deuterium*, is 3669.83 times the electron mass. Thus, it appears that the nucleus must contain a second uncharged particle with a mass approximately the same as the mass of the proton.

This second nuclear constituent is called a *neutron* because it is electrically neutral. Careful measurements give it a value of

$$M_n = \text{neutron mass} = 1838.66m \qquad (4.7)$$

Hence, the structure of heavy hydrogen can be indicated schematically as shown in figure 4.2.

It is believed that protons and neutrons are the *only* constituents of the nucleus. They are called *nucleons*. Although electrons, pho-

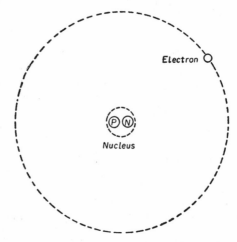

Figure 4.2. Schematic representation of heavy hydrogen.

tons, and other particles are sometimes ejected from nuclei, it is still believed that only protons and neutrons are actually present in the nucleus.

The nucleons are thought to be undergoing rapid motion within some very narrow region of space. This region is thought to be essentially spherical in shape as shown by the dotted circle in figure 4.2.

Although the details of this motion are not entirely known, it appears that in about half of the known nuclei, the nucleus as a whole spins about an axis passing through its center of gravity. Thus, the spinning nucleus has angular momentum just like the spinning electron discussed in chapter 3. Moreover, like the electron, such nuclei will have magnetic spin moments, but the values of the moments are much less than those observed for electrons. Also, as we shall see, both the proton and the neutron are assumed to spin about their own axes.

If you are a careful and observant reader you may have noted that the mass of heavy hydrogen is *not* equal to the sum of the masses of the electron, proton, and neutron. The reason for this is explained in the next section.

4.2. Nuclear binding energy

The values for the neutron and proton masses were given earlier as multiples of the electron mass as follows:

$$m = \text{electron mass} = 9.107 \times 10^{-31} \quad \text{kg}$$
$$M_p = \text{proton mass} = 1836.13m \quad \text{kg}$$
$$M_n = \text{neutron mass} = 1838.66m \quad \text{kg}$$

Nuclear physicists generally express mass in terms of another unit called the *atomic mass unit*, abbreviated amu. This unit is defined as follows:[2]

$$1 \text{ amu} = \tfrac{1}{16} \text{ (mass of oxygen)} = 1.660 \times 10^{-27} \quad \text{kg} \quad (4.8)$$

In this system, the masses of the three particles mentioned so far have the following values:

$$m = \text{electron mass} = 0.000549 \quad \text{amu} \quad (4.9)$$
$$M_p = \text{proton mass} = 1.007593 \quad \text{amu} \quad (4.10)$$
$$M_n = \text{neutron mass} = 1.008982 \quad \text{amu} \quad (4.11)$$

Now, the total energy of any assembled system can be written as follows: let W = energy of the system assembled, W_T = energy of the system completely disassembled, ΔW_a = work on system required to assemble it. Hence,

$$W = W_T + \Delta W_a$$

---

[2] Specifically, the $_8O^{16}$ isotope.

Now, the work required to disassemble a system is equal and opposite to the energy required to assemble it. That is,

$$\Delta W_b = -\Delta W_a = \text{work on system to disassemble it}$$

Hence, $W = W_T - \Delta W_b$

or $\Delta W_b = W_T - W$

When this equation is applied to an atom, terms are defined as follows:

W = energy equivalent of the mass of the assembled atom = Mc^2

W_T = sum of the energy equivalents of the masses of the constituent parts of the atom = $M_T c^2$

ΔW_b = energy required to remove the electron from the atom plus the energy required to disassemble the nucleus

The energy required to remove the electrons from their proper orbits is so small compared to other terms that it is generally neglected. As a result,

$$\Delta W_b = \text{nuclear binding energy} = \Delta Mc^2$$

where ΔM = mass equivalent of the nuclear binding energy. Thus, the equation for the energy required to disassemble the nucleus, which is the nuclear binding energy, is

$$\Delta Mc^2 = M_T c^2 - Mc^2$$

or, after cancellation of the common c^2 factor,

$$\Delta M = M_T - M$$

This equation can now be applied to the case of heavy hydrogen to calculate the energy required to disassemble the nucleus. An atom of heavy hydrogen consists of one electron, one proton, and one neutron. The total mass of its constituent parts is

$$M_T = M_p + M_n + m = 2.017124 \quad \text{amu}$$

However, the mass of the assembled heavy hydrogen atom is experimentally found to be

$$M = 2.014735 \quad \text{amu}$$

Hence, the mass equivalence of the nuclear binding energy is

$$\Delta M = M_T - M = 0.002389 \quad \text{amu}$$

Nuclear physicists generally express energies in *electron-volts*, eV, or *million electron-volts*, MeV. To convert mass in amu to energy in

MeV, use the following equation which was derived from the mass-energy relationship:

$$\text{energy (MeV)} = (\text{mass in amu})(931.162) \tag{4.12}$$

Thus, the binding energy of the proton and the neutron in the heavy hydrogen nucleus is

$$\Delta W = (0.002389)(931.162) = 2.225 \quad \text{MeV} \tag{4.13}$$

This binding energy is believed to arise from strong forces of attraction that appear between protons and neutrons when they are brought very close together. By the word *close*, we mean something of the

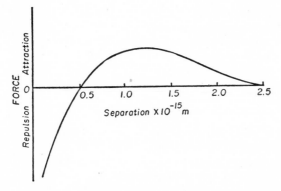

Figure 4.3. Force between a neutron and proton as a function of their separation.

order of 0.5×10^{-15} meter. At separations less than this, the force between a neutron and a proton is repulsive. The general character of the force as a function of the separation between particles is shown schematically in figure 4.3.

4.3. Nuclear notation

Before proceeding to discussions of some of the very interesting aspects of nuclear structure it is helpful to become acquainted with some of the terminology and notation characteristic of this subject. We have seen that the two basic building blocks of atomic nuclei are protons and neutrons. Thus, two important terms are defined as follows:

(1) Z = atomic number = number of protons in the nucleus

(2) A = mass number = number of nucleons (protons + neutrons) in the nucleus

Atoms having the same atomic number Z, but different mass numbers, A, are called *isotopes*. Thus, heavy hydrogen is an isotope of hydrogen. *Tritium*, which is hydrogen of mass number 3, is another hydrogen isotope. It has two neutrons and one proton in its nucleus. Nearly all known elements exist in two or more isotope forms. A partial listing of the stable isotopes of the elements found naturally is given in table 5.

A shorthand system of designating the general properties of nuclei has developed in a form similar to that used in chemistry. In this

Table 5

PARTIAL LIST OF STABLE ISOTOPES

Z	A	*Element*	*Neutral Atom* Mass (amu)	*Protons*	*Neutrons*	*Mass Defect,* amu
1	1	H	1.008142	1	0	0.008142
1	2	H	2.014735	1	1	0.014735
2	4	He	4.003873	2	2	0.003873
3	6	Li	6.017021	3	3	0.017021
3	7	Li	7.018223	3	4	0.018223
4	9	Be	9.015043	4	5	0.015043
5	10	B	10.016114	5	5	0.016114
5	11	B	11.012789	5	6	0.012789
6	12	C	12.003804	6	6	0.003804
6	13	C	13.007473	6	7	0.007473
7	14	N	14.007515	7	7	0.007515
7	15	N	15.004863	7	8	0.004863
8	16	O	16.000000	8	8	0.000000
8	17	O	17.004533	8	9	0.004533
8	18	O	18.004857	8	10	0.004857
9	19	F	19.004456	9	10	0.004456
10	20	Ne	19.998777	10	10	−0.001223
10	21	Ne	21.000504	10	11	0.000504
10	22	Ne	21.998358	10	12	−0.001642
11	23	Na	22.997055	11	12	−0.002945
12	24	Mg	23.992628	12	12	−0.007372
12	25	Mg	24.993745	12	13	−0.006255
12	26	Mg	25.990802	12	14	−0.009198
13	27	Al	26.990071	13	14	−0.009929
14	28	Si	27.985767	14	14	−0.014233
14	29	Si	28.985650	14	15	−0.014350
14	30	Si	29.983237	14	16	−0.016763
15	31	P	30.983550	15	16	−0.016450

notation the mass number and atomic number are specified as subscripts and superscripts about the chemical symbol for the element. Thus, for any nucleus or atom X, we write $_Z X^A$. The atomic number, Z, appears as a subscript to the left of the chemical symbol, while the mass number, A, appears as a superscript to the right. Occasionally, the number of neutrons is specified by a subscript to the right so that we have

$$\text{atomic number} X^{\text{mass number}}_{\text{neutron number}} = {}_Z X^A_{A-Z} \tag{4.14}$$

Thus, the symbol for helium ($Z = 2$) of mass number 4 ($A = 4$) is $_2 He^4$. The symbol for lithium ($Z = 3$) of mass number 7 ($A = 7$) is $_3 Li^7$. The symbol for uranium ($Z = 92$) of mass number 235 is $_{92} U^{235}$. The symbol for a proton is $_1 p^1$ and that for the neutron is $_0 n^1$.

You should familiarize yourself with this symbolism because it is used repeatedly throughout the remainder of the chapter.

4.4. Binding energy per nucleon

The nuclei of atoms heavier than hydrogen become increasingly complicated. However, the nuclear binding energy is calculated by the same method as that outlined in section 4.2. For example, consider the helium atom $_2 He^4$. This atom has two electrons, two protons, and two neutrons. The total mass of the constituent parts of the atom is computed as follows:

$$\begin{aligned}
\text{Total electron mass} &= 0.001098 \quad \text{amu} \\
\text{Total proton mass} &= 2.015186 \quad \text{amu} \\
\text{Total neutron mass} &= \underline{2.017964} \quad \text{amu} \\
\text{Total mass} = M_T &= 4.034248 \quad \text{amu}
\end{aligned}$$

The mass of the $_2 He^4$ atom obtained by careful experimental measurements is

$$M = 4.003873 \quad \text{amu}$$

Hence, the total nuclear binding energy is equivalent to

$$\Delta M = M_T - M = 0.030375 \quad \text{amu}$$

or the binding energy is

$$\Delta W = 28.3 \quad \text{MeV}$$

Similar calculations can be performed for other nuclei. For example, consider the $_3 Li^7$ atom shown in figure 4.4. This atom has three electrons, three protons, and four neutrons. Hence,

$$\begin{aligned}
\text{Total electron mass} &= 0.001647 \quad \text{amu} \\
\text{Total proton mass} &= 3.022779 \quad \text{amu} \\
\text{Total neutron mass} &= \underline{4.035928} \quad \text{amu} \\
\text{Total mass} = M_T &= \overline{7.060354} \quad \text{amu}
\end{aligned}$$

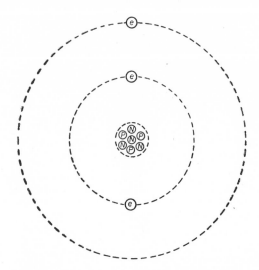

Figure 4.4. Schematic representation of $_3\text{Li}^7$.

However, the measured mass of the assembled atom is

$$M = 7.018223 \quad \text{amu}$$

Hence, the mass difference is

$$\Delta M = M_T - M = 0.042131 \quad \text{amu}$$

This corresponds to a nuclear binding energy of

$$\Delta W \doteq 39.2 \quad \text{MeV}$$

It is interesting to determine how the binding energy changes as more and more nucleons are added to the nucleus. The calculation is most informative if expressed in terms of the binding energy per nucleon. This is simply the total binding energy divided by the number of nucleons. Thus, from data previously computed we can write as follows:

Atom	Binding Energy	No. Nucleons	Binding Energy/Nucleon
$_1H^2$	2.225 MeV	2	1.112 MeV
$_2He^4$	28.3 MeV	4	7.09 MeV
$_3Li^7$	39.2 MeV	7	5.6 MeV

This same method can be used to calculate the binding energy per nucleon for many different atoms. If this is done, a curve of the general form shown in figure 4.5 is obtained.

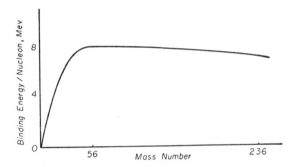

Figure 4.5. Binding energy per nucleon as a function of the mass number.

The binding energy per nucleon of $_1H^1$ has no meaning. For heavier nuclei the binding energy per nucleon increases rapidly to a maximum value of about 8.5 MeV for iron of mass number 56. Then the binding energy per nucleon gradually diminishes as the mass number increases, having a value of about 7.5 MeV for uranium 236.

4.5. Forces between nucleons

We have studiously avoided any discussion of nuclear forces up to this point. This seemed advisable because the mathematical analysis of the experimental data supporting nuclear physics is based upon wave mechanics. Without wave mechanics it is not possible to reflect the ideas of nuclear physicists. Thus, the statements to be made are more in the character of analogies. That is, we will use mental images of a nuclear structure that are analogies of wave mechanical results expressed in terms of classical physics. Statements concerning forces of attraction and repulsion are analogies drawn from classical physics to represent the deductions of wave mechanics.

Classical physics provides no real explanation for the forces of cohesion holding nuclei together. The only force we might anticipate is the Coulomb force of repulsion between protons. Yet, attractive forces must exist between nucleons, otherwise nuclei would not exist.

The simplest nucleus is the single proton representing the nucleus of hydrogen $_1H^1$. The binding energy has no meaning in this case. However, consider the nucleus of heavy hydrogen which is the next simplest case. This nucleus contains a proton and a neutron and the binding energy was previously shown to be 2.225 MeV. In other words, there is a definite force of attraction between a neutron and a proton when they are quite close together, say about 10^{-15} meter separation. This force of attraction between protons and neutrons is taken to be one of the principal sources of cohesion between nucleons.

Rutherford conducted an extensive series of experiments concerned with the properties of the nucleus. He assumed that the electric charge in the nucleus is symmetrically distributed within a distance r of the center of the nucleus. As a matter of convenience, r is regarded as the *radius of the nucleus*. Rutherford's experiments indicated that r is generally, but not always, proportional to the number of nuclear particles according to the equation

$$r \doteq 1.4A^{1/3} \times 10^{-15} \quad \text{meter} \qquad (4.15)$$

where A = mass number $\doteq$ number of nucleons. The volume of the nucleus is

$$V = \tfrac{4}{3}\pi r^3$$

Substitute for the nuclear radius and the equation for the volume is

$$V = (\tfrac{4}{3}\pi)(1.4)^3 A \times 10^{-45} \quad \text{meter}^3$$

This shows that the nuclear volume is ordinarily proportional to the number of nuclear particles. These particles are not tightly packed together like marbles in a bag; instead they are rather loosely distributed throughout the nuclear volume.

If we define the *density* of the nucleus as the number of nuclear particles per unit volume, then

$$\text{nuclear density} = \frac{A}{V} = \frac{10^{45}}{(\tfrac{4}{3}\pi)(1.4)^3} = \text{constant}$$

In other words, the nuclear density is ordinarily independent of the number of nucleons. This means that the distance between nucleons is relatively fixed in all nuclei, regardless of the number of nucleons. As more particles are added to the nucleus, the volume increases proportionately.

From this we conclude that nucleons affect only those nucleons nearby. If remote nucleons were affected, the nuclear density should change as more nucleons are brought in. Thus, it appears that the forces holding nuclei together are very short in range. The limiting distance is taken to be of the order of 10^{-15} meter.

When more than one proton is present in the nucleus, the forces of repulsion between protons tend to partially offset the attraction between protons and neutrons. The simplest such nucleus is $_2\text{He}^4$ which has two protons and two neutrons. Earlier we calculated the nuclear binding energy to be about 28 MeV. The magnitude of energy resulting from proton repulsion in this nucleus can be estimated rather closely. Assume two protons 10^{-15} meter apart. This leads to an energy of about 1.4 MeV and this is clearly quite small compared to the total nuclear binding energy of 28 MeV.

However, the Coulomb repulsion between protons increases rapidly as the number of protons increases. Thus, in the heavier elements where Z is 80 or more, the effect of proton repulsion is of the same order of magnitude as the proton-neutron attraction. This partially accounts for the reduced binding energy per nucleon for the heavier elements as shown in figure 4.5.

In spite of the fact that a neutron has no charge, we have found that there is a force of attraction between a neutron and a proton. Thus, we might guess that there is a similar short-range attraction between two neutrons and between two protons. Careful measurements by Breit, Thaxton, and Eisenbud indicate that such a proton-proton force of attraction does appear when the distance between protons is less than about 3×10^{-15} meter. This attraction is superimposed on the Coulomb repulsion. A similar attraction of the same order of magnitude appears between two neutrons.

4.6. Systematics of stable nuclei

Nuclei can be classified as either *stable* or *unstable*. When *stable*, they retain their identity and do not spontaneously change to other nuclear forms. *Unstable* nuclei *spontaneously* change from one isotope to another, releasing energy in the process. These are called *radio-*

active nuclei. We will consider the unstable, or radioactive, nuclei later. At the moment we are concerned with the characteristics of stable nuclei.

It is helpful to list certain known facts concerning stable nuclei before discussing them systematically. Some of the known facts are summarized as follows:

(1) About seven-eighths of the elements composing the earth's crust have even atomic numbers Z.

(2) Most nuclei contain an even number of neutrons. As a result, ordinarily, (a) when the atomic number Z is even, the mass number is also even, and (b) when the atomic number is odd the mass number is odd. The only stable exceptions to this rule are $_1H^2$, $_3Li^6$, $_5B^{10}$, and $_7N^{14}$.

(3) In most stable light nuclei the number of neutrons is virtually equal to the number of protons.

(4) For nuclei heavier than $_{20}Ca^{40}$, the number of neutrons exceeds the number of protons. The neutron-proton ratio has a maximum value of about 1.5.

(5) All nuclei having more than 83 protons are radioactive, or unstable.

An approximate explanation of these effects is offered in this section.

Consider the light elements first. It was shown earlier that the total binding energy of $_2He^4$ is about 28.3 MeV. The energy arising from proton-proton repulsion was shown to be about 1.4 MeV. This effect is small compared to the proton-neutron attraction. Thus, in light nuclei, the most stable nucleus should result when the number of neutrons is approximately equal to the number of protons.

However, the energy associated with the proton repulsion is proportional to the square of the number of protons (see equation 1.47). This causes the repulsion to increase very rapidly as the number of protons increases. For the heavier elements beyond $_{20}Ca^{40}$, the proton repulsion is quite large. Therefore, stable nuclei ordinarily result only when there is a neutron excess. The neutron excess increases the number of proton-neutron attractions to the point necessary to produce nuclear stability, despite the effects of proton repulsion.

It is important to note that the binding energy per nucleon of $_2He^4$ is 7.09 MeV. This is much larger than the figure obtained for either the next lighter or the next heavier element. Indeed, the maximum binding energy per nucleon in any nucleus is only about 8.5 MeV. Thus, the arrangement of two neutrons and two protons apparently represents a peculiarly stable configuration. Contrast the value of 7.09 MeV of $_2$He^4 with 2.2 MeV obtained for $_1$H^2.

It is believed that the protons and neutrons spin in somewhat the same manner as electrons. Moreover, it is believed that there is a strong tendency for protons of opposite spin to pair up and for neutrons of opposite spin to pair up. This pairing is the apparent cause of the large binding energy per nucleon observed in $_2$He^4. The pairing also presumably accounts for the widespread occurrence of elements having even atomic numbers and the predominance of nuclei with an even number of neutrons. The $_2$He^4 nucleus is the smallest nucleus that can be constructed from neutron and proton pairs.

It seems probable that the nuclei of the heavier elements are made up, in part at least, by groupings of $_2$He^4 nuclei. The $_2$He^4 nuclei are, in turn, held together by forces that are weaker than those internal to the $_2$He^4 nucleus. For this reason, the binding energy per nucleon never greatly exceeds that occurring in $_2$He^4. The occurrence of the $_2$He^4 nucleus is sufficiently frequent to warrant assigning it a special name. It is called an *alpha particle* and is clearly a helium nucleus or a positive, double charged helium ion.

To summarize, neutron and proton spin provide a partial explanation for the widespread occurrence of nuclei with even numbers of protons and neutrons. It also accounts for the marked stability of the $_2$He^4 nucleus. The relationships between proton-neutron attraction and proton-proton repulsion roughly account for the tendency of light nuclei to have equal numbers of protons and neutrons and for heavy nuclei to have a neutron excess.

4.7. The neutrino and neutron radioactivity

In preceding sections we have seen that atomic nuclei are made up of varying numbers of neutrons and protons. In this section we consider the properties of neutrons when they are freed from nuclei.

Suppose that by some method we are able to produce a cloud of free neutrons. A very unique phenomenon now occurs. The neutrons *spontaneously* disintegrate into electrons and protons according to the following reaction:

$$_0n^1 \rightarrow \ _1p^1 + \ _{-1}e^0 \tag{4.15}$$

This is *not* a complete reaction as we shall see later.

The number of neutron disintegrations varies with time. Hence, the actual number of neutrons remaining in the cloud varies as a function of time, gradually decreasing to zero. This variation in the number of neutrons present in the cloud is shown in figure 4.6. It can be shown that the equation for this curve is

$$N = N_n \epsilon^{-\lambda t} \tag{4.16}$$

where N = number of neutrons present at any time t, N_n = original number of neutrons, λ = constant.

The *half life* of this spontaneous nucleon disintegration is the time required for half of the neutrons to disintegrate. The time is experimentally found to be 12.8 minutes when evaluated over a large enough number of disintegrations to be statistically significant.

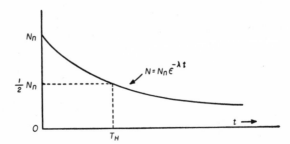

Figure 4.6. Number of neutrons as a function of time.

At the instant of time T_H corresponding to the half life, $N = \frac{1}{2}N_n$. Hence, equation (4.16) becomes

$$\tfrac{1}{2}N_n = N_n \epsilon^{-\lambda T_H}$$

Solve this equation for T_H and the result is

$$T_H = \text{half life} = \frac{1}{\lambda}\ln 2 \tag{4.17}$$

or

$$\lambda = \frac{1}{T_H}\ln 2 \tag{4.18}$$

The *spontaneous disintegration* of neutrons is called *neutron radioactivity*. Any nucleus or nucleon that spontaneously disintegrates is said to be *radioactive*. The neutron disintegration produces energetic electrons as products of the disintegration. High energy electrons are called *beta rays*, denoted by β. Other nuclear disintegrations release high energy photons, called *gamma rays*, γ. Still other disintegrations release double charge helium ions, $_2\text{He}^{4(++)}$. These are called *alpha particles*, α.

It is a fairly simple exercise to calculate the theoretical reaction energy of the neutron disintegration. This calculated value should equal the kinetic energy of the ejected electron. It seems reasonable that the electron should receive virtually all of the reaction energy because its mass is so small compared to the mass of the ejected proton. This should be a fairly precise and specific amount of kinetic energy. Experiments do *not* confirm this hypothesis. Instead, the electron kinetic energy ranges from zero up to the theoretical value of the reaction energy. Something is obviously missing from our model of nuclear behavior.

This difficulty was resolved by Pauli who postulated that some uncharged particle, called a *neutrino*, denoted by ν, was involved in the reaction. The neutrino is assigned zero charge and virtually zero mass, and a spin number of $\frac{1}{2}$. Its purpose is to balance equation (4.15) so that the law of conservation of mass and energy, together with conservation of linear and angular momentum, are not violated. Neutrinos have never been observed experimentally, but the evidence of their existence is very strong.

With the idea of the neutrino established, the neutron radioactive disintegration is written properly as

$$_0\text{n}^1 \rightarrow {}_1\text{p}^1 + {}_{-1}\text{e}^0 + \nu + Q$$

The reaction energy Q is divided between the electron and neutrino in all possible proportions.

4.8. Natural radioactivity

The discussion in section 4.6 is a great help in explaining the broad features of natural radioactivity. These elements fit into three main series as follows:

(1) uranium-radium series
(2) thorium series
(3) actinium series

Before proceeding with the discussion, it is helpful to restate some of the observations made in section 4.6. It was stated there that all nuclei with atomic numbers exceeding 83 are naturally radioactive. It was further stated that this was apparently caused by the large proton-proton repulsion present in the heavier nuclei. This repulsion is so great that nuclei having atomic numbers in excess of 92 do not occur naturally. Moreover, it was also stated that the nuclei of heavier elements may be visualized approximately as an array of loosely bound alpha particles intermixed with some excess neutrons.

Now consider the heaviest known natural element, $_{92}U^{238}$, uranium of mass number 238. This contains 92 protons and 146 neutrons. Because of the strong proton-proton repulsion, the nucleus is radioactive and emits an alpha particle. The emission reduces the number of nuclear protons by two and the number of neutrons by two, converting the nucleus to an isotope of thorium, $_{90}Th^{234}$. This isotope is generally called uranium X1. The half life of the alpha radioactivity is about 4.5×10^9 years. This long half life accounts for the comparatively large deposits of U^{238} still present in the earth's crust.

The neutron excess present in the $_{90}Th^{234}$ nucleus is so great that one neutron changes to a proton and emits an electron (β ray) with a half life of 24.5 days. This converts the thorium to another uranium isotope $_{91}U^{234}$. This is called uranium X2.

The UX2 nucleus is also an emitter of β radiation. This means that another neutron changes into a proton and emits an electron thereby producing $_{92}U^{234}$, another uranium isotope.

The uranium 234 nucleus emits an alpha particle and becomes ionium $_{90}Io^{230}$. This, in turn, emits an alpha particle and is converted into radium $_{88}Ra^{226}$. Through a series of radioactive transformations involving the emission of alpha particles and electrons (β rays), the nucleus is eventually reduced to that of an isotope of ordinary lead. This is $_{82}Pb^{206}$, whereas ordinary lead is $_{82}Pb^{204}$. Lead is not radioactive and this is the end product of the uranium-radium series.

Similar series are observed for thorium and actinium. In all cases the radioactive transformations involve the emission of either alpha particles or electrons. These emissions are often accompanied by energetic photons, called *gamma rays*.

4.9. The positron

In 1932, Anderson detected the presence of a previously unknown particle. This particle was found to have the same mass as the electron and the same charge. However, the charge is *positive* rather than negative. At first, Anderson called the new particle a positive electron. Later, he termed it a *positron*. A positron will be denoted by $_{+1}e^0$ in the notational system used in this chapter.

Positrons are never emitted by the naturally radioactive nuclei. However, they are quite commonly emitted from artificially produced radioactive nuclei. All positron radioactive transformations presently known exhibit very short half lives. As a result, if such elements ever occurred naturally, it is believed that the radioactive transformations have been fully completed during the estimated life of the earth.

When a positron passes through matter it is slowed down and eventually spends some time near an electron. The two charges attract one another, combine, and emit photons according to the following reaction:

$$_{+1}e^0 + _{-1}e^0 \rightarrow \gamma + \gamma$$

This is called *pair annihilation*. Both the electron and the positron disappear and two photons (γ) appear in their place. The energy of each photon is about 0.5 MeV. The two photons travel in opposite directions so that the momentum of the system is conserved.

A reverse process of *pair production* can also occur in certain cases. In this reaction a photon breaks up into an electron and a positron according to

$$\gamma \rightarrow _{-1}e^0 + _{+1}e^0 + Q_1 + Q_2 \qquad (4.19)$$

where Q_1 and Q_2 are the kinetic energies of the electron and positron.

It seems obvious that this reaction can occur only with photons having energies exceeding about 1.02 MeV because this is the energy equivalent of the electron and positron masses.

4.10. Unstable light nuclei

Natural radioactivity was discussed in a previous section. This discussion applied directly to the heavy elements for which Z exceeded 83. The light nuclei can, on occasion, be radioactive. Such nuclei are generally produced artificially by the process described in the next section.

Light nuclei most frequently emit either electrons or positrons. The following rules generally, but not always, apply:

(1) In *unstable light nuclei* having more neutrons than protons, one neutron changes into a proton and an electron is emitted.

(2) In unstable light nuclei having more protons than neutrons, one proton changes into a neutron and a positron is emitted.

A short list of unstable light nuclei is given in table 6. This table lists the type of particle emitted and you should compare this against the neutron-proton ratio to see how the foregoing rules apply.

These transformations are indicated in nuclear notation by the examples discussed in this section. Consider nitrogen 16. This has 7 protons and 9 neutrons. Hence, one neutron changes to a proton and ejects an electron yielding

$$_7N^{16} \rightarrow {}_8O^{16} + {}_{-1}e^0 + \nu + Q \tag{4.20}$$

The half life is about 7.35 seconds.

On the other hand, consider nitrogen 13. This has 7 protons, as before, but only 6 neutrons. Hence, one proton changes to a neutron and a positron is ejected. That is,

$$_7N^{13} \rightarrow {}_6C^{13} + {}_{+1}e^0 + \nu \tag{4.21}$$

Another representative transformation of this type is

$$_7N^{12} \rightarrow {}_6C^{12} + {}_{+1}e^0 + \nu \tag{4.22}$$

Table 6
SOME UNSTABLE LIGHT NUCLEI

Z	A	Element	Mass (amu)	Protons	Neutrons	Emission
1	3	H	3.016997	1	2	electron
2	6	He	6.020833	2	4	electron
3	8	Li	8.025018	3	5	electron
4	7	Be	7.019150	4	3	positron
5	9	B	9.016190	5	4	positron
5	12	B	12.018162	5	7	neutron
6	11	C	11.014916	6	5	positron
6	10	C	10.02061	6	4	positron
6	14	C	14.007682	6	8	electron
7	13	N	13.009858	7	6	positron
7	16	N	16.01074	7	9	neutron
8	15	O	15.007768	8	7	positron
9	17	F	17.007505	9	8	positron
9	20	F	20.006350	9	11	electron
10	19	Ne	19.007952	10	9	positron

4.11. Nuclear reactions

Nuclei of various atoms are often bombarded by energetic particles. These particles may be electrons, protons, neutrons, deuterons ($_1H^2$), or alpha particles. This bombardment often causes *nuclear transformations* to take place. These transformations are denoted by *nuclear reaction equations* using the symbolism discussed briefly in section 4.3.

When nuclear reactions occur, it is assumed that the initial nucleus *captures* the incident particle. The result is called the *intermediate* or *compound nucleus*. The compound nucleus may do any of three things. It may

(1) emit photons and retain its identity,
(2) be radioactive,
(3) be stable, but emit particles such as electrons, protons, neutrons, or alpha particles and reduce to some other nucleus.

We will discuss each of these very briefly.

For example, suppose that we bombard aluminum with protons. The nuclear reaction equation is

$$_1H^1 + {}_{13}Al^{27} \rightarrow ({}_{14}Si^{28}) + \gamma \tag{4.23}$$

In this case, the compound nucleus is $_{14}Si^{28}$. However, after capturing the proton it is in an excited state. It attains the normal state by emitting a photon, or γ ray. The energy of the photon is the *reaction energy* Q, where $Q = Q_m + Q_k$, Q_k = kinetic energy of incident particle, Q_m = energy equivalent of the mass difference between the initial and final particles. This is an example of the first type of action that might be followed by the compound nucleus.

In writing nuclear reaction equations like the one preceding, it is important to note that the total numbers of nucleons and protons are constant throughout the reaction. The nucleons are given by the superscripts and the protons by the subscripts. The sum of the subscripts or superscripts is the same on either side of the equation. This is an important rule to remember in writing nuclear reaction equations.

According to the second possibility, the compound nucleus may be radioactive. If this is the case, then it emits particles with a time delay that can be measured experimentally. For example, consider the proton bombardment of carbon 12. This yields,

$$_1H^1 + {}_6C^{12} \rightarrow ({}_7N^{13}) \tag{4.24}$$

However, nitrogen 13 is unstable, or radioactive, and decays according to the reaction

$$_7N^{13} \rightarrow {_6}C^{13} + {_{+1}}e^0 + \nu + Q \tag{4.25}$$

Now consider the third type of action that might be taken by the compound nucleus. That is, it might be stable, but excited to such an energy that it immediately disintegrates. For example, consider the bombardment of aluminum with alpha particles. This yields

$$_2He^4 + {_{13}}Al^{27} \rightarrow ({_{15}}P^{31}) \rightarrow {_{14}}Si^{30} + {_1}H^1 + Q \tag{4.26}$$

Phosphorus 31 is the compound nucleus in this case. It is stable. However, when it is formed by the capture of the alpha particle by the aluminum nucleus, it is at such a high energy level that it immediately emits a proton and reduces to silicon 30. The reaction energy is calculated as before. The reaction energy usually appears as kinetic energy shared by the product particles. The laws of conservation of momentum and energy can be applied to calculate the distribution of kinetic energy between the final particles.

Another reaction might also result from the bombardment of aluminum with alpha particles. That is, we could have

$$_2He^4 + {_{13}}Al^{27} \rightarrow ({_{15}}P^{31}) \rightarrow {_{15}}P^{30} + {_0}n^1 + Q \tag{4.27}$$

In this case the product nucleus is phosphorus 30 instead of silicon 30. A neutron is emitted instead of a proton. In other words, the *results of a bombardment are not necessarily unique.* More than one transformation may be possible.

We can illustrate this by two more reaction equations using neutrons as the bombarding particles. This yields

$$_0n^1 + {_{13}}Al^{27} \rightarrow ({_{13}}Al^{28}) \rightarrow {_{11}}Na^{24} + {_2}He^4 + Q \tag{4.28}$$

$$_0n^1 + {_{13}}Al^{27} \rightarrow ({_{13}}Al^{28}) \rightarrow {_{12}}Mg^{27} + {_1}H^1 + Q \tag{4.29}$$

So far we have shown transformations yielding only two final particles. This is not always true. It sometimes happens that there are three or more final particles. For example:

$$_1H^2 + {_5}B^{11} \rightarrow ({_6}C^{13})$$
$$\rightarrow {_2}He^4 + {_2}He^4 + {_2}He^4 + {_0}n^1 + Q \tag{4.30}$$
$$_1H^2 + {_7}N^{14} \rightarrow ({_8}O^{16})$$
$$\rightarrow {_2}He^4 + {_2}He^4 + {_2}He^4 + {_2}He^4 + Q \tag{4.31}$$

4.12. Nuclear fission

In all of the reactions discussed in the preceding section, the product nuclei were all closely related to the initial nuclei. Neutron bombardment of *heavy nuclei* may produce another type of action first noted by Fermi in 1934. Neutrons are very effective for bombarding heavy nuclei because they are not repelled by the large number of nuclear protons.

Suppose that uranium 235 is bombarded with slow neutrons. One possible transformation is given as follows:

$$_{0}n^1 + {}_{92}U^{235} \rightarrow ({}_{92}U^{236})$$

$$\rightarrow {}_{38}Sr^{94} + {}_{54}Xe^{140} + {}_{0}n^1 + {}_{0}n^1 + Q \qquad (4.32)$$

In this case you will observe that the compound nucleus breaks up into fragments having moderately heavy nuclei. This process is called *nuclear fission* to distinguish it from the type of reaction previously discussed where the initial and end result nuclei have somewhat the same size.

The reaction energies resulting from nuclear fission are very large. Values as high as 200 MeV or more may be observed. The reaction given in the preceding equation is also interesting because one neutron disintegrating a U^{235} nucleus may produce two neutrons. After these neutrons are slowed to appropriate velocities they can be used to disintegrate two more U^{235} nuclei. This results in four neutrons possibly capable of producing four more nuclear disintegrations, and so on. A process of this type, when carefully regulated, is used in *nuclear chain reactions* in atomic bombs. Under proper conditions of regulation, the reaction can be maintained at a constant and sustained rate and used in *nuclear reactors* for the production of power.

PROBLEMS

4.1. Calculate the nuclear binding energy of $_2He^4$. Express the result in amu and MeV. Calculate the binding energy per nucleon.

4.2. Repeat problem 4.1 for $_4Be^9$.

4.3. Repeat problem 4.1 for $_5B^{10}$.

4.4. Repeat problem 4.1 for $_6C^{12}$.

4.5. Calculate the approximate nuclear radii of $_1H^1$, $_1H^2$, $_3Li^7$, $_4Be^9$,

$_5B^{10}$, $_6C^{12}$, and comment upon the result relative to the binding energy per nucleon.

4.6. Calculate the nuclear reaction energy of

$$_1H^1 + {}_3Li^7 \rightarrow ({}_4Be^8) \rightarrow 2{}_2He^4 + Q$$

Assume the kinetic energy of the proton is 15 MeV.

4.7. Calculate the nuclear reaction energy of the uranium disintegration given in section 4.12. Assume the neutron has a kinetic energy of 20 MeV.

4.8. Where does the reaction energy computed in problem 4.7 appear physically?

4.9. Calculate the minimum neutrino energy possible for a neutron disintegration.

4.10. A cloud of 5×10^{11} neutrons is confined to a chamber at zero time. How many neutrons, protons, and electrons are present one-half hour later?

4.11. Radon is a radioactive element. It emits alpha particles with a half life of 3.82 days. What fraction of radon atoms will disintegrate in a period of: 1 minute; 10 minutes; 1 day?

4.12. Radium D disintegrates with a half life of about 22 years, emitting beta rays in the process. What fraction of radium D atoms will disintegrate in a period of 5 years? 10 years? 20 years?

4.13. Write the nuclear reaction equation for the proton bombardment of $_5B^{11}$. The product includes an alpha particle $_2He^4$. Be sure to show the compound nucleus.

4.14. Why is an alpha particle ejected in problem 4.13? Why not a proton or a neutron? You will find the table of unstable nuclei helpful in answering this.

4.15. The neutron bombardment of $_7N^{14}$ yields a proton as one of the products. Write the nuclear reaction equation showing the compound nucleus.

4.16. What additional reaction will occur after the initial reaction given in problem 4.15?

4.17. Calculate the photon energy in equation (4.23).

4.18. A photon disintegrates yielding an electron and a positron, each having kinetic energy of 0.25 MeV. Calculate the photon energy and wave length.

5

STRUCTURE AND BEHAVIOR
OF METALS

Conductors are materials capable of conducting electric current. At various times and under various conditions, gases, liquids, and solids are all conductors. In this chapter we are concerned only with solid conductors. In particular, we are primarily interested in *metals* because they are easily the most common type of conductor.

Metals are particularly important materials to engineers. The properties of a particular metal may depend somewhat upon the field of engineering. Here we are primarily concerned with the electrical properties of metals.

There are three main subdivisions of material in this chapter, as follows:

(1) structure and models of metals
(2) electronic conduction in metals
(3) electrical properties of metals

The material on extranuclear atomic structure presented in chapter 3 is a necessary prerequisite to the presentation in this chapter.

5.1. Types of solids

The extranuclear structure of single atoms was presented in some detail in chapter 3. At the end of the chapter it was shown that important interactions develop between atoms when they are forced more and more closely together. Depending upon the extent of the interactions, one of the three states of matter, *solid, liquid,* or *gaseous,* is obtained.

The types of *solids* formed as a result of these interactions depend upon the properties of the atoms themselves. Following Kittel[1] and Seitz[2] we will classify solids into five more or less distinct types. The distinctions arise from the differences in the binding forces between the atoms composing the solid. As in any classification system, there are intermediate cases falling somewhere between these main categories. The five types of solids and typical values for the inter-atomic binding energy are given in table 7.

The *binding energy* is the energy required to dissociate the solid into its constituent atoms or ions.

Although the metallic solids are the primary concern of this chapter, it is desirable to comment briefly upon the other solids at this point. We will discuss *ionic* solids first.

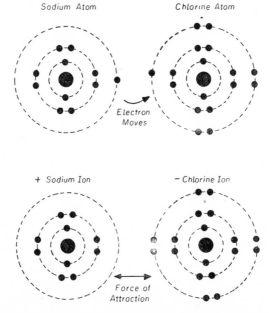

Figure 5.1. Formation of sodium chloride as an example of an ionic solid.

---

[1] Charles Kittel, *Introduction to Solid State Physics*, New York: John Wiley & Sons, Inc., 1953, p. 2.

[2] Frederick Seitz, *Modern Theory of Solids*, New York: McGraw-Hill Book Co., Inc., 1940.

Elements on the left of the periodic table are said to be *electropositive* because they have a tendency to lose their valence electrons and form positive ions. Elements on the right-hand side of the periodic table have a tendency to acquire electrons and become negative ions. They are said to be *electronegative*. These tendencies arise from the general tendency of atoms to form closed stable shells of electrons of the inert gas form.

An extreme case occurs in the interaction of a highly electropositive element with a highly electronegative element. Consider sodium, which is electropositive, reacting with chlorine, which is electronegative. Sodium has one valence electron outside a complete shell. Chlorine has seven valence electrons, lacking just one from an otherwise complete shell.

When the two atoms are brought in close proximity, the sodium atom easily loses its valence electron to the chlorine atom which is avid for electrons. This leaves the sodium atom as a singly-charged positive ion with a stable and closed electron shell as shown in figure 5.1. The chlorine atom becomes a negative ion and the additional electron fills the electron shell as shown in figure 5.1. The two ions are attracted to one another by Coulomb force. Solids held together in this manner are called *ionic solids*.

Table 7

TYPES OF SOLIDS

Type of Solid	Typical Binding Energy—joules
Ionic	13.6×10^{-19}
Covalent	16.0×10^{-19}
Molecular	0.144×10^{-19}
Hydrogen bonded	7.0×10^{-19}
Metallic	4.0×10^{-19}

As the ions are attracted more closely together, a force of repulsion appears that finally exactly offsets the attraction. This occurs when some particular distance remains between ions. The repulsive force arises from the Pauli exclusion principle. As the ions are forced very close together, it becomes necessary to have two electrons with the same set of four quantum numbers. This cannot occur according to the Exclusion Principle. It is prevented from occurring physically by a strong force of repulsion that appears.

It is possible to estimate the distance between ions rather closely from this very elementary analysis. It seems clear that the separation between ions should be approximately equal to the sum of the radii of the constituent ions. Some correction must usually be made for the geometric arrangement of the ions. However, for sodium chloride we have

(1) radius of the sodium (+) ion = 0.98×10^{-10} meter

(2) radius of chlorine (−) ion = 1.81×10^{-10} meter

sum = 2.79×10^{-10} meter

(3) measured value of separation = 2.82×10^{-10} meter

The agreement is quite close as you can see. This agreement is interesting because wave mechanics tells us that no particular meaning can be attached to specific values for ionic radii.

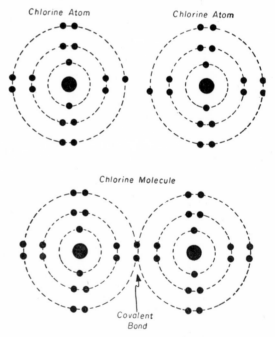

Figure 5.2. Formation of the chlorine molecule as an example of the covalent bond.

Covalent bonds between atoms occur when two or more atoms jointly share electrons. Electrons of opposite spin pair up in these bonds so that there is no violation of the exclusion principle.

Covalent bonds are extremely common. They occur in the molecular structure of the extremely electronegative elements such as fluorine, chlorine, and oxygen as shown in figure 5.2. The covalent bond is produced when two electrons of opposite spin join in a common energy level.

Elements near the center of the periodic table tend to form covalent bonds with other elements and particularly with themselves. Carbon in the diamond form is an outstanding example of a *covalent solid*. This is a covalent solid because all of the atoms in the solid are held together by covalent bonds on a repeating schedule as shown in two-

Figure 5.3. Covalent bonding of carbon atoms to form the covalent solid, diamond; two dimensional representation.

dimensional form in figure 5.3. Note that there is no molecular formation here, just a continued repetition of the covalent bond in particular directions throughout the solid. *Germanium* and *silicon* are two other very important covalent solids. Indeed, they are so important to electrical engineers that all of chapters 6 and 7 are devoted to these materials.

Hydrogen normally forms covalent bonds with other atoms. However, under certain conditions an atom of hydrogen may be attracted by strong forces to two atoms, thereby forming a *hydrogen-bonded* solid. Formic acid, ice, proteins, and hydrogen chloride are representative cases of hydrogen-bonded solids.

We can see how hydrogen bonding comes about by examining the molecular characteristics of such solids. Take hydrogen chloride, for example. The hydrogen electron finds a place in the outer shell of the chlorine atom. The resulting chemical bond has many of the prop-

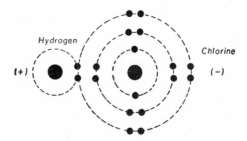

Figure 5.4. Molecular structure of hydrogen chloride, illustrating polar bonds.

erties of the covalent and ionic bonds. This rather complicated force causes a molecule to be formed. Because of the difference in size of the hydrogen and chlorine atoms, the hydrogen end of the molecule is positive while the chlorine end is negative. Therefore, it appears

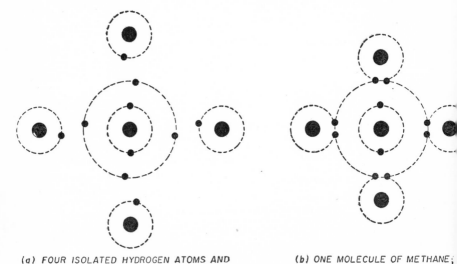

(a) FOUR ISOLATED HYDROGEN ATOMS AND ONE CARBON ATOM

(b) ONE MOLECULE OF METHANE;

Figure 5.5. Basis for the formation of a molecular solid.

that the atoms are held together by ionic and partly covalent bonds while the molecules are held together in solid form by ionic forces between molecules. In particular, the hydrogen can form an ionic bond with a second atom.

The molecular form of hydrogen chloride is shown in figure 5.4. This is often called a *polar bond*. We shall have more to say about this type of material in the chapter on insulators and dielectrics.

Practically all of the organic chemicals, and others as well, are *molecular solids*. A typical example may be found in methane. A methane molecule is shown schematically in figure 5.5. The atoms forming the molecule are held together by covalent bonds. When a number of molecules are aggregated to form a solid, the molecules are held together by rather weak forces called *Van der Waal forces*. It is very difficult to explain the origin of these forces at this point in our discussion. About all that we can conveniently say is that the Van der Waal forces arise from entirely different sources than ionic or covalent bonding forces. We will discuss organic materials at greater length in chapter 10 because they are extremely important as electrical insulators.

The *metals* form an entirely different class of solids and are discussed in the remainder of this chapter.

5.2. Types of metals

Metals are *crystalline* solids where the *crystal* is formed by the regular arrangement of atoms of the element. Some additional information concerning crystal structure is presented in the next section.

Metals are generally classified into four fairly distinct types as follows:

(1) *alkali metals:*
   lithium, sodium, potassium, rubidium, caesium
(2) *noble and platinum metals:*
   copper, silver, gold, platinum, iridium, palladium
(3) *divalent metals:*
   beryllium, strontium, magnesium, calcium, barium
(4) *transition metals:*
   iron, nickel, cobalt, tungsten

The *alkali* metals all have single valence electrons located in an $l = 0$ subshell. Moreover, except for lithium, the valence electron

Table 8

LEVEL OF VALENCE ELECTRONS IN ALKALI METALS

Metal	Atomic Number	Last Filled Level		Valence Level	
		n	l	n	l
Lithium........	3	1	0	2	0
Sodium.........	11	2	1	3	0
Potassium......	19	3	1	4	0
Rubidium......	37	4	1	5	0
Caesium........	55	5	1	6	0

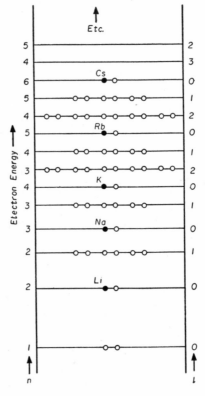

Figure 5.6. Composite energy level diagram for alkali metal atoms; not to scale.

always falls in the $l = 0$ subshell following a completed $l = 1$ subshell. Thus, we find the valence electrons in the subshells specified
in table 8.

The reason for this particular characteristic of the alkali metals
arises from the sequence of energy levels. A composite energy level
diagram for the alkali metals is shown in figure 5.6. This represents
schematically the sequence of energy levels for the alkali metals.
The valence electrons are shown by black dots marked with the
chemical symbol for that element. All other electrons are shown by
white circles. This particular sequence of energy levels results from

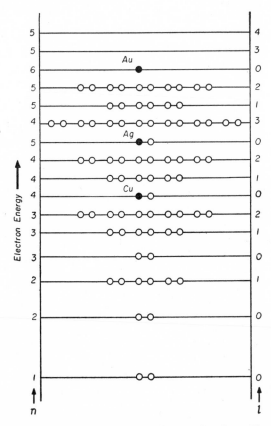

Figure 5.7. Composite energy level diagram for the noble metal
atoms; not to scale.

the particular number of electrons involved in the solution of the many electron atom.

The *noble metals* are also monovalent. They differ from the alkali metals in the general sequence of the electron arrangement in the various quantum states. The difference arises from the difference in the sequence of the energy levels. This sequence is shown by the sketch in figure 5.7.

For all of the noble metals the valence electron always falls in an $l = 0$ subshell immediately following a completed $l = 2$ subshell. This is shown in figure 5.7 and summarized in table 9. This contrasts with the case of the alkali metals where the valence electron followed a completed $l = 1$ subshell.

In comparing the noble and alkali metals it is interesting to observe the location of the valence electron for potassium and copper, rubidium and silver, and caesium and gold. Each pair, which consists of one alkali and one noble metal, has the *same* valence electron. The atoms differ only in the arrangement of the inner electrons and atomic number.

The *divalent* metals are not treated in this volume and the *transition* metals are covered in chapter 11.

Table 9

LEVEL OF VALENCE ELECTRONS IN NOBLE METALS

Metal	Atomic Number	Last Filled Level		Valence Level	
		n	l	n	l
Copper........	29	3	2	4	0
Silver.........	47	4	2	5	0
Gold..........	79	5	2	6	0

5.3. Structure of metals

Metals are aggregations of *crystals*. Although there are many different types of crystals, the three types common to most metals are

        (1) body-centered cubic
        (2) face-centered cubic
        (3) close-packed hexagonal

Sketches of *single cells* from these crystals are shown in figure 5.8.

Crystals are ordered arrays of atoms of the element forming the solid. The metals can be grouped according to crystalline form as shown in table 10. You will observe that the alkali metals together with some others crystallize in the body-centered cubic. The noble metals and some others fit into the face-centered cubic, and so on.

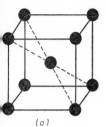 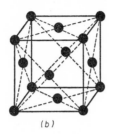 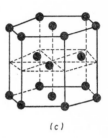

(a)   (b)   (c)

Figure 5.8. Unit cells of crystals found in most metals: (a) body-centered cubic; (b) face-centered cubic; (c) close-packed hexagonal.

Another group of metals including iron, cobalt, and manganese may assume either of two crystalline forms depending upon the temperature. This is shown in table 11.

The properties of solid crystalline materials, such as metals, are controlled by the arrangement of the atoms making up the solid. The arrangement of atoms along one axis of the crystal may be different than it is along some other axis of the crystal. If this is so, the physical properties of the material will be different along these different directions. This fact has great commercial importance as we shall see in chapter 11.

Table 10
CRYSTAL STRUCTURE OF METALS

Body-centered Cubic	Face-centered Cubic	Close-packed Hexagonal
Lithium	Copper	Beryllium
Sodium	Silver	Magnesium
Potassium	Gold	Zinc
Vanadium	Platinum	Cadmium
Tantalum	Iridium	Titanium
Chromium	Palladium	Osmium
Molybdenum	Nickel	
Wolfram	Aluminum	

Table 11

EFFECT OF TEMPERATURE ON STRUCTURE OF SOME METALS[3]

Element	Structure at Low Temperature	Dividing Line Temperature	Structure at High Temperature
Iron.........	Body-centered cubic	906°C	Face-centered cubic
Manganese ..	Cubic (58 atoms)	742°C	Cubic (20 atoms)
Cobalt......	Close-packed hexa-gonal	477°C	Face-centered cubic

You must have been wondering all of this time about how the atoms are held together in these crystals. There is no evidence of ionic or covalent bonding. We can get an idea of the factors involved by studying the forces between two atoms as a function of the distance between them.

As the atoms are forced closer and closer together, forces of repulsion and attraction appear as shown in figure 5.9. These forces become important as the orbital electrons of one atom begin to interpenetrate the orbits of the other atom. Repulsion comes about by the Pauli exclusion principle. The inner quantum levels of the atoms are completely filled with electrons and more electrons cannot be added. This appears as a force of repulsion that increases rapidly as the penetration goes to the innermost quantum levels. At the same time, the penetrating electrons of each atom fall under the attraction

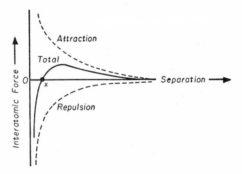

Figure 5.9. Interatomic force between two metal atoms as function of the distance between them.

---

[3] From John W. Boas, *Physics of Metals and Alloys*, New York: John Wiley & Sons, Inc., 1947, p. 45.

of the nucleus of the other atom and this tends to pull the two atoms together. When these two forces are exactly equal, as at x in figure 5.9, equilibrium results and a crystalline structure would evolve if many atoms were present.

5.4. Energy level diagram for metals

In the preceding section we saw that atoms of metallic crystals interpenetrate one another in the process of solidification. Such an interpenetration affects the electronic energy levels of the solid in the

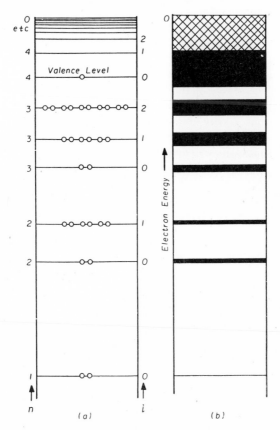

Figure 5.10. Energy level diagrams for a metal, shown schematic-ally.

general way discussed at the end of chapter 3. The purpose of this section is to show the effects of this interpenetration on the energy level diagram.

The approximate energy level diagram for a single copper atom is shown in figure 5.10a. The permitted energy levels are shown by horizontal lines and forbidden levels, or zones, appear as white spaces. Energy levels actually occupied by electrons are indicated by little circles representing the electrons. The allowed energy levels become continuous outside the atom and this is shown by the region at the top of figure 5.10a. Otherwise, the permitted energy levels are *discrete, not continuous.*

When a large number of copper atoms combine into a crystalline solid, the approximate energy level diagram of figure 5.10b is obtained. Here the discrete energy levels characteristic of the single atom have been split up into virtually *continuous bands* because of the interpenetrations of the atoms with one another. Permitted energy levels that are fully occupied are shown by solid black bands; permitted, but empty, bands are shown by cross sectioning. The forbidden zones are white. Actually, we observed the incipient formation of these bands in figure 3.17 of chapter 3 while discussing the splitting of energy levels as five hydrogen atoms were forced more closely together.

As you might expect, the greatest amount of splitting occurs in the valence levels and all higher levels as shown in figure 5.10b. In noble

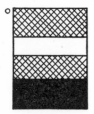 

metals, such as copper, the valence band is only half filled with electrons while all lower bands are completely filled. The occurrence of one *partially filled band* is characteristic of all metals.

It will be clear later that we are primarily interested in the valence energy band and all higher energy bands up to the

Figure 5.11. Band theory models for two types of metals.

zero level at the top of the figure. This is so because the electrons involved in electrical current and related phenomena are always in these energy bands. Thus, for the purposes of this book we will use only that part of the energy level diagram that includes the valence band and all higher bands. The result for copper appears as shown in figure 5.11. This is called the *band theory model* for copper. All of the noble metals can be represented by band theory models having this same general form. Similar models can be constructed for the alkali and divalent metals.

In all of the work that follows, figure 5.11 will be used to represent the energy distribution of the *valence* electrons in metallic solids.

5.5. Electronic conduction in metals—band theory model

The band theory model of metals given in figure 5.11 shows the energy levels of the valence electrons in their lowest energy states. Thus, this figure describes the energy distribution of the valence electrons in metallic solids at the absolute zero of temperature and in the absence of any electric or magnetic fields.

Under these conditions it is a little easier to discuss electronic behavior if we redraw the band theory models of the metals so that the zero level of energy falls at the bottom of the valence band. This is shown in figure 5.12. This simply represents a shift in the location of the *reference energy* level. It is desirable because we are interested only in the energies of the valence electrons. Thus, it seems reasonable to make the lowest energy possible for a

Figure 5.12. Band theory models of metals with new reference energy level defined.

valence electron serve as the reference energy level.

You should recall from our discussion of single atoms that a discrete and definite amount of energy was required to raise the energy level of a valence electron to some higher value. This was so because the permitted energy levels for electrons in a single atom were separated by definite forbidden zones.

This is no longer true for the *valence* electrons in metallic solids. As you can see from figure 5.12, there is a virtually continuous range of empty and permitted energy levels immediately above those valence electrons having the greatest amount of energy. Hence, nearly *any* amount of energy, even very small amounts, can raise the energy levels of some of the valence electrons so that they occupy the previously vacant, higher energy levels.

Suppose that we establish an electric field across a solid piece of metal by raising the potential of one end to a higher value than the potential at the other end. Let the potential difference be V volts so that in figure 5.13

$$V = V_1 - V_2 \quad \text{volts}$$

If the length of the metal sample is d meters, the electric field intensity in the metal is V/d volts/meter. The direction of the field intensity is shown in figure 5.13. This field exerts a force on the valence electrons and causes some of them to move through the metal toward the point of highest potential, in a direction opposite to the electric field intensity.

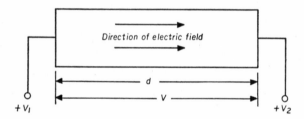

Figure 5.13. Conditions required to produce an electric current in a metal.

Because the electrons move in response to the force exerted by this field, the field does work on the electrons, giving them additional energy. This causes the topmost electrons in the band theory diagram to move up to higher energy levels.

The motion of the electrons constitutes a flow of electric charge or an electric current. Because the charge is carried by electrons, this is called *electronic conduction*. Materials that conduct electricity in this manner at all temperatures are called *conductors*. Hence, alkali, noble, and divalent metals are always conductors while in the solid state.

These materials are always conductors because there are always empty energy levels in the valence band immediately above the filled energy levels. Hence, the valence electrons can always accept energy in any amount from an applied electric field and can therefore conduct electric charge or current. Any *partially filled* energy band is called a *conduction band*.

The electrons in a completely filled band cannot ordinarily take part in electrical conduction because there are no immediately higher permitted energy levels that they can occupy. This is extremely important in materials called *semiconductors* as we shall see in chapter 6.

5.6. Electronic conduction in crystals at absolute zero

From the preceding discussion of electronic conduction in metals you can see that the valence electrons are essentially free to move about inside the crystal under the influence of any applied force. The electrons behave in very much the same manner as the molecules of gas in a closed container.

It is convenient to picture the interior of a metal as having the form of a regular array of positive ions imbedded in a sea or gas of *free* or *conduction* electrons. These valence electrons cannot be specifically assigned to one atom, but are considered to be free and to wander about.

If an electron is present in the deep interior of a metal crystal, and if the electron has zero kinetic energy, it remains at rest if the temperature is at absolute zero. This is possible only because, on the average, the *net* electric field inside the crystal is zero. This condition results from the regularity and symmetry of the arrangement of the crystal's ions. You can convince yourself of this by making a few sketches, because you will quickly see that a force in one direction is offset by an exactly equal force in the opposite direction.

All of the ions in a crystal are stationary at absolute zero. We will also assume that the crystals are perfectly periodic, without imperfections of any kind.

When an electric field is applied to the metal, the free electrons are accelerated in a direction opposite to the direction of the electric field. As the electrons move through the crystal lattice, they undergo strong and periodic variations in potential energy. This is caused by the regular spacing and force of attraction of the positive ions. This strong variation in potential energy acts to slow the electrons so that, generally speaking, they do not move as rapidly as they would in free space.

This result is usually accomodated mathematically by *assuming* that the mass of the electron is decreased. Thus, electrons moving in a crystal are endowed with an *effective mass* that is generally smaller than that obtained in free space. Values chosen to agree with experiment range from 1 to $\frac{1}{4}$ of the free space mass.[4,5]

Thus, at absolute zero we conceive electronic conduction to consist of the motion of wavelike free electrons diffusing through a perfectly periodic variation in electric potential. The electron mass and velocity may be less than the free space values. There is no opposition to the motion of these electrons—once set in motion they will move forever thereafter. Thus, in theory, the *resistance* of the material to the flow of electronic charge is zero at absolute zero temperature.

This may seem surprising now, but in future studies you will find it to be altogether expected. You will find that waves can be propagated without loss of energy in perfectly periodic structures. This is why electrical energy can be transmitted without loss on certain types of transmission lines. It is a characteristic of systems involving wave propagation in perfectly periodic systems.

In practice the periodicity is never perfect. Some impurities are always present in the material; or, some mechanical stress may break up the otherwise perfect periodicity. This generally causes most metals to have some small, but measurable, resistance at absolute zero.

There are a few special materials called *superconductors* that have zero resistance at temperatures above absolute zero. Space limitations prevent us from pursuing this subject.

5.7. Phonons and phantom particles

As the temperature of a solid is raised above absolute zero, both the electrons and atoms in the crystal acquire *thermal energy*. In the case of the valence electrons, those electrons in the upper energy levels of the band theory diagram move to higher energy levels as they acquire kinetic energy from the source of heat.

The atoms in the crystal manifest their acquisition of energy by vibrating vigorously within the framework of the crystal structure.

---

[4] W. Shockley, "Transistor Electronics: Imperfect, Unipolar, and Analogue Transistors," *Proc. I.R.E.*, Vol. 40, No. 11, Nov. 1952, p. 1292.

[5] E. M. Conwell, "Properties of Silicon and Germanium," *Proc. I.R.E.*, Vol. 40, No. 11, Nov. 1952, pp. 1327–1337, esp. p. 1330.

The extent of the vibration is appreciable as shown by the data in table 12. For example, data in this table show that the atoms in the copper crystal vibrate with an amplitude that is 5.6 per cent of the spacing between the atoms in the crystal, assuming operation at room temperature.

This atomic vibration obviously destroys the perfect periodicity of the crystal, which was assumed in the preceding section. Hence, at temperatures above absolute zero we have a slightly different picture of the mechanism of electronic conduction. We must digress for a moment to explain why this is so.

Quite a bit of space was spent in chapter 3 in discussing the various quantizing operations connected with the description of atomic structure. It was shown that light and other electromagnetic vibrations are quantized by assuming that they consist of a stream of photons. In addition, the mechanical motion of the electrons in atoms was described in terms of several quantum conditions.

Thus, it should not be surprising to find that the mechanical vibrations in a solid are also quantized in modern mathematical descrip-

Table 12

AMPLITUDE OF ATOMIC VIBRATIONS IN CRYSTALS AT 20°C [6]

Element	Amplitude in % of Atomic Spacing
Aluminum	6.2
Silver	5.6
Copper	5.6
Nickel	5.1
Zinc	7.1

tions. In this scheme of things we consider the energy in a mechanical vibration in a solid to be carried by a stream of corpuscular *phonons*. The phonons represent mechanical vibrations in the same sense that photons represent electromagnetic vibrations.

As the temperature of the solid is progressively raised above absolute zero, the atoms in the solid acquire additional energy and they

[6] Taken with permission from W. Boas, *Introduction to the Physics of Metals and Alloys*, New York: John Wiley & Sons, Inc., 1947, table 8, p. 61.

vibrate. This is called *thermal vibration*. The energy in this vibration is equivalent to a certain number of phonons. Hence, at temperatures well above absolute zero we conceive the solid as being full of phonons, where the phonons represent the thermal vibrations of the crystal lattice. At absolute zero there are no phonons because there is no energy of lattice vibration.

The phonons constitute energetic imperfections in the otherwise perfect periodicity of the idealized crystalline solid. Hence, an electron set in motion by thermal or electric forces will *not* continue along one path indefinitely. Instead, its motion is occasionally changed through the interference from a phonon. This causes the wavelike electron to be *scattered*, just as light is scattered by imperfections in glass.

It has been shown[7,8] that it is possible to get a better mental visualization of the phenomena inside a heated metal if a new model of behavior is proposed. This consists of introducing a set of *phantom particles* which take the place and have the same effect as the phonons. These phantom particles are conceived to be hard, spherical, uncharged, and perfectly elastic particles. They are assumed to have a mass about 170 times larger than the mass of an electron.

When using this phantom particle model we assume that the atoms forming the crystal are stationary. The thermal energy associated with the atoms, which are actually vibrating, is assigned to the phantom particles. In other words, the solid is conceived to be full of energetic phantom particles moving about within the solid in a random manner while the atoms remain stationary. The energy of the phantom particles equals the vibrational energy of the atoms.

We can now describe the events occurring in a heated solid in a way that is more readily visualized. The electrons and phantom particles in a heated solid are in energetic motion. Every now and then they collide and some energy is exchanged. The electron does not lose very much energy because the phantom particle is very heavy compared to the electron and is perfectly elastic. Thus, the motion of a free electron in a heated solid might have the perfectly random path shown in figure 5.14.

---

[7] W. Shockley, "Transistor Electronics: Imperfect, Unipolar, and Analogue Transistors," *Proc. I.R.E.*, Vol. 40, No. 11, Nov. 1952, pp. 1289–1313.

[8] W. Shockley, "Hot Electrons in Germanium and Ohm's Law," *B.S.T.J.*, Vol. 30, 1951, p. 900.

This figure was drawn by assuming that the electron collides with phantom particles at regularly spaced intervals. This does *not* actually occur. Collisions occur at perfectly random intervals. However, there is some average distance travelled between collisions when the average is computed over a large number of collisions. The *average* distance between collisions is called the *mean free path* of the electron. The mean free path is about 10^{-7} meter at room temperature. The mean free path decreases with increasing temperature because more phantom particles are present and they are moving more rapidly.

Figure 5.14. Possible path of an electron in a heated solid.

Figure 5.14 was drawn by assuming that collisions occur at intervals equal to the mean free path. Although this is obviously untrue, just like the phantom particles, it still gives very accurate theoretical predictions.

5.8. Conduction at temperatures above absolute zero

In section 5.6 we discussed electron motion in perfect metallic solids at absolute zero, when an electric field was applied. We found that it had the general form shown schematically in figure 5.15a. In section 5.7 we discussed the motion of electrons in heated solids in the absence of any electric field. The result was the perfectly random motion shown in figure 5.15b.

In the most common case of interest to engineers, the electrons are in heated solids and an electric field is also present. Thus, the two motions previously discussed separately now occur simultaneously and the result might appear as shown in figure 5.15c. The curvature of the path between collisions with phantom particles is caused by the acceleration of the electrons by the force of the electric field.

Between collisions the electrons receive energy from the electric field. This energy is then transferred to the phantom particles during collision. This causes energy to be transferred from the electric field to the phantom particles by the collision process. This is just another way of saying that the energy of the phantom particles is increased when a voltage is applied across the metal. The increase in phantom particle energy corresponds to increased vibration of the atoms in the solid. Exactly the same thing happens if we raise the temperature of the solid. Thus, it appears that the electron motion, or electric current, in the metal, raises the temperature of the metal.

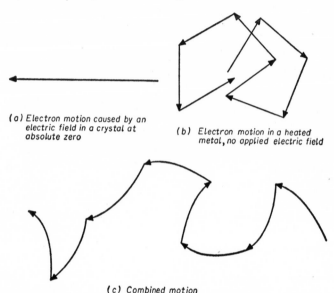

(a) Electron motion caused by an electric field in a crystal at absolute zero

(b) Electron motion in a heated metal, no applied electric field

(c) Combined motion

Figure 5.15. Showing how electric and thermal forces combine to produce the erratic drift of electrons in heated solids with an applied electric field.

While on this same line of thought you can also see that if the temperature of the solid is increased, the thermal agitation of the electrons and phantom particles increases. This causes them to jump about in an increasingly energetic manner, thereby increasing the frequency of collisions.

Because of their frequent starting and stopping, the electrons do not have a fixed and uniform velocity in the direction opposite to the electric field intensity. Nevertheless, over a period of time including many collisions, there is an *average* or *drift velocity*, v_d, in the direction opposite to the electric field. The ratio of this drift velocity to the magnitude of the electric field intensity is called the *mobility*, μ, of the electron in the solid. That is,

$$\mu \overset{\Delta}{=} \frac{v_d}{E} = \text{mobility in m/sec/v/m} \qquad (5.1)$$

where E = magnitude of the electric field intensity. Hence, the drift velocity is

$$v_d = \mu E \tag{5.2}$$

In most cases the mobility, μ, is a constant of the material and is independent of the electric field intensity. However, in some cases where the field intensity is very high, the energy of the random motion of the electrons becomes so large that the collision frequency increases causing the mobility to decrease.[9,10] This change in mobility occurs when the drift velocity is approximately equal to the thermal velocity of the phantom particles.

5.9. Resistance

In the preceding discussion it was shown that an electric current is produced in a conductor when a potential difference is impressed across it. Let V = potential difference in volts, I = current in amperes. The ratio of the voltage to the current is called the *resistance*, R, of the material. That is,

$$R \triangleq \frac{V}{I} = \text{resistance of the material} \tag{5.3}$$

or

$$V = IR \tag{5.4}$$

Equation (5.4) is generally called *Ohm's Law*.

The unit of resistance is the *ohm*, where 1 ohm = (1 volt)/(1 amp). The reciprocal of resistance is called the *conductance*, G, of the material. That is

$$G \triangleq \frac{1}{R} \tag{5.5}$$

The unit of conductance is the *mho*.

Let N denote the number of free electrons per unit volume in a conducting material. If these electrons have an average drift velocity v_d, then according to equation (2.3) of chapter 2, the current is

$$I = N e v_d A \tag{5.6}$$

where A = area of conductor perpendicular to the current, e = charge

---

[9] E. M. Conwell, *op. cit.*

[10] E. J. Ryder, W. Shockley, "Mobilities of Electrons in High Electric Fields," *Phys. Rev.*, Vol. 8, 1951, p. 139.

on an electron in coulombs. Now suppose that the conductor is L meters long and that a potential difference of V volts is applied across it. The various factors involved in this discussion are shown in figure 5.16.

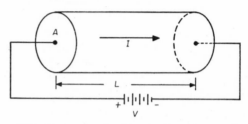

Figure 5.16. Factors involved in the discussion of resistance.

The electric field intensity produced in the conductor by the applied potential difference is

$$E = \frac{V}{L} \tag{5.7}$$

Thus, the drift velocity of the electrons can be expressed as

$$v_d = \mu E = \frac{\mu V}{L} \tag{5.8}$$

where μ = mobility of the electrons. Therefore, the current in the conductor is

$$I = \frac{Ne\mu A V}{L} \tag{5.9}$$

According to Ohm's Law the current can also be computed from

$$I = \frac{V}{R} \tag{5.10}$$

Equate (5.9) and (5.10) and solve for the resistance R. The result is

$$R = \left(\frac{1}{Ne\mu}\right)\frac{L}{A} \tag{5.11}$$

The bracketed factor is called the *resistivity*, ρ, of the material so that

$$\rho \stackrel{\Delta}{=} \frac{1}{Ne\mu} = \text{resistivity} \tag{5.12}$$

This is a very important relationship that we will use many times. Combining equations (5.11) and (5.12) gives

$$R = \rho \frac{L}{A} \quad \text{ohms} \tag{5.13}$$

The reciprocal of the resistivity is the *conductivity*, σ, where

$$\sigma \triangleq \frac{1}{\rho} = Ne\mu \tag{5.14}$$

The units associated with the resistivity are easily computed from equation (5.13). This yields the unit *ohm-meter*. Other units commonly used are the *ohm-inch* and *ohm-centimeter*.

Some representative values for the resistivities of various materials

Table 13

RESISTIVITIES OF SOME COMMON
MATERIALS AT 20°C

Element	ρ in ohm-cm
Aluminum...............	2.67×10^{-6}
Copper (annealed)........	1.724×10^{-6}
Nickel...................	$7.2 \quad \times 10^{-6}$
Nichrome................	$110 \quad\, \times 10^{-6}$
Silver...................	1.64×10^{-6}
Platinum................	$10 \quad\;\, \times 10^{-6}$

are given in table 13. It will be shown in the next section that the resistivity is dependent upon temperature. The resistivities given in table 13 are valid only at 20°C.

One more point remains in the discussion of resistance. We have previously shown that an electric current in a metal causes the metal to heat. This represents a transfer of power from the source of the electric field to the metal conductor. We need some way of calculating this *electrical power*.

In chapter 1 we defined potential difference as the work done per unit charge in moving the charge through this potential difference. Hence, if V = potential difference in volts, and q = total charge transferred in coulombs, then the work done in moving the charge dq through the potential difference of V volts is

$$dW = V \, dq \quad \text{joules} \tag{5.15}$$

The time rate of doing work is power, P. Hence,

$$P = \frac{dW}{dt} \tag{5.16}$$

If we divide both sides of equation (5.15) by dt, the equation for the power reduces to

$$P = V\frac{dq}{dt} \tag{5.17}$$

However, current was defined in chapter 2 as the time rate of change of charge, or $I = dq/dt$. Hence, the electric power is

$$P = VI \tag{5.18}$$

The unit of electrical power is the *watt*, where (1 volt)(1 amp) = (1 watt) = (1 joule)/(1 sec).

From Ohm's Law we know that $V = IR$, or that $I = V/R$. Hence, the electrical power delivered to the resistor can also be computed from

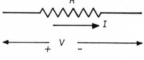

Figure 5.17. Circuit symbol for a resistor.

$$P = I^2R = \frac{V^2}{R} \tag{5.19}$$

This is the amount of electrical power delivered by the voltage source in the process of supplying heat to the metal as a result of electronic collisions with phantom particles. The energy dissipated by the resistor as a result of a constant current is

$$W = Pt = I^2Rt = VIt = \frac{V^2t}{R} \tag{5.20}$$

Resistors are indicated schematically in drawings by the symbol shown in figure 5.17.

5.10. Special units for resistivity

In the preceding section we saw that the MKSC unit for resistivity is the *ohm-meter*. A common unit for resistivity that nearly always confuses young engineers is the *ohms per circular mil foot*.

A *circular mil* is the area of a circle 1 *mil* (1 milli-inch) in diameter. That is

$$1 \text{ circular mil} \stackrel{\Delta}{=} \frac{\pi(0.001)^2}{4} = \frac{\pi}{4} \times 10^{-6} \text{ in.}^2$$

Because wires used in electrical circuits are usually, though not always, round, the area of most wires is given by

$$A \text{ (in.}^2) = \frac{\pi}{4} d^2$$

where d = wire diameter in inches. Factor out a term equal to the area of 1 circular mil so that

$$A \text{ (in.}^2) = \left(\frac{\pi}{4} \times 10^{-6}\right)(\text{diam in mils})^2$$

The area of a wire expressed in *circular mils* is the square of the wire diameter, when it is expressed in mils. That is,

$$A \text{ (circular mils)} \triangleq (\text{diam in mils})^2$$

Consequently,

$$A \text{ (in.}^2) = \left(\frac{\pi}{4} \times 10^{-6}\right)(\text{area in circular mils})$$

or $\qquad A \text{ (circular mils)} = \left(\frac{4}{\pi} \times 10^6\right)(\text{area in in.}^2)$

If the cross-sectional area of a wire is expressed in circular mils and the length in feet, the unit for the resistivity is

$$\rho = \text{ohms}\left(\frac{\text{circular mil}}{\text{ft}}\right)$$

or $\qquad \rho = \text{circular mil ohms per foot}$

Unfortunately, this is frequently expressed as *ohms per circular mil foot*, which is somewhat misleading and incorrect. Nevertheless, it is often used and really means *circular mil ohms per foot*.

5.11. Hall effect

To calculate the resistivity of metals from equation (5.12) we must know both the density and mobility of the *free* valence electrons. One method of determining mobility and electron density is given in this section.

Consider a solid sample of metal as shown in figure 5.18. The sample is assumed to be located in a uniform *magnetic field* of flux density B directed parallel to the z axis as shown. A current I is assumed to exist in the metal and to be directed in the positive x

direction. This current arises from the motion of negatively charged electrons moving along the negative x direction.

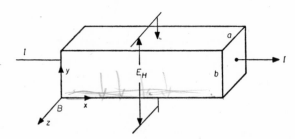

Figure 5.18. Terms involved in the explanation of the Hall effect.

The electrons are moving at right angles to the magnetic field. This causes a force to be exerted on the electrons by the magnetic field. This force is

$$F_m = -e\boldsymbol{v} \times \boldsymbol{B}$$

The velocity $\boldsymbol{v}$ is in the negative x direction. The flux density $\boldsymbol{B}$ is in the positive z direction. Hence, this force is directed downward in the negative y direction. This force tends to sweep the electrons down to the bottom side of the conductor. The *magnitude* of this force in the y direction is

$$F_m = evB$$

The action just described creates a nonuniformity in the charge distribution in the metal sample, producing an excess of electrons on the bottom side of the conductor. This, in turn, produces a *transverse* electric field in the $-y$ direction, tending to force electrons *up* from the bottom. Designate this field as E_H. The production of this field is called the *Hall effect*.

The magnitude of the electrostatic force on an electron in the y direction as a result of the Hall effect electric field is

$$F_e = eE_H \tag{5.21}$$

Under equilibrium conditions the electrostatic force exactly offsets the magnetic force and the accumulation of electric charge will cease. Under this condition

$$eE_H = evB \tag{5.22}$$

According to equation (5.6) the current through a sample is given by

$$I = NevA$$

This corresponds to a current density J, where

$$J = \frac{I}{A} = Nev \tag{5.23}$$

Consequently,

$$ev = \frac{J}{N}$$

and equation (5.22) becomes

$$eE_H = \frac{JB}{N} \tag{5.24}$$

Solve this equation for $1/Ne$. This factor is a constant of the material and we will define it as the *Hall coefficient* and denote it by $\Re$. That is,

$$\Re \overset{\Delta}{=} -\frac{1}{Ne} \tag{5.25}$$

and also

$$\Re = -\frac{E_H}{JB} \tag{5.26}$$

Equation (5.26) is the basis for the experimental measurement of the Hall coefficient. By any one of several methods[11] it is possible to measure the Hall effect field intensity produced in a sample by any combination of values for current density and flux density. The Hall coefficient can then be computed. Knowing the Hall coefficient, the concentration N of electrons can be calculated from equation (5.25).

From the discussion of the resistivity of a material it was shown in equation (5.12) that

$$\rho = \frac{1}{Ne\mu}$$

or

$$\mu = \frac{1}{Ne\rho} = \text{electron mobility}$$

Now substitute equation (5.25) for the density of electrons.

$$\mu = -\frac{\Re}{\rho} \tag{5.27}$$

From this you can see that the electron mobility can be computed

---

[11] Lindberg, "Hall Effect," *Proc. I.R.E.*, Vol. 40, No. 11, Nov. 1952.

from measurements of the Hall coefficient and the resistivity of the metal sample.

5.12. Some circuit concepts

A resistor is one type of *electric circuit element*. An *electric circuit* is formed when several such elements are combined in various geometric configurations. The simplest electric circuits are the *series* and *parallel* circuits shown in figure 5.19. The same current I exists in all elements in the series circuit. The same voltage V exists across all elements in the parallel circuit.

When the current passes through a circuit element in a direction from a point of high potential (+) to a point of lower potential (−), we identify the voltage across that element as a *voltage drop*. Voltage drops occur across all resistors. However, the current passes from a point of low potential (−) to a point of high potential (+) in sources

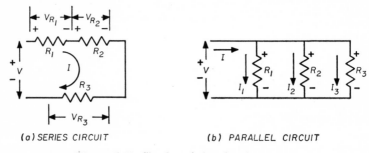

(a) SERIES CIRCUIT   (b) PARALLEL CIRCUIT

Figure 5.19. Simple resistive electric currents.

of electrical energy such as generators and batteries. Such a voltage is identified as a *voltage rise*. We will have occasion to use this terminology in just a moment.

According to the Law of Conservation of Energy, the total energy supplied to a system must be equal to the total energy dissipated by that system, assuming that the system cannot store energy. The total energy supplied to either of the two circuits of figure 5.19 is easily computed from equation (5.20) to be

$$W \text{ (supplied)} = VIt \qquad (5.28)$$

Energy is *dissipated* in each of the three resistors of both circuits in figure 5.19. Using equation (5.20) again, we have for the *series* circuit

$$W_1 = I^2 R_1 t = V_{R_1} I t$$
$$W_2 = I^2 R_2 t = V_{R_2} I t$$
$$W_3 = I^2 R_3 t = V_{R_3} I t$$

For the *parallel* circuit we have

$$W_1 = I_1^2 R_1 t = V I_1 t$$
$$W_2 = I_2^2 R_2 t = V I_2 t$$
$$W_3 = I_3^2 R_3 t = V I_3 t$$

In the case of the *series* circuit, set the energy supplied equal to the total energy dissipated. This gives

$$VIt = (V_{R_1} + V_{R_2} + V_{R_3})It$$

Cancel the product of I and t on both sides of the equation.

$$V = V_{R_1} + V_{R_2} + V_{R_3} \qquad (5.29)$$

or

$$V = I(R_1 + R_2 + R_3) \qquad (5.30)$$

Equation (5.29) can be stated in much more general terms as follows:

The sum of the voltage rises (V) is equal to the sum of the voltage drops $(V_{R_1} + V_{R_2} + V_{R_3})$ around a closed path in an electric circuit.

This is called *Kirchhoff's Loop Law.*

In the case of the *parallel* circuit, equate the energy supplied to the total energy dissipated. The result, after cancelling the common Vt factor, is

$$I = I_1 + I_2 + I_3 \qquad (5.31)$$

or

$$I = \frac{V}{R_1} + \frac{V}{R_2} + \frac{V}{R_3} \qquad (5.32)$$

Equations (5.32) and (5.31) can be stated more generally as follows:

The sum of the currents (I) into a junction of several circuit elements is equal to the sum $(I_1 + I_2 + I_3)$ of the currents leaving the junction.

This is called *Kirchhoff's Node or Junction Law.*

It is sometimes desirable to know the total resistance R_T of a series or parallel combination of resistances. The total resistance of a circuit measured at any pair of terminals is equal to the ratio of the voltage across that pair of terminals to the current into or out of the terminals. Thus, for either of the two circuits in figure 5.19,

$$R_T = \frac{V}{I}$$

Thus, from equation (5.30) for the *series* circuit it is easily shown that

$$R_T \text{ (series)} = R_1 + R_2 + R_3 \qquad (5.33)$$

In other words, the total resistance of a series combination of resistors is equal to the sum of the series resistances.

From equation (5.32) for the *parallel* circuit you can easily show that

$$R_T \text{ (parallel)} = \frac{1}{\dfrac{1}{R_1} + \dfrac{1}{R_2} + \dfrac{1}{R_3}} \qquad (5.34)$$

Hence, the total resistance of a parallel combination of resistors is the reciprocal of the sum of the reciprocals of the parallel resistances. A simpler equation is obtained if we use conductances rather than resistances. Let

$$G_T = \frac{1}{R_T} = \text{total parallel conductance}$$

$$G_1 = \frac{1}{R_1} \qquad G_2 = \frac{1}{R_2} \qquad G_3 = \frac{1}{R_3}$$

Hence, from equation (5.34),

$$G_T = G_1 + G_2 + G_3 \qquad (5.35)$$

The total conductance of paralleled conductances is the sum of the separate conductances.

Kirchhoff's Laws form the basis for the general field of knowledge called *electric circuit theory*. This subject is treated in detail in numerous other books and is not pursued further here.

5.13. Effect of temperature on resistance

From the discussion of resistance in section 5.9 it is apparent that resistance is used as a measure of the amount of energy removed from the electrons by the phantom particles or other crystalline imperfections. Hence, the resistance of a perfect crystal should be zero at absolute zero temperature because there are no phantom particles present. We shall assume that the crystal is devoid of other imperfections. The electrons move through the crystal under the influence of an electric field without interference, collision, or loss of energy.

While this is true in theory, it appears that most metals, such as copper, have crystal imperfections. They may be caused by crystal faults, finite crystal dimensions, or other irregularities. This results in non-zero resistances at absolute zero.[12]

As the temperature is increased slightly above absolute zero, phantom particles are produced and they interfere with the motion of the electrons. This causes the resistance of the material to increase. In a confined range of temperatures the resistance increases very rapidly with increasing temperature, at a rate approximately proportional to the fifth power of the temperature.

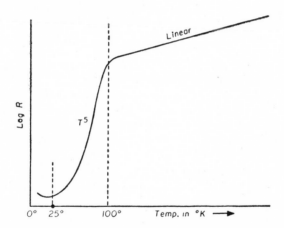

Figure 5.20. Effect of temperature on the resistance of a metal.

At somewhat higher temperatures the resistance becomes a nearly linear function of temperature. This is illustrated by the sketch in figure 5.20, which is generally characteristic of the alkali and noble metals. The cause of the dip in the region near 25°K is not completely understood.[12]

---

[12] C. A. Swenson, A. G. Emslie, "Low Temperature Electronics," *Proc. I.R.E.*, Vol. 42, No. 2, Feb. 1954, pp. 408–413.

The region of the curve where the resistance increases almost linearly as the temperature increases is very important to engineers. An enlarged view of this part of the curve is shown in figure 5.21. In this

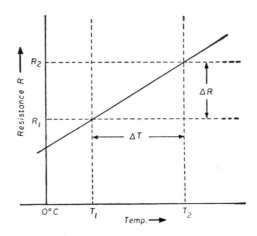

Figure 5.21. Temperature dependence of resistance in the linear region.

figure the resistance is shown on a linear scale rather than a logarithmic scale as used in figure 5.20. Because this section of the curve shown in figure 5.21 is virtually a straight line for most metals, the slope is the same throughout. That is,

$$\text{slope} = \frac{\Delta R}{\Delta T} = \frac{R_2 - R_1}{T_2 - T_1} \tag{5.36}$$

The equation for the line shown in figure 5.21 is easily written. Such an equation would allow us to compute the resistance at any temperature if we know its value at any other temperature. Let R_1 = known resistance at temperature T_1, R_2 = unknown resistance at temperature T_2. Then,

$$R_2 = R_1 + (\text{slope})\Delta T$$

or, if we factor out the R_1, we have

$$R_2 = R_1 \left[1 + \frac{\text{slope}}{R_1} \Delta T \right] \tag{5.37}$$

The second factor inside the brackets in equation (5.37), which is (slope)/R_1, is called the *temperature coefficient of resistance* and denoted by α_{T_1}. That is

$$\alpha_{T_1} \overset{\Delta}{=} \frac{\text{slope}}{R_1} = \left(\frac{R_2 - R_1}{R_1}\right)\left(\frac{1}{T_2 - T_1}\right) \tag{5.38}$$

It is clear that this factor depends upon temperature.

Values for the temperature coefficient of resistance are generally given at 20°C as shown in table 14 for a few typical materials. The temperature coefficient of resistance for pure metals is always positive. Certain alloys may have negative values.

Substitute equation (5.38) back into equation (5.37) and we have the equation for the temperature variation of resistance in its most common form:

$$R_{T_2} = R_{20}[1 + \alpha_{20}(T_2 - 20)] \tag{5.39}$$

It is clear that the resistance at 20°C must also be known to make this calculation. In turn, this requires that you know the resistivity ρ_{20} at 20°C.

The resistivity at any other temperature is easily computed from equation (5.39) to be

$$\rho_{T_2} = \rho_{20}[1 + \alpha_{20}(T_2 - 20)] \tag{5.40}$$

Table 14
TEMPERATURE COEFFICIENTS OF RESISTANCE AT 20°C

Material	α_{20}/°C
Aluminum................	+0.0039
Annealed copper...........	+0.00393
Hard drawn copper.........	+0.00382
Nickel...................	+0.006
Platinum.................	+0.003
Silver...................	+0.0038
Tin.....................	+0.0042

5.14. Fermi distribution of electrons in a metal

We have seen that the close-packed atomic structure of metals produces a nearly field-free space in which the outermost, or valence electrons of the atom can move freely. Of course, strong local irregularities in field strength exist near the atoms, but on the average, the inside of a metal is nearly field-free. Thus, a relatively accurate approximation of the behavior of the valence electrons in a metal is obtained if it is assumed that they behave like the molecules of a perfect gas. This *perfect gas model* is simply another way of interpreting the band theory diagrams of metals given in figure 5.12.

It has been estimated that each atom in a metal contributes approximately one electron to the *electron gas*. Hence, the density of the gas is quite high.

For a perfect gas it can be shown that the gas molecules can have an infinite number of allowed energy levels. We noted the same effect for the valence electrons in metals by the form of the band theory model in figure 5.12.

At absolute zero the electrons revert to their lowest possible energy levels. However, no two electrons in a unit volume exist in the same energy state. So even at absolute zero, the *free* electrons in the metal are distributed in energy as shown in the band theory model. Some electrons have high energies while others have low energies.

The trouble with our band theory model is that it does not show the relative densities of electrons in various energy ranges. It does not tell us whether most of the electrons have high energies, or low energies, or if the number of electrons in each energy range is the same.

An approximate curve showing the distribution of the electron energies is given in figure 5.22. This is the *Fermi distribution* of the energy of the *free* electrons in a metal at absolute zero. It indicates the relative density of electrons in various energy ranges. It is a plot of the distribution of electrons in the various energy ranges in the filled valence band of the metal, evaluated at absolute zero. The symbol $N(W)$ signifies the number of electrons per unit volume per unit range of energy.

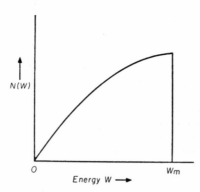

Figure 5.22. Fermi distribution of electrons at 0°K.

This calculated distribution of electrons in a metal is only an approximation. The approximation is very good for high energy electrons, but it is poor at the low energy range. This is not a serious disadvantage in most cases because greatest interest is directed upon the electrons in the high energy ranges. This will be apparent shortly.

When thermal energy is added to the metal, energy is added to the electrons and to the atoms. This affects the energy distribution of the electrons, but the effect is not very large at ordinary room temperatures. However, at high temperatures the effect can be quite pronounced as shown in figure 5.23.

W_m is called the *Fermi* level of the solid. It is shown on figure 5.22 and in figure 5.23. No electron can have an energy greater than the Fermi level at absolute zero.

The only electrons that can acquire thermal energy

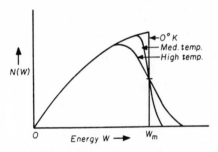

Figure 5.23. Effect of temperature on the Fermi distribution of electrons in a metal.

as the metal is heated are those electrons having energies near the Fermi level. They are the only electrons that have unfilled energy levels immediately above them.

The change in distribution of the electrons as a function of temperature has only a slight effect upon the electrical conductivity. However, it is enormously important in the operation of *vacuum tubes* and some *gas tubes*. In these cases it is necessary to force electrons completely out of the metal and into the surrounding space. This process is called *electronic* emission and it is discussed in some detail in later sections.

It can be shown that the Fermi level can be computed from the following equation:

$$W_m = \frac{h^2}{8m}\left(\frac{3N}{\pi}\right)^{2/3} \quad \text{joules} \tag{5.41}$$

where h = Planck's constant, m = electron mass, N = number of electrons per unit volume. This can be expressed somewhat more compactly as

$$W_m = (3.64 \times 10^{-19})N^{2/3} \quad \text{electron-volts} \tag{5.42}$$

The Fermi level, W_m, varies slightly with temperature, but it is essentially constant up to the melting point for pure metals. It is

* See Appendix III, page 398.

clear from equation (5.42) that the Fermi level depends upon the density of *free* electrons in the material. This is different for different metals so that different metals have different Fermi levels.

5.15. Thermionic emission from pure metals

Despite the fact that the atoms in a metal are electrically neutral, the shielding of the nucleus by the distributed orbital electrons is not complete. As a result, an unattached electron will experience a nuclear attraction from each atom in the crystal. This force is quite difficult to formulate mathematically. In the *interior* of the metal the atoms are regularly arranged in some sort of crystalline array. Thus, the forces on a stray electron inside the metal are nearly the same in all directions and the interior of the metal may be considered to be field-free on the average.

Near the *surface* of the metal the symmetrical arrangement of the nuclei gradually disappears because of the absence of nuclei outside the metal. As a result, a net force is present on an electron tending to pull it back to the interior of the metal. To overcome this force and be ejected from the metal, the electron must be supplied with additional energy from some source. If this energy is supplied by heating, *thermionic emission* of electrons occurs. If the energy comes from electromagnetic radiation, *photoelectric emission* takes place.

The unbalance of forces on an electron near the surface of a metal

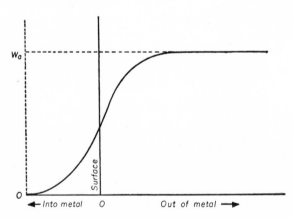

Figure 5.24. Potential energy barrier at a metal surface.

requires that energy be supplied to the electron to move it outside the metal. Assume an electron to be located in the deep interior of the metal and to have zero potential and kinetic energy. Now assume that we start moving this electron toward the surface of the metal. No work is required at first because there is no force of opposition. The potential energy of the electron remains zero.

As the electron nears the surface, a force of opposition develops that grows ever stronger as the surface is approached. Work must be done to move the electron against this force. This causes the potential energy of the electron to increase as shown by the curve in figure 5.24. As the electron is forced out of the metal, the force is still present and the potential energy of the electron increases rapidly. As the electron moves farther away from the surface, the force decreases rapidly so that the potential energy increases much less rapidly. For all practical purposes the force rapidly approaches zero and the potential energy of the electron approaches a maximum limiting value of W_a, as shown in figure 5.24. W_a is the energy of an electron *at rest outside* a solid. Its value may vary by as much as a factor of 2 for different metals.

If the energy distribution bands of the electrons in the metal are superimposed on the potential energy barrier curve, the condition at absolute zero appears as shown in figure 5.25. It is clear from this figure that *electron emission* from the metal will occur if enough energy is added to some electrons to allow them to make the transition from

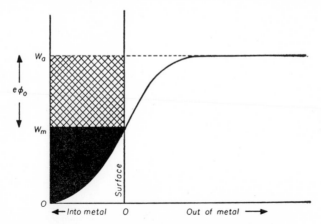

Figure 5.25. Energy relationships at a metal surface.

the energy level W_m to an energy level W_a. This energy difference is called the *work function*, $e\phi_0$, of the metal. Hence,

$$e\phi_0 = W_a - W_m \quad \text{joules} \tag{5.43}$$

where e = charge on an electron in coulombs, ϕ_0 = work function in electron-volts.

The work function, which is the energy that must be added to an electron for it to be emitted, is usually expressed in electron-volts (eV). Some typical values for the work functions of pure, clean metals

Table 15
EMISSION CONSTANTS OF PURE METALS

Element	ϕ_0 in eV	A' amp/cm², °K	Melting Point, °K
Caesium.............	1.81	16	302
Rhodium............	4.80	33	2243
Nickel..............	4.61	30	1725
Tantalum...........	4.05	55	3123
Molybdenum........	4.17	51	2893
Tungsten...........	4.52	60	3643
Platinum...........	5.32	32	2028

are given in table 15. The units can be changed to *joules* by multiplying the work function in eV by the charge on an electron in coulombs.

It was shown earlier in figure 5.23 that the energy distribution of the electrons in a metal is altered when the metal is heated. At temperatures of 1000°K and above, this alteration becomes sufficient to cause a relatively large number of electrons to overcome the surface energy barrier and be emitted. It can be shown[13] that this emission of electrons constitutes an emission current that depends upon temperature according to the following formula:

$$J = AT^2\epsilon^{-e\phi_0/kT} \tag{5.44}$$

where J = emission current density in amp/meter²

ϕ_0 = work function in eV

e = charge on an electron in coulombs

T = temperature in °K

[13] See for example, C. Herring, M. H. Nichols, "Thermionic Emission," *Rev. Mod. Phys.*, Vol. 21, April 1949, p. 185.

$$k = \text{Boltzmann's constant} = 1.380 \times 10^{-23} \text{ joule/}^\circ\text{K}$$

$$A = \text{theoretical constant} = \frac{4\pi m k^2 e}{h^3} \tag{5.45}$$

$$= 120.4 \times 10^{+4} \text{ amp/meter}^2 \,^\circ\text{K}$$

$$m = \text{electron mass in kg}$$

$$h = \text{Planck's constant}$$

Equation (5.44) is generally called the *Richardson equation*.[14] It is also known as the *Dushman* or *Richardson-Dushman equation*.

Typical experimentally determined values for the constant A and work function ϕ_0 are given in table 15 for a few pure metals. The theoretical value for A is 120.4. From table 15 it is obvious that there is a considerable discrepancy between the theoretical and measured values for A.

This deviation can be accounted for in the theoretical development of the Richardson equation by introducing a *reflection coefficient*, γ. That is, because of the wave nature of the electrons, not every electron with the required amount of normally directed energy will actually be emitted. Some will be reflected back into the metal. Thus, a new emission constant A' is defined where

$$A' = A(1 - \gamma) \tag{5.46}$$

Superficially it would appear that metals with the lower work functions would be the best for practical thermionic emitters. This is not generally true, however, because metals with low work functions also have low melting points as a glance at table 15 will show. Metals evaporate rather rapidly at temperatures near their melting points. Thus, by the time a metal with a low work function is heated sufficiently to provide adequate emission, its rate of evaporation is so great that it rapidly burns out. It has a very short useful life. Consequently, tungsten, which melts at 3643°K is the most common pure metallic emitter because it has the highest melting point of usable metals.

Metals are heated to provide emission in vacuum or in atmospheres of inactive gases. This is necessary because metals oxidize very rapidly at high temperatures and the oxides usually evaporate at lower

---

[14] O. W. Richardson, *Emission of Electricity from Hot Bodies*, 2nd Ed., New York: Longmans, Green, and Co., 1921.

temperatures than the pure metal. Also, the work functions of the oxides are generally higher than those of the pure metals.

5.16. Schottky effect and high field emission

The preceding discussion treated the case of thermionic emission of electrons from metals when there was no electric field at the emitting surface to accelerate the electrons away from the metal after emission. The work function, ϕ_0, was defined under this *field-free* condition. Because the presence of an accelerating field tends to assist the electrons in overcoming the surface energy barrier, it seems reasonable that the *effective work function* will be reduced. Precisely this occurs and it is called the *Schottky effect*.

The mathematical derivation of the Schottky effect for the case of pure, clean metal surfaces is not difficult.[15] However, only a brief qualitative discussion is presented here. Most of the factors involved can be illustrated by the simple energy level diagram sketched in figure 5.26. This shows the energy bands of the electrons in the metal referred to the variation in potential energy near the surface. The field-free work function ϕ_0 is identified together with

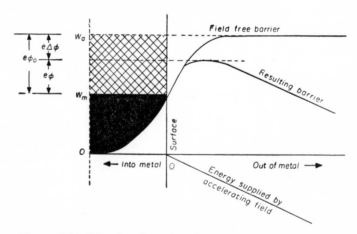

Figure 5.26. Schottky effect—lowering of the surface energy barrier by an applied electric field.

[15] See for example, M.I.T. Staff, *Applied Electronics*, New York: John Wiley & Sons, Inc., 1943, pp. 94–99.

W_a = field-free electron energy when at rest outside the metal

W_m = Fermi level

The potential energy variation introduced by the applied electric field is shown by a straight line drawn from the origin. This is a special case not often met in practice.

The total potential energy variation near the metal surface is the sum of the original surface barrier curve and that caused by the applied accelerating field. The resultant appears as shown in the figure and it is clear that the surface barrier has been reduced by an amount $\Delta\phi$. Consequently, the new work function in the presence of the electric field is

$$\phi = \phi_0 - \Delta\phi$$

and the corrected Richardson equation is

$$J = A'T^2\epsilon^{-e(\phi_0 - \Delta\phi)/kT}$$

or

$$J = (A'T^2\epsilon^{-e\phi_0/kT})\epsilon^{+e\Delta\phi/kT} \qquad (5.47)$$

The bracketed factor in equation (5.47) is the original Richardson equation corrected for the reflection coefficient. The second exponential factor arises from the Schottky Effect. It increases the emission current because it is a positive exponential factor. It can be shown that it has the form

$$\epsilon^{43.89\sqrt{E}/T}$$

where E = electric field intensity at the emitting surface in volts/ meter.

It seems fairly clear that we could increase the electric field intensity at the surface still more. Eventually, the potential energy barrier would be reduced to the point where electrons *tunnel through* the barrier. When this occurs, electrons are easily emitted without the addition of thermal energy. This is called *high field emission* because extremely high field intensities are required. *Tunneling* is explained in more detail in chapter 6.

5.17. Photoelectric emission from metals

The energy of a photon of light is given by

$$W = hf = \frac{hc}{\lambda} \quad \text{joules}$$

where h = Planck's constant, c = velocity of light, f = frequency of light, λ = wave length of light. The energy of a photon is linearly proportional to the frequency and inversely proportional to the wave length. Thus, a blue photon has more energy than a red photon because the wave length of blue light is shorter than that of red light.

If light is directed upon a metal surface, some of the photons are reflected while others enter the metal and collide with atoms. In so doing they release their energy and disappear; an electron associated with the atom receives the photon energy and is excited to a higher energy level. At some wave length the photon energy is sufficient to cause the excited electron to overcome the surface barrier and be emitted. This is called *photoelectric emission*. The wave length corresponding to the onset of photoelectric emission is called the *threshold wave length*, λ_0.

Several important points can be deduced from the preceding discussion. For example, emission commences when the photon energy is equal to the work function, neglecting temperature effects. Hence,

$$e\phi_0 = \frac{hc}{\lambda_0}$$

or
$$\lambda_0 = \frac{hc}{e\phi_0} \tag{5.48}$$

Because different materials have different work functions, they will also have different threshold wave lengths.

Each photon excites only a single electron. The number of photons is directly proportional to the *intensity* of the light. Hence, the number of electrons emitted per second, or the emission current, is a linear function of the light intensity.

As the wave length is decreased from its threshold value, emission continues. However, because the photon energies are increased, they impart more energy to the electrons than they need to surmount the surface energy barrier. As a result, the electrons are emitted with velocities that depend upon the wave length of the incident light. This is expressed mathematically as follows:

$$\begin{pmatrix} \text{photon} \\ \text{energy} \end{pmatrix} = \begin{pmatrix} \text{work} \\ \text{function} \end{pmatrix} + \begin{pmatrix} \text{kinetic energy} \\ \text{of electron} \end{pmatrix}$$

Hence,
$$\frac{hc}{\lambda} = e\phi_0 + \tfrac{1}{2}mv^2 \tag{5.49}$$

This is the *Einstein photoelectric equation*.

5.18. Secondary emission

The energy necessary for an electron to be emitted from a solid can be supplied by the mechanical impact of another electron. The ejected electrons comprise the *secondary* electrons or *secondary emission*. Secondary emission can also be produced by the impacts of other energetic particles such as ions.

The ratio of the number of secondary electrons to the number of incident or primary electrons is called the *secondary emission coefficient,* δ. It is possible that one primary electron may have enough energy to cause several secondary electrons to be emitted. This is shown by the sketch in figure 5.27. In some cases as many as ten or more secondary electrons may be emitted through the action of one primary electron.

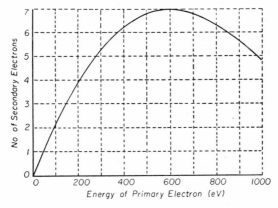

Figure 5.27. Secondary emission as a function of the energy of the primary electron.

In general the number of secondary electrons increases as the energy of the primary electrons increases. This is shown in figure 5.27. This action continues up to a point and then the number of secondary electrons gradually falls off. This falling off is apparently caused by the deep penetration into the metal of the very high energy primary electrons. The penetration becomes so deep that some of the energized electrons are captured by atoms before reaching the surface of the solid.

Readers interested in more details are referred elsewhere.[16]

---

[16] H. Bruining, *Physics and Applications of Secondary Emission*, New York: McGraw-Hill Book Co., Inc., 1954.

5.19. Contact potential

Different metals have different Fermi levels and work functions as shown by the sketches in figure 5.28. Thus, the electrons in one metal have a different maximum energy for a given temperature than the electrons in another metal. The case for 0°K for two different metals is shown in figure 5.28.

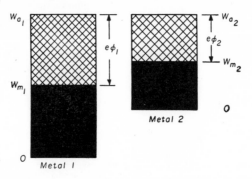

Figure 5.28. Band theory models of two different metals.

When two dissimilar metals are joined together as shown in figure 5.29, the physical barriers between them are destroyed. This permits the electrons from one metal to move across the barrier into the other metal, and vice versa. The energy level diagrams finally combine about a common Fermi level as shown in figure 5.29. The necessity

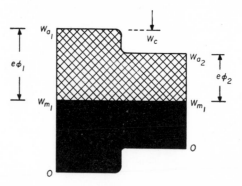

Figure 5.29. Conditions when two dissimilar metals are joined, showing the appearance of the contact potential W_c.

for combining the diagrams in exactly this way will be apparent in a moment.

Suppose that the Fermi level of metal 2 is slightly higher than that of metal 1. This allows the high energy electrons in metal 2 to move into lower unoccupied energy levels in metal 1, causing metal 1 to become negative and metal 2 positive. When a metal is made negative, its energy level diagram moves *up* from its original position because the total potential energy of the electrons is increased. Conversely, when a metal is made positive, its energy level diagram moves *down* from its original position. These two effects act to bring the Fermi levels into alignment regardless of how they may be displaced initially. Under equilibrium conditions when the Fermi levels are equalized, both metals are electrically neutral; neither metal has an excess or deficiency of charge.

The *contact difference in potential* between two metals is the difference in the potential energy of an electron just outside metal 1 and an electron just outside metal 2. This is shown as W_c on figure 5.29. It is clear from this figure that the contact difference in potential is equal to the difference in the work functions of the two metals. That is

$$W_c = e(\phi_1 - \phi_2) \quad \text{joules}$$

or
$$\phi_c = \frac{W_c}{e} = \phi_1 - \phi_2 \quad \text{electron-volts} \tag{5.50}$$

Now consider figure 5.30 where two dissimilar metals are placed in contact at a junction and then bent around so they are separated by

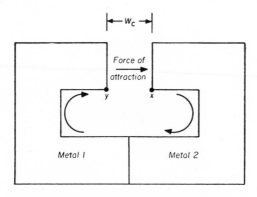

Figure 5.30. Appearance of contact potential W_c.

an air gap at their other ends. Suppose that we take an electron at point x with an energy just sufficient to keep it outside of metal 2. Now move the electron very slowly in a clockwise path as shown by the arrows in figure 5.30. No work is required to move the electron because no change in potential energy is required to keep the electron outside the metal. However, at the junction between the metals, the energy of the electron must be increased by an amount $e(\phi_1 - \phi_2)$ to keep it outside of metal 1. The electron can then be transported to the point y without change of energy.

If the electron is released at point y in the air gap, it has an excess energy $e(\phi_1 - \phi_2)$. It gives up this energy by drifting across the air gap to the point x where it has the same energy it started with. In other words, an electron in this air gap is subject to an electric field of force arising from the contact difference in potential. All measurements of contact potential are made by studying this field in the air gap.

If the two materials are short circuited, the potential drop, corresponding to $e(\phi_1 - \phi_2)$, is produced across the contacts between the metals and the metal providing the short circuit. In any case, the Fermi levels remain equalized.

For most of the purposes of this book the most important point to emerge from this discussion is the following:

When two dissimilar materials are joined together, their band theory models are drawn about a common Fermi level.

PROBLEMS

5.1. In monovalent metals the number of *free* valence electrons per cc can be approximated by assuming it to be equal to the number of atoms per cc. The number of atoms per cc can be computed from the following relationship:

$$\text{atoms/cc} = \frac{(\text{density})(\text{Avogadro's number})}{\text{atomic weight}}$$

Compute the density of free electrons in annealed copper at 20°C. The density of annealed copper at this temperature is 8.89 grams/cc and the atomic weight is 63.57.

5.2. How many electrons must move through a conductor each second to conduct an electric current of 1 amp? 5 amp?

5.3. If 1 amp of electric current exists in a copper conductor 2 cm² in cross-sectional area, what is the average drift velocity of the electrons?

5.4. Compute the average drift velocity in a copper conductor 4 cm² in cross-sectional area and conducting a current of 1 amp.

5.5. Repeat problem 5.1 for tantalum using a density of 16.6 gm/cc and an atomic weight of 180.88. Assume that there is one free electron for every two tantalum atoms.

5.6. Repeat problems 5.3 and 5.4 for a tantalum conductor.

5.7. Compute the ratio of the resistance of the copper conductor to the resistance of the tantalum conductor assuming both conductors have the same length and cross-sectional area.

5.8. Assume that 1 volt is applied across the copper conductor of problem 5.3 and that the wire is 1.149×10^{10} cm long. Calculate the field intensity in the wire and the value for the electronic mobility.

5.9. Calculate the resistance of an annealed copper wire at 20°C if it is 1 meter long, round, with a radius of 5 cm.

5.10. Repeat problem 5.9 for a nichrome wire of the same dimensions.

5.11. Calculate the area in circular mils of wires having the following diameters:

  (a) 0.2043 in. (AWG 4)   (c) 0.0641 in. (AWG 14)

  (b) 0.1019 in. (AWG 10)   (d) 0.0320 in. (AWG 20)

5.12. Calculate the power dissipated in the following resistors if 250 volts is applied across them: 100 ohms, 1000 ohms, 10,000 ohms, 100,000 ohms.

5.13. Compute the resistance of the copper wire in problem 5.9 at 200°C.

5.14. Compute the resistance of a platinum wire of the same dimensions as the wire in problem 5.13 and at the same temperature.

5.15. Compute the resistivity of annealed copper at 200°C.

5.16. The resistivity of annealed copper is measured at 1.724×10^{-6} ohm-cm. The density of conduction electrons was computed in problem 5.1. Calculate the mobility of the electrons.

5.17. What value would you predict for the Hall coefficient for annealed copper?

5.18. If the measured value for the Hall coefficient is twice the value computed in problem 5.17, how would you attempt to determine the source of the error, which could be in either the mobility or the resistivity.

5.19. A given material exhibits the following experimental characteristics: resistivity = 6.5×10^{-6} ohm-cm, Hall coefficient = 1.05×10^{-3} cc/coulomb. Calculate the approximate value for the Fermi level.

5.20. Compute the emission current density from a tantalum surface at 2000°K. Use the theoretical value for A and the field-free work function.

5.21. Repeat problem 5.20 for the experimentally determined value for A'.

5.22. Repeat problems 5.20 and 5.21 for tungsten and compare these results with those for tantalum.

5.23. If an electric field of 10,000 volts/meter is present at the tantalum surface in problem 5.20, compute the increase in emission current brought about by the Schottky effect.

5.24. Calculate the threshold wave lengths of caesium and tungsten. Which of the two materials is the most practical photoelectric emitter?

5.25. Photons of wave length of 5200 Å (1 Å = 10^{-8} cm) strike a caesium surface. Calculate the velocity of the emitted electrons.

6

STRUCTURE AND BEHAVIOR
OF SEMICONDUCTORS

In section 5.1 of the preceding chapter it was shown that *covalent solids* form one of the main types of materials in the solid state. Such materials have remarkably different characteristics from those exhibited by metals. For example, metals conduct at all temperatures up to their melting points while covalent solids conduct at some temperatures, but poorly at others. For this reason they are called *semiconductors*. We can understand the origin of this behavior by studying the crystalline structure of semiconductors. This material is a basic prerequisite to an understanding of the various semiconductor devices such as *transistors*.

The chapter commences with a brief description of the structure of covalent solids. A band theory model is then formulated and this is used to describe the behavior and physical characteristics of semiconductor materials.

6.1. Crystal structure of covalent solids

A two-dimensional sketch of the diamond crystal was shown in figure 5.3 of the preceding chapter as a typical example of a covalent solid. Other covalent solids include germanium and silicon. All three of these materials appear in column four of the periodic table of elements.

When these materials form crystalline solids, each atom is surrounded by four other atoms with which it forms *covalent bonds* as shown earlier in figure 5.3. Each bond of this type consists of a pair of *shared electrons*, and is called an *electron-pair bond*. This is shown by a simplified two-dimensional sketch in figure 6.1 where the atoms appear as black circles and the electron-pair bonds as short, straight, parallel lines.

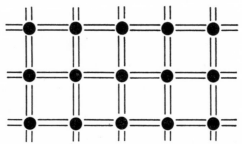

Figure 6.1. Two-dimensional representation of a covalent solid.

In a covalent solid such as that shown in figure 6.1, all four valence electrons of every atom are required to form the crystal. These covalent bonds are very strong, so that each electron is held very strongly to the two atoms sharing it. Hence, there are no *free* electrons such as we found in metals. Here every electron is closely associated with particular atoms. Because there are no free electrons or other free electric charge present, electrical conduction is impossible. If an electric field is applied across such a material there is no progressive motion of charge, there is no current, and the electrical resistance of the material is theoretically infinite.

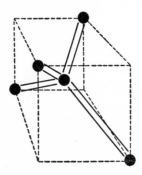

Figure 6.2. Schematic representation of a single crystal element of a tetravalent solid such as carbon in the diamond form, or germanium (After W. Shockley).

As the temperature of the solid is raised above absolute zero, the atoms in the crystal vibrate. At relatively high temperatures the thermal vibration may become so intense that valence bonds occasionally break. When this occurs, electrons are released from each broken bond and they behave in the same way as the free electrons in a metal. Electrical conduction is now possible because free charges are available to move in response to an applied electric field.

When a valence bond is broken and an electron is released, the perfection of the crystal is destroyed; one or more bonds are missing. These missing bonds are called *holes*. They play a very important part in semiconductor operation as we shall see later.

Although we have shown covalent solids in two-dimensional form only, they actually crystallize in three dimensions. The array of atoms in such a crystal is shown in the three-dimensional sketch of figure 6.2.

6.2. Band theory model—intrinsic semiconductors

Perfect covalent solids without crystalline imperfections of any kind are called *intrinsic semiconductors*. The theoretical interest in such materials is very great and is very necessary background for the analysis of other cases.

The data presented in the preceding section can be used to formulate a band theory model for an intrinsic semiconductor. First, you must recall that semiconductor materials do not conduct electricity at absolute zero. This implies that the *valence energy band* must be *completely filled* with electrons at absolute zero temperature. If it were only partially filled, electrical conduction would be possible at absolute zero as it is with metals.

Electrical conduction in semiconductors occurs only when enough thermal energy is added to break one of the valence bonds. This occurs at some fairly definite temperature. Hence, at this temperature an energy band must suddenly become partially filled so that conduction can take place. We can conceive this to occur only if the band theory model for semiconductors has *two permitted energy bands separated by a forbidden zone*. This is illustrated by the band theory model shown in figure 6.3.

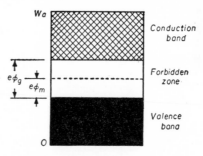

Figure 6.3. Electronic energy levels in an intrinsic semiconductor at absolute zero. This is our band theory model.

This diagram shows the energy distribution of electrons in a semiconductor material at absolute zero. The solid black region is the *valence band* of energies; it is completely filled with electrons at absolute zero temperature. The crosshatched section at the top of the figure is called the *conduction band*. It is completely empty at absolute zero, representing permitted, but presently empty, energy levels. The two energy bands are separated by the white *forbidden zone*.

The width of the forbidden zone is different for different materials. The values given in table 16 are representative approximate values.

At absolute zero, the valence band is completely filled and the conduction band is entirely empty. There are no partially filled bands, and electrical conduction is impossible. As the temperature of the material is progressively increased, the thermal vibration of the atoms eventually causes a bond to rupture; an electron is released and a hole is created. The amount of energy required to rupture the bond is equal to the width of the forbidden zone in the band theory model. Thus, when the bond is ruptured, an electron in the valence band jumps the forbidden zone and ends up in the conduction band.

We now have two partially filled bands. The conduction band has a few free electrons while the valence band has a few electron vacancies or holes. Electrical conduction is now possible.

The electrical resistivity of a solid was defined in chapter 5 and was written as

$$\rho = \frac{1}{Ne\mu} = \text{resistivity} \qquad (6.1)$$

where N = density of free charges, e = charge on an electron, μ = mobility of the charges. The electrical resistivity of the semiconductor is high at low temperatures because there are only a few free charges available for conduction; N in equation (6.1) is small. Further temperature increases cause more electrons to jump the forbidden zone and more charges can take part in conduction; N in

Table 16

APPROXIMATE WIDTHS OF FORBIDDEN ZONES

Material	ϕ_g in eV
Carbon (diamond).............	6.5
Silicon........................	1.1
Germanium....................	0.7
Cu$_2$O........................	1.6

equation (6.1) increases. Hence, the resistivity of the material decreases as the temperature increases. This causes intrinsic semiconductors to have a negative temperature coefficient of resistance. In contrast, pure metals have positive temperature coefficients of resistance.

Conwell (see footnote 2) gives empirical relations for the resistivities of germanium and silicon as

$$\rho_i = (0.23 \times 10^{-4})\epsilon^{4350/T} \quad \text{ohm-cm for Ge}$$

$$\rho_i = (0.29 \times 10^{-4})\epsilon^{6450/T} \quad \text{ohm-cm for Si}$$

6.3. Fermi level—intrinsic semiconductor

In an intrinsic semiconductor the number of conduction electrons is always equal to the number of holes. Let N_e = density of free electrons in the conduction band, N_h = density of holes in the valence band. In addition, refer back to figure 6.3 where the following terms are defined:

ϕ_g = width of the forbidden zone in eV

ϕ_m = Fermi level in eV, measured from the top of the valence band

Kittel[1] proves from the Fermi distribution function that the density of electrons in the conduction band of an intrinsic semiconductor can be computed from the following equation:

$$N_e = 2 \left(\frac{2\pi mkT}{h^2}\right)^{3/2} \epsilon^{-e(\phi_g - \phi_m)/kT} \text{ per M}^3 \tag{6.2}$$

where m = mass of an electron in kg, k = Boltzmann's constant, h = Planck's constant, T = temperature in °K, e = charge on an electron in coulombs. Other terms were defined earlier.

Kittel also derives a similar formula for the number of holes in the valence band. He shows that

$$N_h = 2 \left(\frac{2\pi m_h kT}{h^2}\right)^{3/2} \epsilon^{-e\phi_m/kT} \text{ per M}^3 \tag{6.3}$$

where m_h = effective mass of the hole.

In an intrinsic semiconductor the densities of holes and electrons are equal. Therefore,

$$N_e = N_h \tag{6.4}$$

[1] Charles Kittel, *Introduction to Solid State Physics*, New York: John Wiley & Sons, Inc., 1953, pp. 275–276.

Establish this equality using equations (6.2) and (6.3), cancel common terms, and solve for the Fermi level. The result is

$$e\phi_m = \tfrac{1}{2}e\phi_g + \tfrac{3}{4}kT \log_\epsilon \frac{m_h}{m} \qquad (6.5)$$

This shows that the Fermi level is slightly dependent upon temperature.

It is clear from equation (6.5) that the Fermi level of an intrinsic semiconductor falls exactly in the middle of the forbidden zone at absolute zero temperature. Hence,

$$e\phi_m\,(0°\mathrm{K}) = \tfrac{1}{2}e\phi_g \qquad (6.6)$$

The same equation results if the electron mass and effective hole mass are equal. However, this does not appear to be true. For example, for silicon, the mass ratio m_h/m is taken to be about 0.67.

The theoretical equations for the electron and hole densities in intrinsic semiconductors are given by equations (6.2) and (6.3). Empirical formulas obtained for silicon and germanium are given below:[2]

$$N_e = N_h = (9.7 \times 10^{15})T^{3/2}\epsilon^{-4350/T} \quad \text{for Ge per CC}$$

$$N_e = N_h = (2.8 \times 10^{16})T^{3/2}\epsilon^{-6450/T} \quad \text{for Si per CC}$$

6.4. Conduction in an intrinsic semiconductor

The mechanism involved in the conduction of electricity by *free* electrons in crystals was discussed in some detail in chapter 5, particularly in section 5.8. This type of conduction also takes place in heated semiconductors. Electrons jump the forbidden zone and enter the conduction band at elevated temperatures; a hole is left behind in the valence band.

Once in the conduction band, the electrons act just as they would in a metal because essentially the same conditions prevail. The free electrons in a metal travel through the intercrystalline space of the metal when acted upon by an electric field. Under normal conditions at room temperature, they may travel a thousand crystal lattice constants before being scattered by a thermally agitated atom, or phantom particle. The free electrons in a semiconductor behave in the

[2] E. M. Conwell, "Properties of Germanium and Silicon," *Proc. I.R.E.*, Nov. 1952, pp. 1327–1337.

same manner, regardless of whether they originate from a broken valence bond or from some other source to be discussed later. Thus, electrical conduction by free electrons is called *electronic conduction* without regard to the nature of the solid.

An entirely different situation prevails when holes are present. Under the stimulus of an applied electric field, a hole will be filled by an electron from an adjoining valence bond, which creates a new hole as a result. This, in turn, is filled by another electron moving in from another bond, and another hole is produced. Charge motion, or electric current, results and to be absolutely correct, the current arises from the motion of electrons. However, these electrons are not free, but move from valence bond to valence bond, progressively filling holes. This is in sharp contrast to the free electron which might go a thousand lattice constants without being noticeably affected by the crystal. Evidently some method must be used to distinguish this conduction process from the usual electronic conduction.

As the electrons move from bond to bond, the hole *apparently* moves in the reverse direction. Actually the hole does not move; the electrons do. However, the progressive vacancies created give the impression of hole motion. Accordingly, this is called *hole conduction* to distinguish it from the conventional electronic conduction. In the presence of an electric field, the holes move in a direction opposite to the motion of the electrons. Thus, the holes *behave as though* they had a *positive charge* equal to the charge on an electron.

There are equal numbers of holes and free electrons in an intrinsic semiconductor at any temperature. Therefore, current arises from the motion of both the electrons and the holes. The total current is the sum of the two separate currents. That is,

$$I_T = I_e + I_h \qquad (6.7)$$

where I_T = total current, I_e = current from electronic conduction, I_h = hole current. Let N signify the density of holes and the density of free electrons.

Further, let v_e = electron velocity, v_h = hole velocity, A = cross-sectional area of semiconductor perpendicular to the direction of charge motion, e = charge on an electron. Hence,

$$I_T = N(v_e + v_h)eA \qquad (6.8)$$

It was shown in chapter 5 that the velocity of a charged particle is equal to the product of the electric field intensity and the mobility. Hence,

$$v_e = \mu_e E$$
$$v_h = \mu_h E$$

where E = electric field intensity, μ_e = electron mobility, μ_h = hole mobility. Hence, the total current in an intrinsic semiconductor is

conductivity $$I_T = NE(\mu_e + \mu_h)eA \qquad (6.9)$$

Because of the difference in the character of the motion of the holes and electrons you would expect them to have different mobilities. In particular, you would expect the electron mobility to be larger than the hole mobility. This is true; for germanium[3]

$$\mu_e = 3600 \pm 180 \quad \text{cm/sec/v/cm}$$
$$\mu_h = 1700 \pm 90 \quad \text{cm/sec/v/cm}$$

and for silicon

$$\mu_e = 1200 \pm 120 \quad \text{cm/sec/v/cm}$$
$$\mu_h = 250 \pm 50 \quad \text{cm/sec/v/cm}$$

The mobilities are constant up to fairly high values for the electric field intensity. According to Conwell,[4] the departure from the constant mobility in germanium occurs at 900 v/cm for electrons and 1400 v/cm for holes. Larger field intensities are required to produce this departure in the case of silicon.

Because of the difference in the electron and hole mobilities, the electrons produce a larger current than the holes even though equal numbers of each are present. The difference arises from the difference in charge velocities.

6.5. Effect of impurities in the crystal

Impurities have a considerable effect upon the properties of semiconductors. The effect can be quite pronounced even when only minute traces of 1 part in 10^7 or 10^8 are present. The *nature* of the phenomenon produced depends upon the effect of the impurity atoms upon the crystalline structure of the semiconductor. The *magnitude* of the effect depends upon the number of impurity atoms present.

---

[3] *Ibid:* p. 1330.
[4] *Ibid:* p. 1333.

Now suppose that germanium or silicon of valence 4 is crystallized with a few impurities of valence 5 such as arsenic, antimony, or phosphorous. Such impurities can enter the crystal lattice of the germanium, but only four of the five valence electrons enter into the interatomic valence bonds. This is shown in figure 6.4 where the black circles represent germanium atoms and the white circle is an atom of valence 5. The extra valence electron that does not enter into an interatomic bond is also shown.

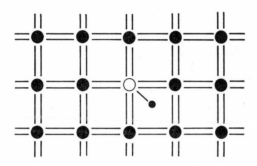

Figure 6.4. Crystal lattice of germanium showing a valence 5 impurity.

This fifth electron is only loosely bound to its parent atom by the relatively weak attraction of its nucleus. Hence, the fifth electron is readily dissociated from its parent atom by thermal vibration at temperatures well below 20°C. Such electrons are then free to wander about the intercrystalline space of the semiconductor and take part in electrical conduction.

Impurities of this type are called *donors* because they donate free electrons to the semiconductor. Observe that holes are *not* created in this process, although some people prefer to assume that a hole is created and trapped on the donor atom. When the fifth electron is removed from the parent atom, the crystal structure is complete and characteristically that of a covalent solid. It differs from a pure germanium or silicon crystal only because the impurity atom is now a *positive ion*, not a neutral atom. All valence bonds about the impurity atom are complete and there are no holes.

The positive ion cannot take part in conduction because it is firmly bound to the remainder of the crystal. Hence, the only free charges available for conduction are electrons. Electrons carry a negative electric charge. Thus, this type of *impurity semiconductor* is said to be *n-type*, where the *n* stands for *negative*.

The reverse situation can also be obtained. Impurities of valence 3 such as boron, aluminum, indium, and gallium, can also enter the crystal structure of germanium or silicon. When such impurities are present they lack one valence bond from the normal four-bond structure. This is shown in figure 6.5.

These distortions remain in the crystal lattice at low temperature; no electrons are present to complete the bonding array. However, at higher temperatures, as the valence bonds are stressed by thermal vibration, the incomplete bond of the impurity atom also exerts a force of attraction upon nearby bonded electrons. A temperature is

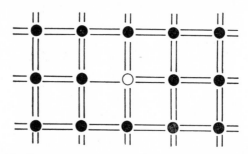

Figure 6.5. Crystal lattice of germanium showing a valence 3 impurity.

eventually reached where these forces cause an electron from an all-germanium or all-silicon array to be trapped into the valence bond vacancy associated with the impurity. This leaves a *hole* in the valence bond structure of the germanium while the impurity becomes a bound *negative ion*.

The only free charges present in this type of impurity semiconductor are the positive holes. The negative ions cannot take part in conduction because they are firmly bound into the crystal lattice. Hence, electric current results from the motion of the positively charged holes. The semiconductor is said to be *p-type* where the *p* stands for *positive*.

The impurity in a *p*-type semiconductor is called an *acceptor* because it accepts electrons from the semiconductor.

The properties of an *intrinsic* semiconductor can be simulated by an impurity semiconductor containing equal numbers of acceptors and donors. The *deliberate* introduction of impurities, which is called *doping*, may produce only 1 impurity atom for every 10^7 semiconductor atoms. Hence, even very pure semiconductors will *inadvertently* contain impurities. For this reason it is almost impossible to obtain a true intrinsic semiconductor.

Practically all commercial semiconductors are of the impurity type. Both donors and acceptors are present, but the density of one ordinarily exceeds that of the other. The semiconductor is then specified as *n*- or *p*-type depending upon the identity of the *majority charge carrier*. The *minority charge carrier* is often important, however.

6.6. Impurity semiconductors—band theory models

The discussion of impurity semiconductors in the preceding section can be summarized by constructing appropriate band theory models. The proposed models for *n*- and *p*-type semiconductors are shown in figures 6.6 and 6.7.

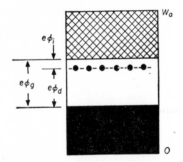

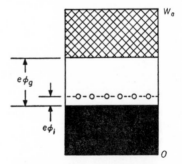

Figure 6.6. Relationship of donor impurity energy levels to semiconductor energy levels; *n*-type semiconductor model.

Figure 6.7. *p*-type semiconductor; energy level relationships.

First consider the case of an *n*-type semiconductor. From the preceding section you will recall that the *donor* impurity atoms have a very loosely bound electron that is not required in the covalent bonding of the crystal. This extra electron has a comparatively high potential energy relative to the bound valence electrons because it is quite easily detached from the parent atom. Let $e\phi_i$ denote the energy required to detach the extra electron from the impurity atom, an action which ionizes the donor. Figure 6.6 can now be constructed as a logical band theory model for an n-type semiconductor; $e\phi_i$ is the donor ionization energy.

Figure 6.6 shows the regular band theory model for the host semiconductor. The line of black circles in the forbidden zone represents the effect of the impurities. In a pure or intrinsic semiconductor there are no permitted energy levels in the forbidden zone. However, the introduction of valence 5 impurities into the crystal creates new energy levels. These new energy levels appear in the otherwise forbidden zone of the semiconductor, $e\phi_i$ units of energy below the conduction band. These new energy levels are filled with electrons, the extra electrons associated with the donors, at absolute zero.

Free electrons for conduction are produced by exciting electrons from these new energy levels to the conduction band of the semiconductor. This corresponds to the release of the loosely bound electrons from the donor impurity atoms as described in the preceding section. Once in the conduction band, the electrons behave just like the free electrons in metals or intrinsic semiconductors.

It is clear that holes are *not* produced in this process. Electrons are *not* removed from the valence band of the semiconductor. The conduction electrons come from the new energy levels created by the donor atoms; the valence band of the semiconductor remains completely filled. The donor atoms that lose electrons become positive ions firmly tied into the crystal structure. They cannot take part in electrical conduction.

The value for $e\phi_i$ in figure 6.6 is much less than the width of the forbidden zone. For example, the width of the forbidden zone for silicon is about 1.1 eV, whereas ϕ_i has a value of about 0.054 eV.[5] As a result, electrons are excited from the donor atoms to the conduction band at much lower temperatures than those required to excite electrons from the valence band of the semiconductor.

A similar, but slightly different, model can be constructed for the p-type semiconductor. The result is shown in figure 6.7. The standard band theory diagram is used here to represent the host semiconductor. Then a line of white circles is shown in the forbidden zone.

---

[5] G. L. Pearson, J. Bardeen, *Phys. Rev.*, Vol. 75, 1949, p. 865.

These represent new, but empty, energy levels created by the acceptor impurity atoms. These electronic energy levels are empty at absolute zero. They are the representations of the missing valence bonds resulting from the crystallization of valence 3 impurities with a valence 4 semiconductor.

ϕ_i is only about 0.08 eV[5] for silicon. This is much less than the width of the forbidden zone. It is very easy to excite electrons from the valence band into these empty energy levels. This excitation takes place at comparatively low temperatures.

When excitation occurs, free electrons are *not* produced because there are no electrons in the conduction band. Instead, the acceptor atoms become negative ions and holes are produced in the valence band of the semiconductor. These positive holes take part in electrical conduction as described in the preceding section. However, the negative ions are rigidly bound into the crystal and do not contribute to the current.

The Fermi levels of intrinsic semiconductors were shown to be approximately in the middle of the forbidden zone. The displacement away from the central position depends upon the temperature. A similar situation prevails for impurity semiconductors. However, here the Fermi levels fall midway between the energy levels associated with the impurities and the nearest permitted energy level of the semiconductor. This is shown in figure 6.8.

For example, for n-type semiconductors the Fermi level falls midway between the donor energy level $e\phi_d$ and the bottom of the con-

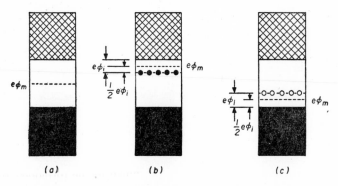

Figure 6.8. Fermi levels in intrinsic and impurity semiconductors: (a) intrinsic; (b) n-type; (c) p-type.

duction band of the semiconductor. This is shown in figure 6.8. The Fermi level of the p-type material falls midway between the acceptor energy level $e\phi_i$ and the top of the valence band of the semiconductor as shown in figure 6.8. This information is very important in chapter 7 and you should carefully note the locations of the Fermi levels with respect to the forbidden zone.

6.7. Hall effect

The essential characteristics of the Hall effect and the Hall coefficient were discussed in section 5.11. The same general phenomenon is observed with semiconductors. However, in intrinsic semiconductors equal numbers of electrons and holes are present. In general, impurity semiconductors will contain both electrons and holes, but one type of charge carrier will predominate in density.

When such a material is inserted in a magnetic field as described in section 5.11, the electrons and holes are forced to opposite sides of the semiconductor and both contribute to the build up of the Hall effect transverse electric field.

For metals, which have only free electrons, the Hall coefficient was shown to be

$$\Re_H = \frac{1}{Ne}$$

where $e = $ *negative* charge on an electron. This leads to a negative Hall coefficient for virtually all metals.

Suppose that we have an n-type impurity semiconductor in which the hole concentration is assumed to be zero. Because the distribution of electron velocities in semiconductors is different from the velocity distribution in metals,[6] it can be shown that the Hall coefficient in this special case is

$$\Re_H = \frac{3\pi}{8} \frac{1}{N_e e} \quad \left(\begin{array}{c}\text{for semiconductors} \\ \text{with electrons only}\end{array}\right) \tag{6.10}$$

The $3\pi/8$ factor arises from the different velocity distribution and N_e denotes the concentration of conduction electrons while e is the negative charge on an electron. Hence, the Hall coefficient is negative.

[6] F. Seitz, *Modern Theory of Solids*, New York: McGraw-Hill Book Co., Inc., 1940, p. 192.

For a p-type semiconductor with only holes involved in the conduction process, the Hall coefficient is

$$\mathcal{R}_H = \frac{3\pi}{8}\frac{1}{N_h e} \quad \left(\begin{array}{c}\text{for semiconductors} \\ \text{with holes only}\end{array}\right) \text{M}^3/\text{coul} \qquad (6.11)$$

where N_h = concentration of holes, e = positive charge on a hole. The Hall coefficient is positive.

When both electrons and holes are present in a semiconductor, it can be shown that the Hall coefficient is[7]

$$\mathcal{R}_H = \frac{3\pi}{8e}\frac{(N_e a^2 - N_h)}{(N_e a + N_h)^2} \text{M}^3/\text{coul} \qquad (6.12)$$

where $a = \mu_e/\mu_h$ = mobility ratio, e = negative electron charge.

6.8. Thermionic emission

With the foregoing models of semiconductors in mind we can visualize the mechanism of thermionic emission from a semiconductor. The essential factors are set forth in figure 6.9. Only n-type semiconductors are used for thermionic emitters.

As the semiconductor is heated, the donor impurities become ionized as they donate electrons to the conduction band of the semiconductor. Higher temperatures increase the number of electrons in

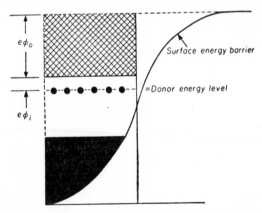

Figure 6.9. Thermionic emission from an n-type semiconductor.

[7] Charles Kittel, *Introduction to Solid State Physics*, New York: John Wiley & Sons, Inc., 1953, p. 283.

the conduction band; some of them acquire sufficient energy to overcome the surface energy barrier and be emitted. Only those electrons in the conduction band of the semiconductor contribute to the emission.

From this viewpoint it is apparent that the emission of electrons from an n-type semiconductor is a two-stage process, with each stage dependent upon temperature as follows:

(1) Ionization of the donor impurities and consequent donation of electrons from the impurities to the conduction band of the semiconductor.

(2) Emission of the electrons from the conduction band of the semiconductor.

Because of this double dependence upon temperature we should expect the emission current to have a different temperature dependence than that exhibited by metals.

It can be shown from material presented by Kittel[8] that the number of electrons donated to the conduction band of the semiconductor by the impurities is given by

$$N_e = \frac{K}{2}\left(\sqrt{1 + \frac{4N_0}{K}} - 1\right) \quad \text{per meter}^3 \qquad (6.14)$$

where

$$K = \left(\frac{2\pi mkT}{h^2}\right)^{3/2} \epsilon^{-e\phi_i/kT} \qquad (6.15)$$

$$= (2.405 \times 10^{21})T^{3/2}\epsilon^{-1.161\phi_i \times 10^4/T} \qquad (6.16)$$

N_0 = density of donor impurities per meter^3

m = electron mass in kg

T = temperature in °K

k = Boltzmann's constant in joules/°K

h = Planck's constant in joule-sec

ϕ_i = donor ionization energy in eV

At low temperatures only a small fraction of the donors are ionized. This makes N_e very much less than N_0 and equation (6.14) becomes

$$N_e \doteq \sqrt{N_0 K} \qquad (6.17)$$

Once the electrons are free in the conduction band of the semiconductor they act like the free electrons in a metal. Thus, they are

---

[8] *Ibid:* p. 281.

emitted through the same general mechanism as for metals. The difference here is that the number of electrons available for emission depends upon temperature as shown by equation (6.14). The number of electrons available for emission from metals is constant, independent of temperature. Calculation of this added temperature dependence for semiconductors leads to the *Fowler equation*[9] for the emission current density from an *n*-type semiconductor. The equation is

$$J = AT^2N_0^{1/2}\left(\frac{h^2}{2\pi mkT}\right)^{3/4}\epsilon^{-e(\phi_0+\phi_i/2)/kT} \tag{6.18}$$

where $A = 120.4 \times 10^{+4}$ amp/m^2 °K, ϕ_0 = width of conduction band in eV, e = charge on an electron in coulombs. All other terms were defined under equation (6.14).

Equation (6.18) can be rewritten in a simplified and more common form as follows:

$$J = aT^{5/4}\epsilon^{-b/kT} \tag{6.19}$$

This shows that the emission current density depends upon the $\frac{5}{4}$ power of temperature instead of upon the square of temperature as in the case of metals. The factor b in the exponent is independent of temperature, but the coefficient a depends upon temperature because it is governed by the number of impurity centers in the semiconductor. The coefficient a is not a universal constant like the A in the original Richardson equation.

At this point you might wonder why the possible electron contribution to the conduction band from the valence band of the semiconductor has been neglected. It seems that the width of the forbidden zone in most semiconductors is so large that a very small number of electrons acquire sufficient energy to traverse the gap at ordinary operating temperatures. For this reason, semiconductors are not very active emitters until the donor impurities are added.

Two of the most common semiconductor emitters are thorium oxide and a mixture of barium-strontium oxides. For further information the reader is referred elsewhere.[10]

---

[9] W. E. Danforth, "Elements of Thermionics," *Proc. I.R.E.*, Vol. 39, May 1951, pp. 487–495.

[10] J. P. Blewett, "The Properties of Oxide Coated Cathodes," *J. App. Phys.*, Vol. 10, Oct. 1939, pp. 668–679; and Dec. 1939, pp. 831–848.

6.9. Photoconduction and photoemission

From figure 6.9 and equation (6.14) you can see that at ordinary temperatures a few electrons are excited from the donors into the conduction band of the semiconductor. Hence, the resistance of the semiconductor is high, but not infinite. If the semiconductor is in darkness, a small current results when a voltage is applied across the semiconductor. This is called the *dark current*. If a beam of light is focused on the sample and if the photon energy, $W = hf$, is high enough, some of the electrons associated with the donors are excited by the photons into the conduction band of the semiconductor. This increase in the density of free electrons lowers the resistance of the semiconductor. Thus, larger electrical currents exist through the action of the same voltage difference creating the dark current. This phenomenon of lowered resistance when exposed to light is called the *photoconductivity effect*. When the light is removed, the electrons recombine with the positive donor ions and the material assumes its *dark resistance* again.[11]

If the photon energy is increased sufficiently by increasing the frequency of the incident light, it is apparent that some electrons may acquire sufficient energy to be emitted. Therefore, *photoelectric emission* is readily secured at the blue end, or high-energy end, of the light spectrum. Photoconduction is most common at the red end, or low-energy end, of the spectrum.

6.10. Thermistors

It was explained in section 6.2 that all semiconductors exhibit negative temperature coefficients of resistance. A semiconductor designed to exhibit this effect to a pronounced degree is called a *thermistor*. The name is coined from a contraction of *therm*al and res*istor* and is used to specify a group of electric circuit elements whose resistance is a function of temperature.

The current-voltage characteristic of a small thermistor with low thermal inertia is shown in figure 6.10. The rather remarkable shape of this curve can be explained rather easily.

---

[11] J. N. Shive, "The Phototransistor," *Bell Lb. Rec.*, Vol. 28, No. 8, Aug. 1950, pp. 337–342.

Assume that the temperature of the atmosphere about the thermistor is constant. Also assume that the thermistor is supplied from an adjustable source of electric current. The thermistor exhibits some initial conductivity because the temperature of the semiconductor is high enough to excite some electrons into the conduction band. However, only a few electrons are excited and the resistance of the material is relatively high. Thus, a small current supplied to the thermistor causes a relatively large voltage drop to appear across it. The current is very small so that the I^2R loss and body heating of the thermistor are small. Therefore, the resistance of the material is almost constant and a nearly linear current-voltage characteristic is obtained. This corresponds to the first part of the curve in figure 6.10.

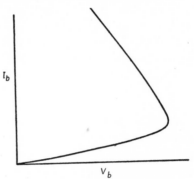

Figure 6.10. Current-voltage characteristic of a small thermistor.

However, a point is soon reached where the temperature rise of the thermistor caused by the current through the thermistor is sufficient to cause a large number of electrons to be excited into the conduction band. This reduces the electrical resistance of the semiconductor and the curve departs from linearity as shown in figure 6.10. This action increases very rapidly so that, before long, the drop in resistance more than offsets the increase in current and the voltage across the thermistor *decreases*.

A different curve is obtained for different temperatures of the atmosphere surrounding the thermistor. This is so because the temperature rise of the thermistor for a given electric current depends upon the temperature difference between the thermistor and the surrounding atmosphere.

The data for the curve of figure 6.10 should be taken only after thermal equilibrium is attained following an increase in current. Some thermal inertia is inevitable in an element of finite size. Hence, it is also inevitable that equilibrium will be established only after some finite time delay. As a result, thermistors can be used to produce finite and relatively long time delays. A typical characteristic is shown in figure 6.11, where an ideal battery is connected to the terminals of the thermistor at $t = 0$. The resulting rise in current is shown as a function of time.

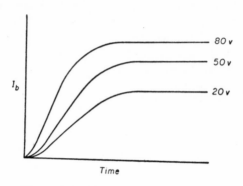

Figure 6.11. Time delay in a thermistor.

The semiconductor materials used in thermistors are generally of two types:

(1) a mixture of manganese and nickel oxides, and

(2) a mixture of manganese, nickel, and cobalt oxides.

Strangely enough, these materials actually have partially filled bands like metals and should behave like metals. However, they do *not* behave like metals and this discrepancy in the band theory model is treated elsewhere.[12]

6.11. Luminescence

The term *luminescence* is used to denote the absorption of energy by some substance and the subsequent re-emission of energetic photons with wave lengths near that of visible light. The energy required to institute the process may come from high energy photons, electrons, positive ions, heating, or other sources of energy.

If the re-emission of energy occurs in less than 10^{-8} second after the absorption, the material is said to be *fluorescent*. If the re-emission

---

[12] J. H. DeBoer, E. J. W. Verwey, "Semiconductors With Partially and Completely Filled Third Bands," *Proc. Phys. Soc.*, London, England, Vol. 49, Aug. 31, 1937, pp. 59–71.

takes place more than 10^{-8} second after absorption, the material is said to be *phosphorescent.*

This is a very large and complicated field that is incompletely understood at the present time. We touch the subject only lightly for this reason.

One of the better known *fluorescent* crystals is thallium-activated potassium chloride. This is an ionic solid of the same general type as sodium chloride. It consists of positive alkali ions and negative halogen ions arranged into a cubic crystal. During the crystallization a small quantity of thallium ions is substituted for potassium ions. However, thallium has a valence of 3 while potassium has a valence of only 1. Thus, distortions in the otherwise perfect crystal are localized about the thallium ions.

The general form of the thallium-activated potassium chloride crystal is shown in figure 6.12. This shows the normal crystal structure of potassium chloride and one thallium impurity ion is also

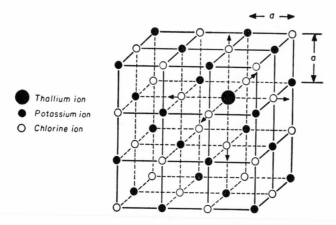

Figure 6.12. Thallium-activated potassium chloride crystal structure.

shown. Let a designate the distance between the chlorine and potassium ions as shown in figure 6.12. From this figure it is clear that every interior potassium ion has six chlorine ion neighbors, all a units away from the potassium.

When thallium ions of valence 3 are embodied in the crystal, the crystal structure is slightly deformed from the otherwise perfect regularity. In particular, it is found that the six chlorine neighbors of the thallium ion are pushed further away from the thallium ion than they are from the potassium ions. This is shown diagrammatically by small arrows on the chlorine ions in figure 6.12.

The *fluorescent* effect observed with this crystal comes about because of relative motion between the thallium ion and its six chlorine neighbors. A detailed study of this subject is beyond our scope, but the discussion in the remainder of this section covers the principal ideas.

Williams[13] has constructed an energy level diagram for the thallium ion to explain the observed phenomenon. His model is reproduced in figure 6.13. The energy of the thallium ion is plotted vertically in this figure and expressed in electron-volts. The symmetrical displacement of the six neighboring chlorine ions is plotted on the horizontal axis. The origin of the horizontal axis represents the positions of the chlorine ions about a positive potassium ion in the crystal. Thus the horizontal axis shows the positive and negative deviations of the chlorine ions from this reference position. A positive deviation signifies that the chlorine ions move further away from the thallium ion. Conversely, a negative deviation signifies that the chlorine ions move closer to the thallium ion.

Two curved lines are shown in figure 6.13. The bottom curve rep-

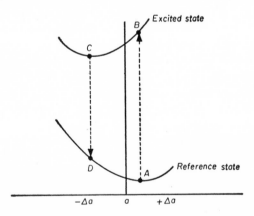

Figure 6.13. Energy level diagram for a thallium ion in a potassium chloride crystal.

[13] F. E. Williams, *J. Chem. Phys.*, Vol. 19, 1951, p. 457.

resents the allowed energy levels of the thallium ion in its unexcited state. The upper curve shows the allowed energy levels for the thallium ion when it is excited. The only energies allowed the thallium ion are those corresponding to points on these two curves; intermediate energies are not possible.

In the unexcited state at 0°K the thallium ion is located on the point A in figure 6.13. This is the trough of the potential energy curve corresponding to the point of least potential energy. At this point the chlorine ions are displaced away from their reference positions creating a local irregularity in the crystal.

Now suppose that an ultraviolet photon with a wave length of 2490 Å strikes the thallium ion. The energy received by the ion from the photon is sufficient to excite it to the point marked B on the upper permitted energy levels of figure 6.13. However, because of the slope of the energy curve at this point, the thallium ion potential energy diminishes as the ion rolls down the potential energy hill to the lowest point in the trough at point C. In doing so it releases energy which is transferred to vibrational energy of the crystal lattice. At the same time, the chlorine ions crowd in more closely to the thallium ion.

After a brief interval of less than 10^{-8} second the thallium ion ejects a photon and drops in energy by an amount equal to the photon energy. Thus, the ion drops in energy from point C to point D of the lower energy level curve. This difference in energy corresponds to a photon with a wave length of 3050 Å. Because photon ejection is instantaneous, the chlorine ions do not have an opportunity to regain their initial positions until *after* the transition to point D. Then they relax and move outward, further away from the thallium ion. This reduces the potential energy of the thallium ion to that corresponding to point A. Equilibrium is again established. The energy difference between points D and A is dissipated as lattice vibrations in the crystal. After a long period of operation, the temperature of the solid increases because of this constant absorption of energy by the crystal lattice.

6.12. Phosphors

Slightly different phenomena are involved in *phosphorescent* crystals such as copper-activated zinc sulfide. These are impurity semiconductors rather than ionic solids. Aside from the presence of the usual donor and acceptor impurities discussed earlier, *activator impurities* can also be introduced at energy levels within the forbidden zone of the host semiconductor as shown in figure 6.14. Through the con-

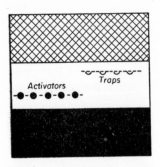

Figure 6.14. Activator and trap energy levels in a semiconductor.

trolled use of impurities it is also possible to establish electron traps in the forbidden zone of the semiconductor. The method of introducing these traps is not covered here.

Suppose that ultraviolet photons or energetic electrons are directed onto the surface of this semiconductor crystal. Occasionally these incident particles ionize an activator atom. The freed electron becomes caught in one of the electron traps. It receives enough energy to make this transition, but not enough to reach the conduction band. The trapped electron may be released by the absorption of more energy. Once free, it has some probability of recombining with an ionized activator, releasing a photon when it does so. The photon is green in the case of copper-activated zinc sulfide.

PROBLEMS

6.1. The following data applies to a barium-strontium oxide emitter. Compute the emission current density.

$\phi_0 = 2.475$ eV $\qquad\qquad T = 2073°$K

$\phi_i = 0.05$ eV $\qquad\qquad A = 120.4 \times 10^{+4}$ amp/meter^2 °K^2

$N_0 = 2.39 \times 10^{17}$ per cc

6.2. Compute the resistivity of an *n*-type germanium sample containing 3×10^{14} electrons/cc.

6.3. Repeat problem 6.2 assuming 3×10^{14} holes/cc.

6.4. Calculate the minimum photon wave lengths required at the onset of photoconduction in germanium, silicon, and the diamond crystal.

6.5. Calculate the photon wave lengths associated with the onset of photoconduction in *n*- and *p*-type silicon.

6.6. Calculate the density of free electrons and holes in intrinsic silicon at 20°C and 200°C. Make separate calculations using the theoretical and empirical formulas and compare the results.

6.7. Repeat problem 6.6 for intrinsic germanium.

6.8. Calculate the Fermi level for germanium at 0°K and 293°K assuming the effective electron and hole masses are the same.

6.9. Repeat problem 6.8 for silicon assuming the mass ratio to be 0.67.

6.10. Calculate the density of ionized donors in n-type silicon at 20°C and 200°C. Assume that there are 10^{18} donors/cc.

6.11. From the results in problem 6.10, calculate the resistivity of silicon.

6.12. A certain semiconductor sample measures 0.060 in. $\times$ 0.060 in. $\times$ 0.020 in. in rectangular form. It has 10^{15} free charges/cc at 20°C. A potential difference of 50 volts is applied across the sample between two narrow opposing faces. Assume the charge mobility to be 300 cm/sec/v/cm. Calculate the electric current.

6.13. How many photons must impinge on the broad face of the sample in problem 6.12 to produce a photoconduction current of 10 milliamperes? Assume that 50 per cent of the incident light is reflected. What is the dark current? How can it be reduced without reducing the photo current?

6.14. Calculate the Hall coefficient of intrinsic silicon at 20°C and 200°C. Use the theoretical equations throughout your calculations.

6.15. Calculate the Hall coefficient for n-type silicon having 10^{18} donors/cc at a temperature of 20°C. (a) First assume there are no holes present. (b) Recalculate the Hall coefficient considering contributions from the valence band.

6.16. A given sample of n-type semiconductor at 20°C has a Hall coefficient of -77.5 cc/coulomb. Calculate the density of electrons. Assuming the material is silicon, compute the density of donors neglecting contributions from the valence band.

6.17. Would it be possible to produce electron emission from p-type semiconductors? Explain your answer in detail.

6.18. Would the phenomenon of photoconduction be observed in noble metals? Explain your answer in detail.

7

SEMICONDUCTOR DEVICES

The band theory of solids developed in the preceding chapters is used here to discuss the operation and characteristics of various solid electronic devices. These devices are called *semiconductor diodes, varistors,* and *transistors.* In these components the electrical conduction process is entirely within the solid structure.

The material presented in the preceding two chapters is a prerequisite to an understanding of this chapter. The discussion here is far from complete. More details will be found in the various sources listed in the footnotes. The subject is growing very rapidly and the reader would be well advised to follow developments in the periodical literature.

7.1. Terminology associated with semiconductor devices

The various semiconductor devices include *semiconductor diodes* and *varistors* and *transistors.* These components are manufactured in many geometrical shapes and sizes and are of several different types.

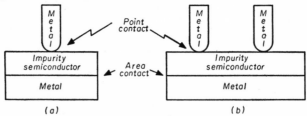

Figure 7.1. Two types of semiconductor devices: (a) point contact varistor; (b) point contact transistor.

Point contact types are sketched in figure 7.1. These sketches show
an impurity semiconductor as the principal structure and one or two
metal electrodes in point contact with the semiconductor. The bottom electrode in each case makes *area contact* with the semiconductor.
The point contact devices form one important class of semiconductor
devices.

The second main group of semiconductor components are classified
as *junction types*. This signifies a junction between two dissimilar
semiconductors. Some of the various possibilities of such contacts
are shown by the sketches in figure 7.2, which also gives the names

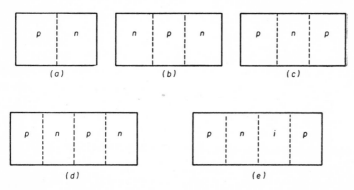

Figure 7.2. Junction type semiconductor devices: (a) *p-n* junction;
(b) *n-p-n* junction transistor: (c) *p-n-p* junction transistor; (d)
p-n-p-n junction transistor; (e) *p-n-i-p* junction transistor.

of the devices. Note that *point contact* and *area contact* denote a
metal-to-semiconductor connection, whereas *junction* type signifies a
contact between two dissimilar semiconductors.

Junctions between dissimilar materials are of two general types as
follows:

(1) *rectifying*

(2) *nonrectifying*

In the *nonrectifying* or *ohmic* contact, electric charge passes across
the contact with equal ease in both directions. This leads to a current-
voltage characteristic of the form shown in figure 7.3. The characteristic has the same slope for currents in both directions. Thus, the
resistance of the nonrectifying contact, which is the reciprocal of the
slope of the curve, is the same in both directions of current.

In a *rectifying* contact, electric charges easily move across the junction in one direction, but move with great difficulty in the reverse direction. This action corresponds to the curved characteristic shown in figure 7.3. In this case the resistance of the contact is low in the positive current direction and the resistance is high in the negative

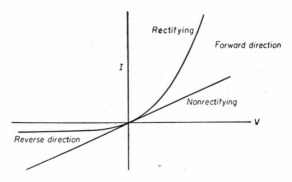

Figure 7.3. Distinction between rectifying and nonrectifying contacts.

current direction. This is the *unique* characteristic that identifies a *rectifier*. That is, all rectifiers or rectifying contacts exhibit low resistance in one direction of current and high resistance to current in the opposite direction. The low resistance direction is called the *forward* direction. The opposite, high resistance direction is called the *reverse* direction.

All semiconductor devices have nonrectifying contacts somewhere in their structure. More important, except for the thermistor, all semiconductor devices have *at least one rectifying junction, or contact*. Indeed, the properties of these devices of interest to engineers arise from the rectifying contacts. For this reason we will spend a large portion of this chapter examining physical phenomena relating to rectifying contacts.

Semiconductor devices are often classified according to the number of different electrodes used, as follows:

(1) Two-electrode devices are called *semiconductor diodes* or varistors. They all have one rectifying and one nonrectifying contact.

(2) Three-electrode devices are called *semiconductor triodes* or

transistors. They all have two rectifying contacts and at least
one non-rectifying contact.

(3) There are some four-electrode devices called *transistor tetrodes.*

It is often convenient to specify the kind of semiconductor material
used. This might include copper oxide, selenium, germanium, silicon,
or copper sulfide.

7.2. The p-n junction in thermal equilibrium

This is the first of a series of sections devoted to an explanation of
the physics and characteristics of *rectifying* junctions. The discussion
begins with an analysis of a junction between an *n*-type and a
p-type semiconductor in thermal equilibrium with zero voltage applied across the junction. The theory of the *p-n* junction was origi-
nated by Shockley.[1]

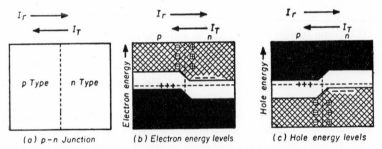

Figure 7.4. Electron and hole energy level diagrams for the *p-n*
junction; zero applied voltage: $\ominus$ = negative ion; $\oplus$ = positive
ion; $-$ = free electron; $+$ = hole.

The essential elements of a *p-n* junction are shown in figure 7.4a.
When the two materials are initially joined, the electrons and holes
in the region of the contact recombine. This leaves the positive
donor ions and negative acceptor ions as the only charges in the
region of contact. This double layer of charge sets up an electric field
across the contact that is directed so that it acts to prevent further
intermixing of electrons and holes. Equilibrium results when the
Fermi levels of the two materials come into alignment as shown in
figure 7.4b.

---

[1] W. Shockley, *B.S.T.J.*, Vol. 28, 1949, p. 435; and *Proc. I.R.E.*, Vol. 40,
Nov. 1952, p. 1289.

Figure 7.4b shows the electronic energy level diagram. Electron energy is plotted vertically *up* in this diagram and the hole energy is plotted *downward* on the vertical axis. The action of the holes is more readily understood if we redraw the diagram upside down as shown in figure 7.4c. The hole energy is plotted vertically up in this figure.

When the energy level diagrams of the two materials are combined about a common Fermi level, a potential energy *hill* or *barrier* appears between the two materials. This arises from the electric field produced by the double layer of electrically charged ions. The electric field is the negative of the slope of the potential curve. That is $E = -dV/dr$. The direction of this field is such as to force the holes back away from the junction and deeper into the p material. It also acts to force the electrons farther to the right, away from the junction and deeper into the n material.

Now assume that the temperature of the junction is raised above absolute zero. This causes two distinctly different things to happen, as follows:

(1) Some of the holes in the p material occasionally acquire sufficient energy from the source of heat to overcome the repelling field at the junction and enter the n material. Similarly, some electrons in the n material are excited to high enough energies to overcome the energy hill and enter the p material.

(2) The temperature increases the energy of the atoms in the n and p materials. Every now and then a valence bond breaks, and a free electron and hole are produced by thermal action.

We will discuss each of these two phenomena separately.

The holes entering the n material from the p region drift to the right. Eventually these holes recombine with electrons in the n region, releasing photons, or increasing the vibrational energy of the crystal. The same thing happens to the electrons moving into the p region from the n region. These two actions give rise to an electric current directed from left to right across the junction. We will call this the *recombination current, I_r*.

At the same time the thermal production of holes and electrons continues in both regions. The direction of the electric field at the contact is such that thermally produced holes in the n region drift to the left across the junction producing a current from right to left. Similarly, thermally produced electrons in the p region drift across the junction to the right into the n region. We shall call this the *thermal current*, I_T.

Under conditions of thermal equilibrium with zero voltage applied across the junction, these two currents must be exactly equal and opposite so that

$$I_r = -I_T$$

or, the total junction current is

$$I_j = I_r + I_T = 0$$

In the next two sections we will examine the effect that a voltage across the junction has on these two currents and the total junction current.

7.3. Reverse voltage applied to the p-n junction

The discussion in the preceding section revealed the presence of two equal and opposite currents across a *p-n* junction at thermal equilibrium and with zero voltage applied. Our problem now is to determine how a junction voltage acts upon these currents to produce a contact with high resistance in one direction and low resistance in the other.

The exact balance between the thermal and recombination currents across the junction is upset when a potential difference is produced across the junction. For example, suppose that we make the p region negative with respect to the n region as shown in figure 7.5a. If the

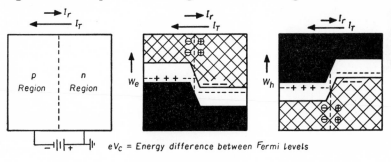

(a) Circuit connections   (b) Electron energy   (c) Hole energy

Figure 7.5. Relations in a *p-n* junction when a reverse potential difference of V_c volts is applied.

n region is assumed to be the reference, or *ground*, potential, then the electronic potential energy diagram of the p region is displaced vertically *up* from the position where the Fermi levels were aligned. This is shown in figure 7.5b. The figure is redrawn upside down in figure 7.5c to show hole energy plotted vertically up. Note that the relative displacement of the potential energy diagram of the p region is equal to eV_c, where e is the charge on an electron and V_c is the potential difference across the contact.

The effect of this applied voltage across the junction is evident in figures 7.5b and 7.5c. The *height* of the potential energy hill between regions is increased. This makes it more difficult than before for holes to diffuse to the right against the electric field intensity across the junction region. Thus, hole current from the p region into the n region is reduced. For the same reason, the electron diffusion from the n region to the p region is also reduced. As a result, the recombination current, I_r, from left to right, is reduced.

However, the thermal current I_T is unaffected. This is so because the thermal production of holes and electrons in both regions continues as before, being affected only by temperature. Holes produced in the n region drift to the left, fall down the potential energy hill and enter the p region. Thermally produced electrons in the p region move down the electronic potential energy hill and into the n region. The number of charges involved is the same as when there is no voltage across the junction. Thus, the thermal current I_T remains constant.

The total junction current is then

$$I_j = I_r + I_T$$

However, I_T is directed opposite to I_r and is larger than I_r. Hence, the total junction current is quite small and is directed in the same sense as the thermal current I_T. This is shown in figure 7.5.

This is called the *reverse* direction of operation. Because only a small net current is produced even when the junction voltage is quite large, the resistance of the contact is high in this direction of current.

It is also apparent that the reverse current will increase only as long as the recombination current decreases. This is so because the thermal current is constant at a constant temperature. It seems clear that when very large voltages are applied across the contact, the recombination current will be reduced nearly to zero and the junction current will essentially equal the thermal current I_T. This thermal current does not depend upon the junction voltage so the junction current remains constant when the junction voltage is increased beyond this point. When the reverse current becomes independent of the junction voltage, the junction is said to be saturated.

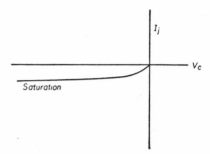

The *reverse* current-voltage characteristic for a *p-n* junction is shown in figure 7.6. The form of this curve should be understood from the preceding discussion.

Figure 7.6. Reverse characteristic for a *p-n* junction.

When the junction voltage is opposite to that applied in this section the junction is said to be operated in the *forward* direction. This is covered in the next section.

7.4. Forward voltage applied to the p-n junction

Suppose that the p region of a *p-n* junction is made positive with respect to the n region as shown in figure 7.7a. This is exactly opposite to the case discussed in the preceding section. In the example shown in figure 7.7 the potential energy diagram of the p region is

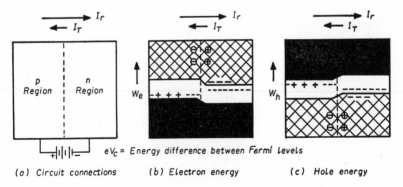

Figure 7.7. Relations in a *p-n* junction with a forward potential difference of V_c volts applied.

lowered with respect to the n region. It is lowered by an energy eV_c, where V_c is the positive junction voltage difference. The energy eV_c is the difference in potential energies between the Fermi levels of the two regions.

Because the application of a positive or *forward* potential to the p region lowers the electronic energy levels relative to the reference n region, the height of the potential energy hill between regions is reduced. This has no effect on the thermal current I_T as explained in the preceding section, as long as the temperature remains constant. However, the recombination current I_r increases because more holes and electrons in the two regions acquire sufficient thermal energy to climb the lowered hill. Thus, the net current across the junction is directed the same as the recombination current from the p region to the n region as shown in figure 7.7.

It can be shown from statistical mechanics that the recombination current is given by

$$I_r = I_T \epsilon^{eV_c/kT} \tag{7.1}$$

where I_T = thermal current in amperes, e = charge on an electron in coulombs, V_c = voltage difference across the junction measured from the p region to the n region, k = Boltzmann's constant, T = temperature in °K. V_c is negative when *reverse* voltage is applied and this makes the recombination current I_r less than the thermal current I_T as described in the preceding section. For the *forward* direction of operation under discussion here, it is clear from equation (7.1) that V_c is positive and that the recombination current I_r is larger than the thermal current I_T.

The total junction current is the sum of the thermal and recombination currents, or

$$I_j = I_r + I_T = I_T(\epsilon^{eV_c/kT} - 1) \quad \text{amp} \tag{7.2}$$

According to this equation the junction current is zero when the junction voltage V_c is zero. When the junction voltage is positive, which is the condition for *forward* operation, the junction current increases exponentially as shown by the current-voltage characteristic in figure 7.8. For *reverse* operation the junction voltage is negative and the junction current decreases exponentially toward the saturation current I_T. The positive direction of current in figure 7.8 corresponds to the direction associated with the recombination current I_r.

The *forward* current is quite large even when the junction voltage is quite small. Hence, the junction resistance is very low in the forward direction of operation.

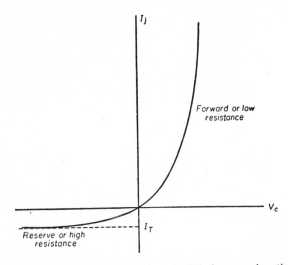

Figure 7.8. Current-voltage characteristic for a *p-n* junction.

When the forward voltage is quite large, the potential energy hill between the p and n regions is completely wiped out. This results in very large concentrations of charge moving across the junction and equation (7.2) is no longer valid.

7.5. Depletion layers and Zener currents

The effect of the junction voltage on the potential energy hill between regions is explored in more detail in this section. The effect of the junction voltage on this hill and on the associated charge distribution is shown in figure 7.9.

The conditions existing in thermal equilibrium are shown in the three sketches of figure 7.9a. This is the case for zero voltage applied across the junction. When the p and n regions are joined, the free electrons and holes in the region of contact combine so that the contact region is devoid of *free* charge. However, the impurities remain as *bound* ions, either positive or negative depending upon the character of the impurity. Therefore, all of this region is depleted of free charge and is called the *depletion layer*. Although there is no free charge, there is a *net* charge arising from the bound ions. The net charge is negative in the *p* region and positive in the *n* region. This is shown by the sketch of charge density in figure 7.9a. This region is sometimes called the *space charge layer* because there is a net, spatially distributed bound charge. Except in this depletion region the net charge density is zero.

The variation in net charge density produces a change in electrostatic potential as shown in the bottom sketch in figure 7.9a. This is the origin of the potential energy hill noted earlier.

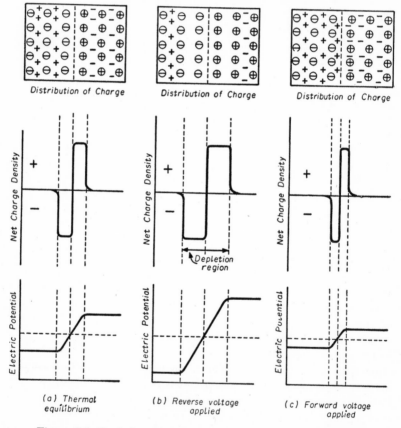

Figure 7.9. Depletion region in a *p-n* junction showing the effect of junction voltage.

When a *reverse* voltage is applied across the junction, the sketches in figure 7.9b apply. This shows that the depletion layer is widened as reverse voltage is applied. This is caused by an increased number of recombinations of electrons and holes and results in a larger potential energy hill. Application of a *forward* voltage across the junction produces the converse effect as shown by the sketches in figure 7.9c.

The *conductivity* of any material is directly proportional to the density of *free* charges. This was proven in chapter 5. There is no free charge in the depletion layer, so it has zero conductivity or infinite resistance. There is free charge in the other regions so that they have finite resistances. For this reason the entire junction voltage appears across the depletion layer. Therefore, the height of the potential energy hill in the depletion layer is equal to the junction voltage added to the difference in Fermi levels. That is,

$$W \text{ (height of hill in joules)} = (W_{F_n} - W_{F_p}) - eV_c$$

where V_c = junction voltage as defined earlier, W_{F_n} = Fermi level of the n material, W_{F_p} = Fermi level of the p material. The width of the depletion layer is of the order of 2.5×10^{-5} meter.

The depletion layer is very thin as noted above and the entire junction voltage appears across it. Hence, the electric field intensity E_c across the junction is quite high. This is so because $E_c = V_c/d$, where d = thickness of the depletion layer. When this field intensity reaches certain rather high values, a new phenomenon called the *Zener effect*[2] is observed.

The electric field intensity in the depletion layer eventually becomes so intense that the force on the bound valence electrons and the atomic cores is large enough to produce relative displacements. Ultimately, this causes the valence bonds to rupture. According to Zener's theory, the valence bonds actually rupture *before* the electric field intensity produces rupture directly.

Each time a bond breaks a hole and an electron are produced. They move as directed by the electric field and an electric current results. This is the *Zener current*. The onset voltage of the Zener current can be controlled over a wide range by varying the densities of the impurities in the p and n regions during the manufacture of the

[2] C. Zener, "A Theory of Electrical Breakdown of Solid Dielectrics," *Proc. Roy. Soc.*, London, Vol. 145, 1934, p. 523.

junction. The *Zener voltage* is usually the maximum *reverse* voltage that can safely be applied across a *p-n* junction.

7.6. Surface states of semiconductors[3,4]

In all of our work so far, attention was restricted to volume properties of essentially perfect crystals. No consideration was made of the surface properties of semiconductor crystals. A brief, simplified description of surface states is presented here as an introduction to the discussion of metal-semiconductor contacts.

Consider the case of a perfect covalent semiconductor solid. The crystal is assumed to be perfect up to the last row of atoms representing the surface. This last row cannot be perfect because the valence bonding is imcomplete. Moreover, there are always some contaminating atoms on the surface. The unused bonds of the semiconductor atoms combine with the atoms of the surface contaminants to form a special surface material called the *skin*. This *skin* is only 1 or 2 atoms thick; it has the form of a two dimensional solid. The properties of this surface solid will be quite different from the properties of the semiconductor crystal because the type, orientation, and concentration of atomic contaminants on the surface will vary over a wide range.

Thus, the structure of the surface *skin* tends to be nonuniform and irregular. For this reason we would *not* expect the *skin* to have a regular band theory model with clearly defined allowed and forbidden zones. Rather, the disorderly structure leads us to think that the energy band structure is also disorderly. In particular, the introduction of so many impurities of various types suggests that many new allowed energy levels are created in the otherwise forbidden zone of the semiconductor. It seems likely that there is a *virtual continuum* of allowed electron energies at the surface of the crystal.

With these points in mind we can construct a band theory model for a semiconductor to show surface states. The proposed model for an *n*-type semiconductor at absolute zero is shown in figure 7.10.

---

[3] J. Bardeen, "Surface States and Rectification At a Metal-Semi-Conductor Contact," *Phys. Rev.*, Vol. 71, Apr. 15, 1949, pp. 208–225.

[4] W. E. Bradley, "Principles of Surface Barrier Transistors," *Proc. I.R.E.*, Vol. 41, Dec. 1953, pp. 1702–1709.

This figure shows the valence and conduction bands of the semiconductor separated by a forbidden zone. The donor impurities in the crystal introduce new energy levels in the forbidden zone as described earlier. These energy levels are filled at absolute zero and are shown by small black circles.

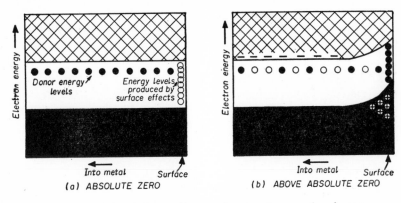

Figure 7.10. Band theory diagram for an n-type semiconductor, showing surface effects.

The surface impurities create a continuum of allowed energy levels in the otherwise forbidden zone. These levels are empty at absolute zero as shown by the white circles in figure 7.10a.

As the temperature of the material is increased, the donors become ionized and free electrons are produced in the conduction band. These electrons tend to revert to the lowest possible potential energy. Hence, they tend to drift to the surface and drop into one of the lower, but empty, surface states. Thus, a negative charge builds up on the surface, causing the potential energy of this region to increase as shown in figure 7.10b. This action produces a potential energy hill similar to that across a p-n junction.

At the same time that all of this takes place, valence bonds in the surface solid rupture, producing holes. The freed electrons move up into one of the allowed, but empty, surface states. This is shown in figure 7.10b.

The potential energy hill shown in figure 7.10b prevents any more electrons from proceeding to the surface and also keeps the holes confined to a thin layer just below the surface. This negative space charge produces a repelling electric field as indicated by the potential hill. Hence, a charge-free, or intrinsic, region is produced just below the surface.

In summary, the surface states produce a surface charge layer followed by a *p* region, an intrinsic point, and thence to the original *n* material of the crystal. Presumably, a similar effect is observed for *p*-type semiconductor materials.

These ideas are quite important in the discussion of metal-semiconductor contacts later in the chapter.

7.7. Metal-semiconductor contacts[5,6]

Up to this point we have considered only rectification at a *p-n* junction. It is also possible to produce rectification at a metal-semiconductor contact, but the mechanism is somewhat more involved and not so well understood. The material presented in the preceding section is used here to partially explain the effect.

When a metal electrode is brought into contact with the surface of an *n*-type semiconductor, the band theory diagrams combine about a common Fermi level as shown in figure 7.11*a*. The diagram used here for the semiconductor was developed in section 7.6. The number of holes produced just under the surface of the semiconductor appears to depend upon the type of metal used for the contact.[7] The potential energy hill prevents any transfer of electrons from either material into the other. A depletion layer appears much like that in the *p-n* junction.

Suppose that the metal is made positive with respect to the semiconductor as shown in figure 7.11*c*. This wipes out the barrier between materials and two things happen:

(1) Electrons from the conduction band of the semiconductor readily flow into the metal.

(2) Holes in the valence band of the semiconductor are repelled by the metal into the semiconductor.

Each of these constitutes an electric current so that the total current is the sum of the hole and electron currents. New holes are

[5] J. Bardeen, *op. cit.*

[6] R. F. Schwartz, J. F. Walsh, "The Properties of Metal-to-Semiconductor Contacts," *Proc. I.R.E.*, Vol. 41, Dec. 1953, p. 1715.

[7] W. E. Bradley, *op. cit.*

created as the original ones are repelled by a complicated condition produced by the surface states of the metal and semiconductor.

This current is further enhanced as the material is made progressively more positive and the current across the contact increases. This is the *forward* direction of operation.

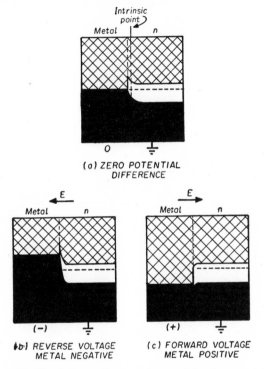

Figure 7.11. Band theory diagrams for a metal n-type semiconductor contact.

When the contact is operated in the *reverse* direction, the energy level diagram of figure 7.11b applies. In this case the metal electrode is negative with respect to the semiconductor. Electrons in the metal are urged toward the semiconductor. However, the relatively large and steep potential energy hill prevents all but a few high energy electrons from crossing the contact. Thus, the reverse current is quite small as expected. There will be a small hole current from the semiconductor to the metal.

As the reverse voltage is made increasingly larger, the Zener effect sets in and the reverse current commences a rapid increase with increasing voltage. At this point a secondary effect enters that acts to increase the Zener current.[8] This is called *tunneling*.

When the metal is very negative relative to the semiconductor, as shown in figure 7.11b, the forbidden zone between the filled band of the metal and the conduction band of the semiconductor becomes very, very thin. Electrons from the metal can then *tunnel through* into the semiconductor in relatively large numbers. The reverse current increases rapidly and the contact may burn out. Thus, a maximum inverse voltage is normally specified to prevent this from happening.

Metal-semiconductor contacts are seldom of the simple *unformed* character discussed here. Normally they receive a special treatment called *forming* which alters their characteristics. This forming process and the proposed theories used to explain it are discussed later in the chapter.

7.8. Commercial diodes

Commercial *semiconductor diodes* or *varistors* may be of the *point-contact* or *area-contact* type. In the latter case the rectifying junction is in contact with the semiconductor over a wide area instead of at a point. A depletion layer is formed in essentially the same manner in either case. The depletion layer is always found under the point contact in point-contact devices.

Several types of semiconductor diodes are shown in figure 7.12. The current-voltage characteristics in the forward direction for several diodes of the same general power capability are shown approximately in figure 7.13.

The forward current through a diode can be approximated by an equation of the form[9]

$$I_b = AV_b^n \tag{7.3}$$

where A and n are experimentally determined constants. The value of n varies between 2 and 4, although silicon carbide varistors exhibit values as high as 7 under certain conditions.[9]

[8] K. B. McAfee, E. J. Ryder, W. Shockley, M. Sparks, "Observations of Zener Current in *p-n* Junctions," *Phys. Rev.*, Vol. 83, 1951, p. 650.

[9] F. R. Stansel, "The Characteristics and Some Applications of Varistors," *Proc. I.R.E.*, Vol. 39, Apr. 1951, pp. 342–358.

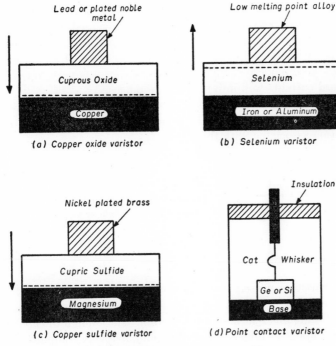

Figure 7.12. Types of varistors.[10]

Commercial area-contact diodes range in size from $\frac{1}{16}$-in. discs to rectangular plates several inches wide and as much as a foot long.

For copper oxide diodes the continuous reverse working voltage is usually limited to a value of the order of 6-18 volts, although higher voltages can be withstood for short periods of time. The voltage ratings of selenium units generally exceed those of corresponding copper oxide varistors, but the reverse characteristics of selenium tend to be somewhat more variable.

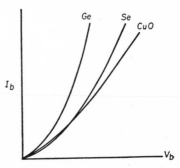

Figure 7.13. Current-voltage characteristics for various types of varistors.

---

[10] *Ibid.*

The point-contact germanium and silicon varistors are usually made in small cartridges of various shapes governed by the projected use. Typical units will pass 10–60 milliamperes of forward current and will withstand inverse voltages ranging from 10 to 150 volts or more. More modern diodes of this type can pass very much larger forward currents well into the ampere range.

The electrical circuit symbol for a semiconductor diode or varistor is shown in figure 7.14. The arrowhead always points in the forward direction associated with the diode.

Figure 7.14. Circuit symbol for a semiconductor diode or varistor.

All varistors possess interelectrode capacitance (see chapter 10) because of their geometrical configuration. All of the elements of a capacitor are inherent in its construction. The amount of capacitance depends upon the area of the contact and, in a very complicated way, upon the frequency and voltage of the signal impressed across the junction.

7.9. Carrier injection[11]

From this point in this chapter our discussion is confined to semiconductor *triodes* or *transistors*. However, before discussing actual transistors it is important that you understand the idea of *carrier injection* because this is an essential mechanism in transistor operation.

Consider the case of an *n*-type germanium semiconductor rod connected to the terminals of a voltage source by two nonrectifying contacts as shown in figure 7.15. The positive donor ions are fixed in position so that conduction through the semiconductor is ideally

---

[11] W. Shockley, G. L. Pearson, J. R. Haynes, "Hole Injection in Germanium— Qualitative Studies and Filamentary Transistors," *B.S.T.J.*, Vol. 28, July 1949, pp. 344–366.

by electrons only. When the voltage source is connected, an electric field is produced lengthwise down the rod and electronic conduction in the usual sense occurs with the free conduction electrons drifting toward the positive electrode. The semiconductor is electrically neutral; at all times it contains equal numbers of electrons and positive

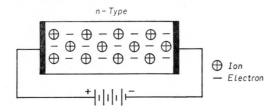

Figure 7.15. Electronic conduction in n-type germanium.

donor ions. This situation must prevail even when an electric current exists. Even small deviations from this condition of neutrality cause enormous space charges to build up that exert tremendous forces to re-establish the neutral state. In other words, the flow of electrons is essentially incompressible. As one electron is injected at the negative end, one moves out of the positive end of the rod.

You can readily see that the density of charge carriers, electrons in this example, remains constant throughout the semiconductor rod at all times. Of course, the density of free electrons and positive ions can be altered by changing the temperature, but the material remains electrically neutral. It is not possible to alter only the density of the electrons by injecting more electrons. Thus, it is not possible to increase the density of charge carriers by injecting more charges of the same sign as that of the free charges normally present in the material.

However, no such restriction is imposed if free charge carriers of the *opposite* sign are injected. This is so because the space charge they create can be neutralized by an increased concentration of the carriers normally present. This increased concentration of the carriers normally present can be supplied by the voltage source.

Now apply the preceding statement to the n-type semiconductor shown in figure 7.15. Free electrons represent the charge carriers normally present. The carrier concentration can be increased by injecting *holes* into the n-type semiconductor. The space charge of the holes is exactly neutralized by an increased density of electrons supplied by the source of electric potential. The term *carrier injection* is used to identify this process of injecting charges into a material where the injected charges have a polarity opposite to that of the charges normally present in the material.

Carrier injection is the origin of the transistor principle. It is discussed in the next section with reference to a particular transistor.

7.10. p-n-p junction transistor[12]

A *transistor* is a three-terminal semiconductor device, or triode, in contrast to the diodes discussed so far. Every transistor has two rectifying junctions and at least one nonrectifying junction. The essential structure of a *p-n-p* junction transistor is shown in figure 7.16 together with its electrical circuit symbol.

The three electrodes of a transistor are the *emitter, base,* and *collector* as shown in figure 7.16. Rectification occurs only at the junctions

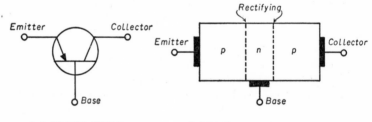

(a) CIRCUIT SYMBOL   *(b) ESSENTIAL STRUCTURE*

Figure 7.16. *p-n-p* junction transistor.

between the *n*-type base region and the adjoining *p*-type emitter and collector regions. All three electrodes are brought out to external circuit connections by wires attached to the three regions in ohmic, or nonrectifying, contact.

The general operation of a transistor is reasonably easy to understand in a general way with reference to the preceding discussion of carrier injection. All transistors are normally operated so that the

---

[12] W. Shockley, M. Sparks, G. K. Teal, "P-N Junction Transistors," *Phys. Rev.*, Vol. 83, No. 1, July 1951, pp. 151–162; also W. Shockley, "The Theory of P-N Junctions in Semiconductors and P-N Junction Transistors," *B.S.T.J.*, Vol. 28, July 1949, pp. 435–489.

emitter injects charge carriers into the base region; the injected charge carriers have a sign opposite to that of charge carriers normally in the base region. The collector is adjusted in potential so that it serves to attract and collect the injected charge carriers after they drift through the base region.

For the *p-n-p* junction transistor the base region is *n*-type material containing electrons as the charge carriers normally present. Hence, the emitter must be made positive with respect to the base so that it injects holes into the base region. The holes drift across the base region toward the collector, which is negative with respect to the base. The injected holes are collected as an increment of collector current. In substance, this is the *transistor principle*. Its real meaning will be more apparent in a few minutes.

The best method of gaining an understanding of this process is through the use of the band theory diagrams. The band theory model for a *p-n-p* junction transistor is shown in figure 7.17. Figure

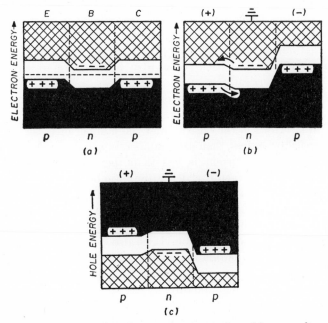

Figure 7.17. *p-n-p* junction transistor operation: (a) zero voltage applied; (b) voltage applied for normal operation; (c) figure (b) inverted to show hole energy.

7.17a shows the band theory model under conditions of thermal equilibrium with zero potential difference across each of the two rectifying junctions. Holes in either p region are prevented from entering the n-type base by the potential energy hill associated with the depletion layers. This also prevents electrons from the base from moving into either p region.

To inject holes into the base from the p-type emitter region, it is obvious that the height of the potential energy hill in the depletion layer must be reduced. If you refer to the discussion in section 7.4 you will find that this can be accomplished by making the p region positive with respect to the n region as shown in figure 7.17b. Hence, *the emitter is operated in the forward direction.* This is the low-resistance direction across the junction.

The collector must attract the injected charge carriers. To do this it must be negative with respect to the base when the injected carriers are holes. This corresponds to *reverse* operation of the p-n junction because the height of the potential energy hill is increasing by the widening of the depletion layer. Thus, *the collector is operated in the high-resistance reverse direction.* This is clear from figure 7.17b.

The *electronic* energy level diagram for normal operation is shown in figure 7.17b. It has been redrawn in figure 7.17c to show *hole* energy plotted vertically up.

Holes injected by the emitter enter the base region and diffuse rather slowly toward the collector. Occasionally, some holes recombine with electrons in the base so that the number of holes arriving at the collector is less than the number injected by the emitter. Thus, the collector current is less than the emitter current. The current amplification factor, which is the ratio of collector to emitter current, is always less than unity in this type of transistor. It can be made to approach unity rather closely by using a very thin base region; this reduces the time the hole is in the base region and reduces the probability of recombination. It is also possible to reduce the probability of recombination by reducing the number of electrons in the base region. This can be controlled by adjusting the donor impurity density during manufacture.

At this point the transistor probably sounds like a pretty ineffective device. We inject current at the emitter and less current, say 90–95 per cent as much, appears at the collector. The important points are:

(1) The current is injected across the low-resistance emitter operated in the forward direction.

(2) A large part of this current is collected at the high-resistance collector operated in the reverse direction.

The importance of this idea is readily shown by a simplified numerical example. The resistance of the emitter circuit might be something of the order of 200 ohms. The resistance in the collector circuit might be something of the order of 20,000 ohms. So, assume that

$$R_\epsilon = 200 \text{ ohms} = \text{emitter resistance}$$

$$R_c = 20,000 \text{ ohms} = \text{resistance in collector circuit}$$

The emitter current might be about 1 milliampere and the collector current might be about 0.9 milliampere. Hence,

$$I_\epsilon = 1.0 \text{ ma} = \text{emitter current}$$

$$I_c = 0.9 \text{ ma} = \text{collector current}$$

Now compute the power levels in the emitter and collector circuits as

$$P_\epsilon = I_\epsilon^2 R_\epsilon = 2 \times 10^{-4} \text{ watt}$$

$$P_c = I_c^2 R_c = 162 \times 10^{-4} \text{ watt}$$

Thus, the practical importance of the transistor arises from its characteristic of *power amplification*. The power amplification results from current injection at a low-resistance level followed by current collection at a high-resistance level.

Please understand that power is *not* created by the transistor. The collector power is actually supplied by the voltage source connected between the collector and base electrodes. The transistor provides the means whereby power at a low level in the emitter circuit is used to *control* power at a high level in the collector circuit.

7.11. n-p-n junction transistors

The essential structural form of an *n-p-n* junction transistor is shown in figure 7.18a. In actual units the central base layer is very thin in comparison to the emitter and collector regions. This device differs from the *p-n-p* transistor only in the arrangement of semiconductor materials. For normal operation the emitter is operated in the forward direction so that it will inject electrons into the *p*-type

base region. This requires the emitter to be negative with respect
to the base. The collector is operated in the reverse direction so that
it can collect the injected electrons. It must be positive with respect
to the base to accomplish this. These voltages are exactly the reverse
of those for the *p-n-p* transistor.

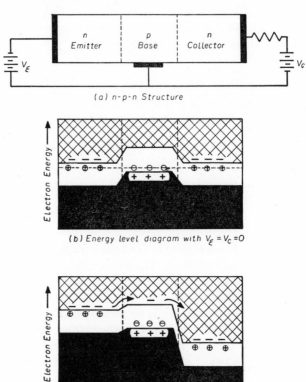

(a) n-p-n Structure

(b) Energy level diagram with $V_\mathcal{E} = V_c = 0$

(c) Energy level diagram, normal operation

Figure 7.18. A *n-p-n* junction transistor: $+$ = electron, $\oplus$ = donor ion, $\ominus$ = acceptor ion. (After W. Shockley, M. Sparks, G. K.
Teal, *Phys. Rev.*, Vol. 83, No. 1, July 1951, pp. 151–162.)

The electronic energy level diagram for the *n-p-n* structure is shown
in figure 7.18b when both the emitter and collector voltages are zero.
This diagram is constructed by equalizing the Fermi levels of the
n- and *p*-type semiconductor energy level diagrams and then connecting the valence and conduction bands by smooth curves. The

potential hill caused by the central p layer is so high that electrons from the n regions do not have enough energy to surmount it without the aid of an applied field.

In figure 7.18c the electronic energy level diagram is shown for normal operating conditions with forward voltage applied to the emitter and reverse voltage applied to the collector.

The applied emitter voltage lowers the potential hill at the emitter junction so that a relatively large number of injected electrons climb the hill and diffuse into the p-type base region. This is the process of injecting charge carriers of the sign opposite to that normally present in the base region. If the base region is thin enough, the injected electrons will diffuse to the collector junction with only a small recombination loss. Once the electrons reach the collector junction they are collected as an increment of collector current.

Some hole conduction from the base to the emitter region may occur. However, as long as the conductivity of the emitter region is much larger than that of the base, the hole current will be small compared to the electron current.

The electrical circuit symbol for an n-p-n transistor is shown in figure 7.19. It differs from the symbol used for the p-n-p transistor only in the direction associated with the arrowhead on the emitter. This arrow always denotes the direction associated with electric current in the emitter circuit. In the n-p-n transistor the emitter injects electrons into the base. This corresponds to an electric current directed from the base toward the emitter, as shown by the arrowhead in figure 7.19. Conversely, holes are injected into the base of the p-n-p transistor and this corresponds to electric current directed from the emitter to the base.

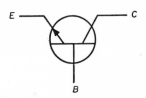

Figure 7.19. Circuit symbol for the n-p-n transistor.

7.12. Hook collector

In section 7.10 it was observed that the current amplification of the p-n-p junction transistor was always less than unity. The same is true of the n-p-n transistor. However, it is found that the current amplification can be made larger than unity if a fourth semiconductor layer is added to either of the two types of junction transistors. In other words, an extra *n*-type layer is added to the *p-n-p* structure making it a *p-n-p-n* transistor. In the same way, a second *p*-type layer is added to the *n-p-n* device making it an *n-p-n-p* transistor.

For the sake of discussion, consider the *p-n-p-n* structure shown in figure 7.20a. Observe that this is essentially a *p-n-p* transistor of

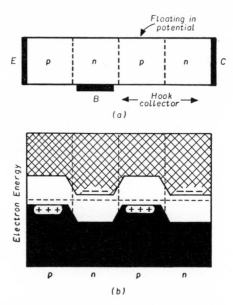

Figure 7.20. Junction transistor with hook collector: (a) structure; (b) electronic energy level diagram in thermal equilibrium, zero voltage difference across the junctions.

the type discussed in section 7.10, except that a second *n* region has been added. As in the *p-n-p* transistor, the first *p* region serves as the emitter and the first *n* region serves as the base. However, the second *p* region is left *floating* in potential and the last *n* region functions as the collector. The last *p-n* layers constitute a *hook collector*.

The electronic energy level diagram for this device under conditions of thermal equilibrium is shown in figure 7.20b. As in all transistors:

(1) The emitter operates in the forward direction and injects

charges into the base with a sign opposite to that of the charges normally present.

(2) The collector operates in the reverse direction.

This requires that the p-type emitter region be made positive with respect to the base to reduce the height of the potential hill. Reduction of the height of this hill allows holes to be injected into the base by the emitter. This operating condition is shown in figure 7.21a and is redrawn in figure 7.21b to show hole energy. The collector must necessarily be operated in the reverse direction by making it negative with respect to the base. This is also shown in figure 7.21.

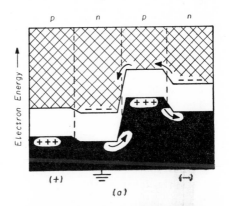

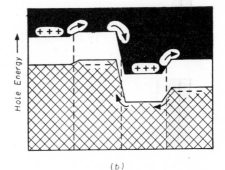

In figure 7.21b you can see that holes injected by the emitter into the base diffuse over to the floating p region and fall down the potential energy hill at this junction. Once the holes enter this p region they are trapped there because they do not have enough energy to surmount the potential energy hill at the collector junction. Thus, the holes are caught in the *hook* in the hole potential energy curve.

As the emitter injects more and more holes into the base, more and more of these become trapped in the floating p region. As a result, the floating p region soon acquires a net positive charge and this increases the hole potential energy of the region. This increase in potential energy causes the floating p region to move up with respect to the n-type base and collector regions. In so doing, the height of the

Figure 7.21. A p-n-p-n junction transistor with voltages applied for normal operation. (After Ref. 12, Fig. 4.)

potential energy hill at the collector is reduced. When equilibrium is finally established, the height of the hill is reduced to the point where one hole moves out of the hook for each hole that enters and becomes trapped.

However, the reduction in the height of the potential energy hill at the collector junction allows a considerable increase in the number of electrons diffusing from the n-type collector into the floating p region. These electrons then diffuse to the base. The total collector current is the sum of the hole and electron currents. Under normal operating conditions, the total collector current exceeds the injected hole current from the emitter. This leads to current amplifications of 2, 3, or more.

The *hook theory* just used to explain current amplifications in excess of unity is not entirely satisfactory. The *trap theory*[13] seems more nearly in agreement with experimental results. In substance, this theory assumes the presence of *hole traps* in p material and *electron traps* in n material. Thus, the injected charge carriers fall into these traps in the floating region of the hook collector. The trapped charges build up and produce the same action and effect as predicted by the hook theory. While the difference in theories appears slight from this superficial presentation, there is good evidence to support the trap theory in preference to the hook theory.

7.13. Point contact transistor[14]

Two types of point contact transistors are shown in figure 7.22.[15] In each case there is a small wafer of an impurity semiconductor making a nonrectifying contact with a metal base electrode. The semiconductor, which can be either n- or p-type, serves as the *base region* of the transistor. Two sharp-pointed metal electrodes are placed firmly on the surface of the semiconductor. These electrodes make rectifying contact as explained in section 7.7.

If the pointed electrodes are sufficiently close together, this device

---

[13] W. R. Sittner, "Current Multiplication in the Type A Transistor," *Proc. I.R.E.*, Vol. 40, April 1952, pp. 448–454.

[14] J. Bardeen, W. H. Brattain, "The Transistor, A Semiconductor Triode," *Phys. Rev.*, Vol. 74, 1948, p. 230.

[15] W. E. Koch, R. L. Wallace, Jr., "The Coaxial Transistor," *Elec. Eng.*, Vol. 68, Mar. 1949, pp. 222–223.

will operate as a transistor. At an early date it was found that the current amplification could be increased by *forming* the collector electrode.

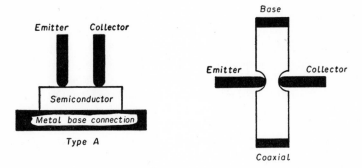

Figure 7.22. Point contact transistors.

The *forming* process consists of passing a large and controlled *reverse* current through the collector. Valdes[16] studied the properties of formed electrodes. In the case of an n-type base region, he found that the properties of the material immediately under the formed electrode were changed to those shown in figure 7.23. You can see that two new regions are produced: an n region is located immediately

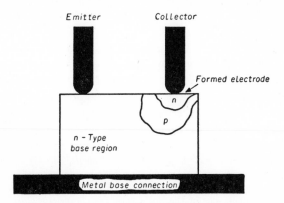

Figure 7.23. *Formed* area under a metal electrode showing the formation of a *p-n* hook.

---

[16] L. B. Valdes, "Transistor Forming Effects in n-type Germanium," *Proc. I.R.E.*, Vol. 40, April 1952, pp. 445–448.

under the electrode and this is followed by a floating p region. This region *floats* in electric potential because it is not directly in contact with a source of potential. This array of materials provides exactly the same structure as that associated with the hook collector. Thus, it appears that the large current amplifications observed in point contact transistors are associated with a hook collector structure.

One of the factors acting to limit the highest usable frequency of a transistor is the time required for the injected charge to travel from the emitter to the collector. In the point contact transistor this time can be computed from the following approximate formula:[17]

$$T \text{ (in sec)} \doteq \frac{S^3}{\rho \mu I_\epsilon} \tag{7.4}$$

where S = electrode spacing in cm, ρ = resistivity of the semiconductor in ohm-cm, μ = mobility of the charge carrier in cm/sec/v/cm, I_ϵ = emitter current amperes.

7.14. Surface-barrier transistor[18]

The *surface-barrier* transistor has two metal-semiconductor rectifying contacts. In this sense it is similar to the point contact transistor. However, unlike the point contact transistor, the electrodes in the surface-barrier transistor make contact over a wide area and are not *formed*.

The operation of this device closely parallels that of the p-n-p transistor. Operation depends upon the production of holes just under the surface of the semiconductor at the emitter contact. These holes are injected into an n-type base region and diffuse over to the collector. The general physical principles involved may be understood in a qualitative way from the discussion of surface state effects in section 7.7 and the transistor principle in section 7.9.

---

[17] B. N. Slade, "Survey of Transistor Development," *Radio and TV News*, Oct. 1952, p. 65.

[18] All of the following articles are from the *Proc. I.R.E.*, Vol. 41, Dec. 1953: W. E. Bradley, "Principles of the Surface-Barrier Transistor," p. 1702; J. W. Tiley, R. A. Williams, "Electrochemical Techniques for Fabrication of Surface-Barrier Transistors," p. 1706; J. B. Angell, F. P. Keiper, Jr., "Circuit Applications of Surface-Barrier Transistors," p. 1709; R. Kansas, "On the High Frequency Performance of Transistors," p. 1712.

7.15. p-n-i-p transistors[19]

It was briefly noted in section 7.8 that there is a *capacitance* (see chapter 10) associated with a *p-n* junction. The value of this capacitance may be estimated from the following equation, which is derived in chapter 10:

$$C = \epsilon \frac{A}{d} = \text{capacitance of the junction in farads}$$

where ϵ = dielectric constant of the intrinsic semiconductor forming the depletion layer of the junction, A = area of the junction, d = width of the depletion layer. The value of this capacitance is one of the main factors in determining the limiting useful frequency of the junction, or the transistor of which the junction is a part. The maximum useful frequency is increased as the junction capacitance is decreased.

The most important capacitance in a transistor is the one formed at the *p-n* junction between the base and collector electrodes. This is called the *collector capacitance*.

One way of reducing the collector capacitance is to increase the width of the depletion layer. This can be accomplished in a controlled manner by inserting an *intrinsic*, or *i*-type, region of semiconductor material between the base and collector regions. Such a move converts the *p-n-p* transistor to a *p-n-i-p* transistor; or, it changes the *n-p-n* device to an *n-p-i-n* structure.

Such transistors have been made and they operate at substantially higher frequencies than their *p-n-p* or *n-p-n* counterparts. With the exception of the change in collector capacitance and some attendant variations of a similar nature, the *p-n-i-p* and *n-p-i-n* transistors operate in the same manner as their counterparts.

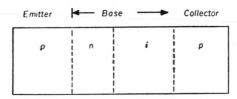

Figure 7.24. Structure of the *p-n-i-p* transistor.

[19] J. M. Early, "P-N-I-P and N-P-I-N Junction Transistor Triodes," *B.S.T.J.*, Vol. 33, May 1954, pp. 517–534.

The general structural form is shown in figure 7.24 for the case of the p-n-i-p device. Note that the n-type base region is very thin and that the i-type region fills most of the base. The combined width of the n and i regions is approximately the same as the total base thickness in the p-n-p structure.

The net density of impurities in each region is approximately as follows:

$$\text{net acceptors in } p \text{ regions } = 10^{18}\text{-}10^{19} \text{ per cc}$$

$$\text{net donors in the } n \text{ region } = 10^{16}\text{-}10^{17} \text{ per cc}$$

$$\text{net impurities in } i \text{ region } = \text{less than } 3 \times 10^{13} \text{ per cc}$$

7.16. Transistor characteristics

Although they vary considerably in range, the direct current electrical characteristics of transistors have essentially the same form regardless of type. Because a transistor is a three-terminal circuit element, it involves four variables, as follows:

I_ϵ = emitter current I_c = collector current

V_ϵ = emitter-base voltage V_c = collector-base voltage

Hence, the data describing the behavior of the device can be organized into four different families of curves as follows:

(1) *Input characteristics*

V_ϵ vs. I_ϵ with I_c as the family parameter

(2) *Output characteristics*

V_c vs. I_c with I_ϵ as the family parameter

(3) *Forward characteristics*

V_c vs. I_ϵ with I_c as the family parameter

(4) *Feedback characteristics*

V_ϵ vs. I_c with I_ϵ as the family parameter

Representative characteristic curves obtained during early developmental stages are shown in figure 7.25.

Consider the output characteristic, which shows the relationship between collector current and voltage when the emitter current is the family parameter. When the emitter current is zero, there is no carrier injection and the curve is essentially the current-voltage characteristic of the collector circuit operating as a diode. As the emitter current is increased, carriers are injected that appear as an increment of collector current. As a result, an increased collector current appears and the characteristic curve shifts over to a higher current region. The translation of the curve is the principal effect, although slope changes are apparent in certain types of transistors.

The *current amplification factor*, denoted by α, is defined as follows:

$$\alpha = \frac{dI_c}{dI_\epsilon}\bigg|_{V_c=\text{const.}} \tag{7.5}$$

The change in collector current produced by a change in emitter current, when the collector voltage is held constant, is the current amplification factor of the transistor.

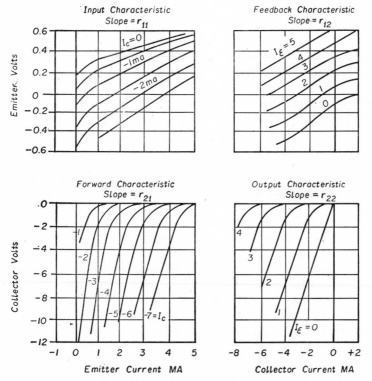

Figure 7.25. Representative characteristics of a point contact transistor. (After J. A. Morton, "The Present Status of Transistor Development," *B.S.T.J.*, May 1952, p. 416, Fig. 4.)

The slopes of the characteristic curves have the dimensions of volts/amperes = ohms. Thus, they are designated as the *slope resistances* and identified as follows:

r_{11} = slope of the input characteristic
    = input resistance

r_{22} = slope of the output characteristic
    = output resistance

r_{12} = slope of the feedback characteristic
    = feedback resistance

r_{21} = slope of the forward characteristic
    = forward resistance

The characteristic curves are not straight lines, so these slope resistances are different when evaluated at different points. Also, like any semiconductor device, transistors and their characteristics are temperature sensitive, highly so in some cases.

The use of slope resistances to represent transistor operation has not been very satisfactory to circuit designers. A number of alternative and interesting proposals have been made. However, no one method was accepted at the time of manuscript preparation. Indeed, at that time the circuit designer counted himself fortunate to have *any* characteristic curves of any type available.

7.17. A junction phototransistor

With some modification, the *n-p-n* junction transistor described in section 7.11 can be used as a phototransistor. When used in this fashion it operates with a hook collector.

The necessary circuit connections required to convert the *n-p-n* transistor to a phototransistor are shown in figure 7.26a. Note that the former base connection *floats* in potential. Moreover, the polarity of the applied voltage has been reversed from that used for the *n-p-n* structure of figure 7.18. The electronic and hole energy diagrams for the phototransistor are shown in figures 7.26b and 7.26c.

When there is no light on the left-hand *p-n* junction, the potential energy hill produced by the *p* region is too high to be surmounted by many electrons. A few do overcome the barrier, drift to the left and constitute the *dark current* of the phototransistor.

Now suppose that light shines on the left-hand *n-p* junction. If the wave length is short enough, the photons produce hole-electron pairs in the boundary region. By virtue of the potential energy hill in the junction region, the electrons and holes are separated with the holes flowing to the right into the *p* region and the electrons flowing to the left into the *n* region. Some of the holes become caught in the *hook*. As more holes accumulate in the hook, they act to reduce the height of the potential energy hill between the two *n* regions and allow more electrons to flow out of the collector. When the light is removed, the diffusion of holes continues and the holes

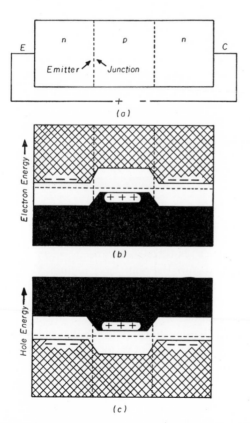

Figure 7.26. *n-p-n* phototransistor: (a) circuit connections; (b) electronic energy level diagram; (c) hole energy level diagram.

gradually disappear as they recombine with free electrons. Finally, the dark current is re-established.

7.18. Point contact phototransistor[20]

The creation of a *p-n* hook as a result of the collector *forming* process has led to the development of a point contact phototransistor. In physical appearance it closely resembles a coaxial transistor as shown in figure 7.27. It consists of a thin, impurity semiconductor wafer, closely fitted into a cartridge that serves as the base electrode. One side of the semiconductor wafer is dimpled and placed in rectifying contact with a collector electrode. There is no emitter. Instead, light is focused on the side of the semiconductor wafer opposite from the collector.

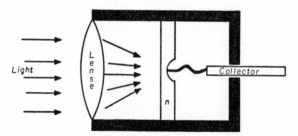

Figure 7.27. Point contact phototransistor.

From the point of view of the incident photons, this device is the same as the junction phototransistor discussed in section 7.17. The light shines on and into the thin base region. Very near the illuminated surface, as a result of the dimple and the forming process, a *p-n* hook exists. The nonreflected photons enter the semiconductor base region and produce hole-electron pairs in the transition region between the *n*-type base assumed, and the floating *p* region produced by forming. Thereafter, the device operates just like the junction phototransistor.

The electric field produced in the semiconductor between the collector electrode and the base is more intense in the region of the *formed* area than it is elsewhere. Thus, hole-electron pairs produced

[20] J. N. Shive, "The Phototransistor," *Bell Lab. Rec.*, Vol. 28, No. 8, Aug. 1950, pp. 337–342.

near the collector are quickly separated before they recombine. However, the lines of force near the periphery of the semiconductor disc are less intense, charge separation is much less rapid, and considerable recombination occurs before transistor action is produced at the collector. Through this effect, the point contact phototransistor has a high spatial resolving power. In other words, it is very sensitive when light falls near the contact area and much less sensitive when the light is displaced away from this position. According to Shive[20] the response is down to $\frac{1}{2}$ its maximum value when the spot of light is displaced ± 0.004 in. from optimum.

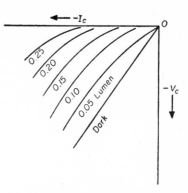

Figure 7.28. Current-voltage characteristics of a phototransistor. (After Ref. 20.)

The current-voltage characteristic of a phototransistor is shown in figure 7.28. Maximum sensitivity with a germanium semiconductor is obtained at a wave length in the infrared part of the spectrum. This is ordinarily quite an advantage over photoelectric emission processes.

PROBLEMS

7.1. Sketch the energy level diagram for a surface-barrier transistor and briefly outline the mechanism of operation.

7.2. Suppose that an area type varistor has two metal electrodes separated by a thin layer of n-germanium. Assume that when 10 volts is applied across the contact in the forward direction, the depletion layer is 10^{-5} cm thick. Assume that the electric field does not fringe and that the entire voltage drop occurs at a uniform rate across the junction. Compute the velocities and transit times of the charged particles traversing the depletion layer. Let $N_e = 10^{16}$ per cc.

7.3. If the measured current through the varistor in problem 7.2 is 40 ma and if 25 per cent of the current arises from hole injection, compute the numbers of electrons and holes crossing the depletion layer each second.

7.4. Draw the energy level diagram for an n-p-i-n transistor and briefly describe its operation.

7.5. Calculate and plot the junction current as a fraction of the thermal current and as a function of the potential difference across a p-n junction.

7.6. The spacing between point electrodes in a point contact transistor is 0.003 in. If the emitter current is 1 ma, compute the transit time of the injected charge carriers. Assume n-type germanium with $N_e = 10^{17}$ per cc.

7.7. Make a sketch of the probable energy relationships at a *non-rectifying* metal-semiconductor junction. Assume the semiconductor is n-type.

7.8. Repeat problem 7.7 for a p-type semiconductor.

7.9. Evaluate the slope resistances of a point contact transistor using the static characteristic curves given in figure 7.25. Assume that operation is to be at the point corresponding to $V_c = -6$ v and $I_c = -2.0$ ma.

VACUUM TUBES

In chapters 5 and 6 it was shown that electrons can be emitted from solids and into the surrounding medium; the emission may be produced thermionically, photoelectrically, or by energetic particle bombardment. When a solid operates as a source of electrons, it is called a *cathode*. If a cathode is enclosed in an evacuated space with one or more other electrodes, the resulting device is called a *vacuum tube*.

There are hundreds of different types of vacuum tubes and there are probably just as many methods of classifying them. The mechanism involved in electronic emission is used here as the first broad distinction between types. Thus, *thermionic* vacuum tubes are those in which electrons are emitted from a hot cathode. *Photoelectric* vacuum tubes require light energy to produce electronic emission. Thermionic tubes are the most widely used and exhibit the greatest diversity of types. For these reasons they receive the greatest emphasis in this chapter.

Thermionic tubes are further classified according to the number of active electrodes in the tube. That is,

(1) diodes = two-electrode tubes
(2) triodes = three-electrode tubes
(3) tetrodes = four-electrode tubes
(4) pentodes = five-electrode tubes

Within each of these groups various subclassifications are made, depending mainly upon the planned use of the tube. In addition, there are a number of special purpose tubes that are not readily classified at all.

The purpose of this chapter is to explain how vacuum tubes work using physical principles covered in previous chapters. The discussion is mainly descriptive, rather than analytical. Readers interested in more detail are referred elsewhere.[1,2] For information on the physical appearance, structure, and electrical characteristics of the many tube types, reference should be made to the handbooks published by the various tube manufacturers.

8.1. Cathode structures and materials

There are two main types of vacuum tubes that are generally sub-divided as follows:
  (1) Thermionic—which are further subdivided as:
    (a) directly-heated
    (b) indirectly-heated
  (2) Photoelectric
Secondary emission also occurs frequently in vacuum tubes, either intentionally or by accident. This problem will be discussed in a later section of this chapter.

The two types of *thermionic* cathodes used in vacuum tubes are sketched in figure 8.1. In the *directly-heated cathode*, a *heater current* is passed through the cathode. The cathode has a filamentary form like the incandescent element in an ordinary electric light bulb. This current produces I^2R heating and raises the filament tempera-

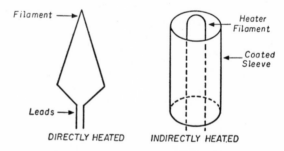

Figure 8.1. Thermionic cathode types.

---

[1] See, for example, Karl Spangenberg, *Vacuum Tubes*, New York: McGraw-Hill Book Co., Inc., 1948.

[2] See, for example, William G. Dow, *Fundamentals of Engineering Electronics*, New York: John Wiley & Sons, Inc., 1937.

ture to a point where electrons are emitted. In the *indirectly-heated cathode* structure, a filamentary *heater* element supplies heat as its principal function, not electrons. The heat it generates is partially absorbed by the surrounding coated sleeve. This coating then becomes hot enough to emit large quantities of electrons.

In any vacuum tube there are always small amounts of residual gas present. The perfect vacuum is never obtained. Moreover, the emitted electrons are usually accelerated away from the cathode by some externally supplied electric field. Because of this acceleration, the electrons may acquire enough kinetic energy to ionize a gas atom if a collision should occur. The massive positive ion so created is then accelerated toward the cathode by the applied electric field. It strikes the cathode with considerable kinetic energy. The impact may be sufficiently strong to cause the cathode material to be sputtered off. If the emitter consists of a thin coating of some material on a base material, the thin coating may be sputtered off and emission thereby lost. For this reason, indirectly-heated, coated cathodes are seldom used in high-power tubes where there is the probability of considerable and energetic positive ion bombardment of the cathode.

High-power tubes are generally constructed with directly-heated tungsten filaments. Because of its large work function, tungsten must be operated at very high temperatures, about 2400°K, to achieve the desired emission current. Thus, large heating currents and large amounts of heating power are required. This is a major shortcoming to the use of tungsten, but it is tolerated because tungsten is strong and can withstand relatively intense positive ion bombardment without sustaining serious damage.

Most small, *low-power* tubes use indirectly-heated, *oxide-coated* cathodes. There are several reasons for this. The amount and intensity of the positive ion bombardment is considerably less than in high-power tubes because the accelerating fields in low-power tubes are not so intense. Thus, a thin oxide film on a base is capable of withstanding the reduced bombardment without serious effects. As a result, low work function, semiconductor oxides can be used and these produce large emission currents even at relatively low temperatures. A comparatively small amount of filament heating power is required. Moreover, the use of an indirectly-heated cathode, wherein the cathode is an equipotential surface, avoids the disadvantages caused by the voltage drop along the length of the directly-heated cathode.

Finally, the higher *thermal inertia* of the large, indirectly-heated cathode reduces *hum effects* when alternating current is used for filament heating.

In a typical low-power tube, the heater is a filamentary tungsten wire electrically insulated from the cathode. The cathode surrounding the heater consists of a nickel sleeve, called the *base* or *core*, and the emitting material is coated on this. The emitting material is quite generally the barium-strontium (BaSr) oxide semiconductor. The cathode temperature is typically of the order of 1000°K.

The directly-heated, *thoriated tungsten* filament has characteristics intermediate between those of the tungsten and the oxide-coated cathodes. As might be expected, it is used mainly in medium-power tubes.

Photoelectric cathodes are usually selected to provide a useful emission at wave lengths near that of visible light. This requires the use of low work function solids such as caesium. Composite materials of various types, and complicated layer-type constructions are in common use. The *caesium-on caesium oxide-on silver* is one example of the layer-type construction used to achieve low work functions.

The photoemission current per square centimeter from a cathode is generally very small compared to thermionic emission current densities. Thus, photoelectric cathodes are designed to have large surface areas to increase the total emission current.

8.2. Space charge limited current

When electrons are emitted from a solid, some have more energy than others. Thus, some will have relatively high velocities and others will have low velocities. On the average, the electron velocity after emission will have a mean value as shown by the distribution curve in figure 8.2. This shows that the electron velocities vary over a wide range, but are generally clustered about a mean value.

If the electrons are emitted into a field-free space, they initially form a cloud in the region of the cathode. This is called the *space charge cloud*. As time goes on, more and more electrons are emitted, the charge density of the cloud increases, and this accumulation of negative charges exerts a repelling force on electrons emerging from the cathode. This repulsion soon becomes strong enough to prevent low-energy electrons from being emitted. In effect, the potential

energy barrier at the surface is increased causing an apparent increase
in the work function. The effect is rather like the Schottky effect in
reverse (see section 5.16).

Some electrons in the emitter acquire enough energy to overcome
the repelling force and enter the space charge cloud. This increases
the charge density and in-
creases the repelling force at
the cathode surface. Eventually equilibrium is reached
when the space charge density is so great that the
repelling force at the cathode
prevents even the highest
energy electron from being
emitted.

If the space around the
cathode is enclosed and if an
attracting field is set up inside
this space, the field acts to
remove some of the electrons
from the space charge cloud.
This decreases the charge

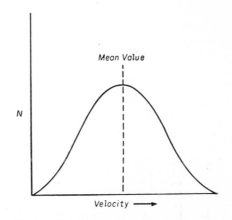

Figure 8.2. Maxwellian distribution of
electronic velocities.

density, reduces the repelling force at the cathode, and allows some
high-energy electrons to be emitted. Thus, a new equilibrium condition is established in which the number of electrons removed from
the cloud is just equal to the number emitted from the cathode.
The current resulting from the motion of the electrons under the influence of this electric field is called the *space charge limited current*.

If the electric field is increased, more electrons are removed from
the space charge cloud, decreasing its repelling effect at the cathode,
and allowing more electrons to be emitted. Thus, the space charge
limited current also increases. It seems clear that the space charge
acts as a reservoir of free electrons that can be attracted by the
applied field. In the process it behaves in a selective manner, allowing
only those electrons with certain energies to be emitted while sup-
pressing the emission of others. Under space charge limited conditions
the cathode is not emitting as many electrons as it would in the
absence of the space charge.

It seems proper to point out that this is merely one viewpoint that serves to describe the behavior of the device. Other models are often used. It is often assumed that the space charge is held at an equilibrium density by two currents:

(1) the emission current into the space charge

(2) the return current from the space charge cloud back to the emitter

The space charge limited current is equal to the difference between these two currents.

Because the *net* emission of electrons from the cathode is less when the current is space charge limited than when there is no space charge, it is clear that it is the space charge and the electric field that control the amount of current. The filament material and temperature have no effect upon the space charge limited current. It can be shown[3] that the equation for the space charge limited current is

$$I_b = KV_b^{3/2} \text{ amps} \tag{8.1}$$

where I_b = space charge limited current, V_b = voltage between the attracting electrode providing the accelerating field and the cathode, K = *perveance* of the tube = constant depending upon the geometry of the electrode configuration. Equation (8.1) is called the *space charge equation*, $3/2$ *power law*, or *Child's Law*.

Departures from this equation are frequent. This is caused by the fact that the assumptions made in deriving the equation are always violated to some extent in practical cases. These assumptions usually include the following:

(1) The electrodes are of infinite extent.

(2) The electrodes are perfectly parallel or perfectly coaxial.

(3) The electric field between electrodes does not fringe.

(4) There is no voltage drop along the cathode.

(5) There is no residual gas in the device.

This device, which includes two electrodes in a vacuum, is called a *thermionic vacuum diode*, if emission is provided by a thermionic cathode.

The general theoretical form of the space charge equation is not affected by the character of the emitter or by the geometry of the electrodes. The 3/2 power law is valid for any geometry; only the

---

[3] See, for example, M.I.T. Staff, *Applied Electronics*, New York: John Wiley & Sons, Inc., 1943, pp. 114–124.

perveance, K, varies. Approximate values for the perveance are given in the following two formulas[4]:

$$K \begin{pmatrix} \text{parallel} \\ \text{plane diode} \end{pmatrix} \doteq (2.331 \times 10^{-6}) \frac{A_c}{S^2} \tag{8.2}$$

where A_c = cathode area, S = distance between cathode and attracting electrode.

$$K \text{ (cylindrical)} \doteq (2.331 \times 10^{-6}) \frac{A_c}{r_c r_a \beta^2} \tag{8.3}$$

where r_c = cathode radius, r_a = radius of attracting electrode, β = constant dependent upon r_a/r_c; assumed unity when this ratio exceeds 10. The numerical factor in front of each equation arises from a term of the form

$$\frac{\sqrt{2}}{9} \sqrt{\frac{e}{m}}$$

where e and m are the charge and mass of an electron.

8.3. Vacuum diode—thermionic and photoelectric

When an emitting electrode, or cathode, is enclosed in an evacuated space with another electrode, the device is called a vacuum *diode*, signifying a two-electrode tube. The added electrode, which serves to establish the electric field to attract electrons away from the cathode, is called the *anode* or *plate*. The addition of the plate makes it possible to establish the electric field to produce current through

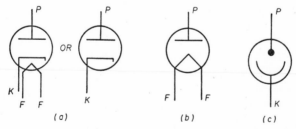

P = Plate; K = Cathode; F = Filament

Figure 8.3. Circuit symbols for various vacuum diodes: (a) thermionic diode, indirectly heated cathode; (b) thermionic diode, directly heated; (c) photoemissive cell.

[4] Dow, *op. cit.*, pp. 101, 107–108.

the tube. Because the plate attracts electrons, it is operated at a positive potential with respect to the cathode.

If a thermionic cathode is used, the tube is called a *thermionic diode*. If a photoelectric cathode is used, the resulting diode is called a *photoemissive cell*. The electrical circuit symbols for these components are shown in figure 8.3.

Suppose that we connect a thermionic diode in series with a voltage source as shown in figure 8.4. A voltmeter V is connected to measure the plate-to-cathode voltage drop V_b and an ammeter A is connected to measure the plate current I_b. The voltage difference applied across the plate and cathode establishes an electric field within the diode, acting to pull electrons from the space charge cloud around the cathode over to the plate.

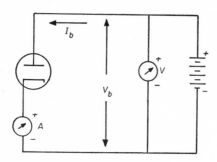

Figure 8.4. Circuit connections for a diode to measure its current-voltage characteristic.

The external current-voltage characteristics of a thermionic diode are easily deduced. For a given cathode temperature and with zero electric field in the space between plate and cathode, some particular equilibrium space charge density is established. Now, as the plate-to-cathode voltage V_b is increased in the positive direction, the current I_b through the tube increases according to the space charge equation. Finally, at some relatively high voltage, electrons are removed from the region about the cathode as rapidly as they are emitted by the cathode. Even those electrons emitted with zero velocity are attracted to the plate. The space charge is thereby destroyed and the current is no longer limited by space charge effects. Instead, the tube now follows Richardson's equation as modified by the Schottky effect. When this occurs the current is said to be *temperature limited* or the diode is said to be drawing *saturation current*. The complete current-voltage characteristic of the tube then appears as shown in figure 8.5.

If the filament temperature is increased from T_1 to T_2 the space charge density for a given plate voltage is greater than before. Thus, the space charge limited current extends over a wider range of plate voltages. Saturation occurs at a higher current, which is anticipated from the Richardson equation. The fact that the transition between the space charge limited and saturation currents is not abrupt, but rounds off into a *knee*, is thought to be caused by geometrical imperfections in the tube.

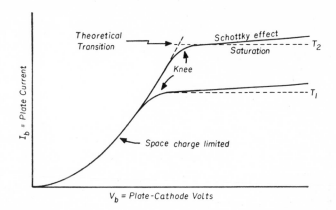

Figure 8.5. Current-voltage characteristics of a thermionic diode.

In the space charge region of operation, the space charge exerts a force opposing the emission of electrons. In the Schottky region the plate exerts a force aiding the emission of electrons. At the theoretical transition point between these two regions, the electric field intensity at the cathode is zero. This is the only instant when the Richardson equation and Child's Law are satisfied. This is so because each equation is derived on the assumption of zero electric field at the cathode. The point of validity for these equations is marked on figure 8.5. This is the operating condition that must be established when the emission constants of the cathode material are measured.

The tube current is not quite zero when the plate voltage is zero. As a matter of fact, the 3/2 power law is invalid over a small range of positive and negative plate voltages. Instead, the plate current appears to be a logarithmic function of the plate voltage. Interested readers are referred elsewhere.[5]

In nearly all cases of practical interest, the saturation and Schottky

[5] Valley and Wallman, *Vacuum Tube Amplifiers*, Rad. Lab. Ser., Vol. 18, New York: McGraw-Hill Book Co., Inc., 1948, pp. 412–418.

region of operation of thermionic diodes is of little value to the circuit engineer. The tubes are nearly always operated over the space charge limited region and published data are generally given just for this part of the characteristic at one specified filament temperature.

Photoemissive cells exhibit current-voltage characteristics that are inherently of the same shape as those of thermionic diodes. The main difference is that the space charge limited region is quite small for a photoemissive cell because of the limited emission. The shape of the curves, shown in figure 8.6, is easily explained. Assuming the

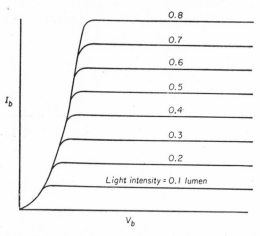

Figure 8.6. Current-voltage characteristics of a photoemissive cell.

cathode to be illuminated by a light of fixed intensity, then in the absence of any plate voltage, the emitted electrons form a space charge cloud. Over a small range of anode voltages the current is space charge limited. Subsequently, the tube saturates and the current increases only slightly through the action of the Schottky effect. If the light intensity is increased, the saturation current increases because there are more incident photons and, correspondingly, more emitted electrons.

While thermionic diodes are always operated on the space charge limited part of the curves, photoemissive cells are always operated in the saturation region. In this way the current through the photo tube is a linear function of the incident light intensity.

There is another important vacuum diode called a *magnetron*. It operates on a fundamentally different principle than the other tubes discussed in this chapter. Treatments both brief[6] and detailed[7] may be found elsewhere.

Before proceeding to other tube types, we must consider one other geometric aspect of the diode. Because the diodes have electrodes of definite area separated by a definite distance by a vacuum, there is a capacitance (see chapter 10) between electrodes. A diode has such a capacitance, C_{pk}, the plate-to-cathode capacitance.

8.4. Energy level diagram of a vacuum diode

Energy levels diagrams were used extensively in preceding chapters to explain the various electronic phenomena of solids. These were diagrams of the energy distribution of the valence electrons in the solids.

A similar technique can be used in the discussion of vacuum tubes except that the diagrams will show the potential energy of an electron in the spaces between the electrodes of vacuum tubes. This proves to be a very useful model for visualizing the operation of many electron tubes.

Consider the hypothetical and idealized case of a thermionic diode with plane and parallel electrodes of infinite extent. Suppose that the

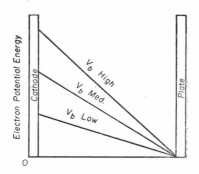

Figure 8.7. Electronic energy level diagram in an unheated thermionic diode, showing the effect of plate voltage variations.

cathode is unheated so that no electrons are emitted. Furthermore, assume that the plate is positive with respect to the cathode. Under these conditions, for a given value of plate-to-cathode voltage, V_b, the potential energy of an electron is given by the curves of figure 8.7 for several different values of V_b.

---

[6] T. L. Martin, Jr., *Ultrahigh Frequency Engineering*, Englewood Cliffs, N. J.: Prentice-Hall, Inc., 1950, chap. 10.

[7] "Magnetron as a Generator of Centimeter Waves," *B.S.T.J.*, Vol. 25, No. 2, April 1946.

Assume a particular value for the plate voltage V_b and then assume that the cathode is heated sufficiently to produce copious emission.

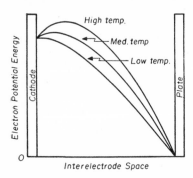

Because electrons are emitted more rapidly than they are collected by the plate, a negative space charge builds up in the interelectrode space in the region near the cathode. This increases the electronic energy level in this region as shown in figure 8.8, just as the trapping of holes in a *p-n* hook causes the electronic energy level of that region to be depressed. Hence, if the cathode temperature is increased, the space charge density will be increased and the height of the potential energy hill will be raised. An electron can move from the cathode surface to the plate only if it has enough kinetic energy to overcome the hill in the energy distribution curve.

Figure 8.8. Electronic energy level diagram for a thermionic diode showing the potential energy hill created by the space charge as affected by cathode temperature variations.

The effect of plate voltage variations with constant cathode temperature is shown in figure 8.9. For low values of V_b, the potential energy hill is quite high and only a few of the emitted electrons have enough kinetic energy to overcome it. Thus, the plate current is low. The height of the hill is decreased as V_b is increased, allowing more electrons to overcome the hill and increase the plate current. Finally, the plate voltage can be made so high that the hill is completely wiped out; this results in the saturation current. Further increases in plate voltage increase the plate current only because of the Schottky effect.

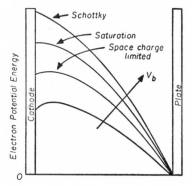

Figure 8.9. Diode energy level diagram showing the effect of plate voltage variations.

In all of these diagrams the plate has been used as the reference

electrode. Thus, in all cases the cathode is negative with respect to
the plate and an increase in plate voltage increases the electronic
potential energy at the cathode.

8.5. Triodes

In 1906, Dr. Lee DeForest inserted a third electrode in a vacuum
tube and made one of the most far-reaching innovations of modern
times. Out of this seemingly simple idea came much that is the
modern electronics industry of today. The third electrode is called
the *control grid* and the resulting three-electrode tube is a *triode*. The
grid takes the form of a small wire mesh structure interposed between the cathode and the plate, generally quite close to the cathode.
Grids are also made in the form of helical windings, parallel wires,
and vertical rods, the type depending upon the function of the grid
and the application of the tube. The electrical circuit symbols for
vacuum triodes are shown in figure 8.10.

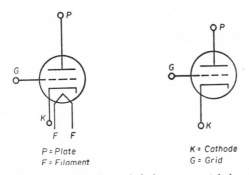

P = Plate
F = Filament

K = Cathode
G = Grid

Figure 8.10. Circuit symbols for vacuum triodes.

In the preceding section it was shown that the space charge in the
vicinity of the cathode acts to regulate the current through the tube.
The space charge achieves this action because of the relatively strong
electric field it produces at the cathode surface opposing the emission
of electrons. Variations in plate voltage cause the space charge
density to change, thus altering the repelling force at the cathode
surface. In turn, this allows more or fewer electrons to be emitted,
thereby varying the space charge limited current through the tube.
Now suppose that a grid is inserted between the plate and cathode.

By establishing a potential difference between the grid and cathode, an electric field is established that can aid or oppose the field produced by the plate voltage. Despite the insertion of the grid, electrons can still travel over to the plate through any of the many openings in the grid.

The grid is much closer to the cathode than is the plate. As a result, the electric field intensity produced by the grid voltage is much larger than that produced by an equal plate voltage.

Now connect a triode to two voltage sources as shown in figure 8.11. The grid, which normally aids the space charge, is made negative with respect to the cathode. A voltmeter V_c is used to measure the grid-to-cathode voltage. Because the grid is negative, theoretically

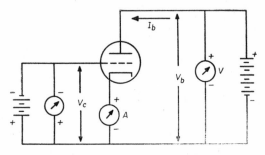

Figure 8.11. Circuit connections to measure the characteristics of a triode.

the grid current is zero. Thus, there is no ammeter in the circuit to record grid current. The plate-cathode connections are the same as those used for the diode. The circuit shown in figure 8.11 is used to determine the current-voltage characteristics of vacuum triodes.

If the grid voltage V_c is set to zero and the current-voltage characteristic of the triode is measured over the space charge limited range, the curve appears as shown in figure 8.12. Now suppose the grid is made a volt or so negative with respect to the cathode. The repelling field that results at the cathode must be overcome by the attracting plate before any plate current is produced. Once this is accomplished, the plate current follows essentially the same variation as before and the new curve is very similar to the first, but displaced sidewards. A whole family of curves can be obtained in this manner and the result appears in figure 8.12. These are called the *static plate characteristics* of the tube. *Static* signifies that the measurements were made with time invariant (d-c) currents and voltages. Because the current and voltage are measured in the plate circuit, the curves are *plate* characteristics.

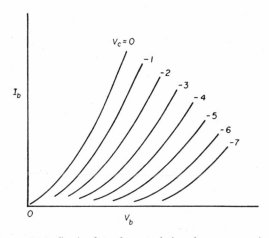

Figure 8.12. Static plate characteristics of a vacuum triode.

From this discussion it is clear that the plate current depends upon both the plate and grid voltages. This dependence can be expressed analytically by the following equation:

$$I_b = K' \left(V_c + \frac{V_b}{\mu} \right)^{3/2} \tag{8.4}$$

where K' = triode perveance, μ = voltage amplification factor; see equation (8.7). Equation (8.4) is the equation for the static plate characteristics of figure 8.12.

An approximate expression for the perveance of a cylindrical triode is given by Kusunose[8] as

$$K' \doteq (2.331 \times 10^{-6}) \frac{A}{r_p r_g \left(\dfrac{\mu + 1}{\mu} \right)^{3/2}} \tag{8.5}$$

where A = area of the plate, r_p = plate radius, r_g = grid radius.

[8] Q. Kusunose, "Calculation of Characteristics and the Design of Triodes," *Proc. I.R.E.*, Vol. 17, Oct. 1929, p. 1709.

It is often convenient to represent triode characteristics in another way. In this case the plate voltage is held constant and the variation in plate current is plotted as a function of the grid voltage. A different curve is obtained for each parametric value of the plate voltage. The resulting family of curves is shown in figure 8.13 and is called the *static transfer* characteristics. The term *transfer* is used because

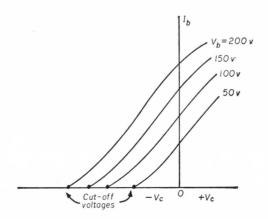

Figure 8.13. Static transfer characteristics of a vacuum triode.

these curves express the relationship between the grid voltage and plate current and thereby relate two quantities in different circuits.

For a given value of plate voltage it is clear from figure 8.13 that there is some value of grid voltage that will make the plate current zero. This is called the *cut-off voltage*.

8.6. Electronic energy levels in a triode

The variation in the electronic potential energy in the interelectrode space of a vacuum triode can be illustrated by the same method as that followed for diodes, simply including the potential variation caused by the grid. In doing this, several possibilities exist because the grid, being a meshlike structure, is not a true equipotential surface. Thus, the potential variation introduced by the grid will depend upon the path taken through the interelectrode space. This difficulty can be avoided by assuming an *average* potential along the plane of the grid; this value is used in the potential energy model.

With the foregoing in mind, triode operation is easily visualized in a rather crude way by drawing the electronic energy level diagram for an idealized triode having parallel, plane electrodes of infinite extent. The result, with fixed plate voltage and variable grid voltage, is shown in figure 8.14. According to this diagram, a negative grid voltage increases the height of the potential energy hill at the cathode and reduces the plate current relative to the zero grid voltage condition. Thus, the grid voltage can be made sufficiently negative that the height of the potential energy hill would be so great that no electrons would be emitted with sufficient energy to surmount it. Plate current would then cease and the *cut-off* condition is attained.

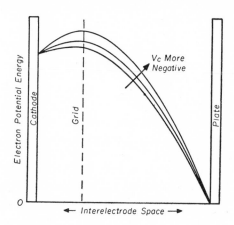

Figure 8.14. Energy levels in a triode, showing the effect of grid voltage variations.

If the grid voltage is fixed at some constant value and the plate voltage is varied, the electronic potential energy diagram appears very nearly the same as that shown for the diode in figure 8.9. Of course, the variation in plate current resulting from changes in plate voltage will be slightly different for different fixed values of the grid voltage because of the alteration in the overall potential energy diagram. This partially accounts for the translation and the change in slope of the triode characteristic curves as the grid is made progressively more negative.

8.7. Triode coefficients

The triode characteristics discussed in the preceding section were obtained under static, or time invariant, test conditions. The behavior of vacuum triodes when small current and voltage variations are involved is usually characterized in terms of three *variational coefficients* specified as follows:

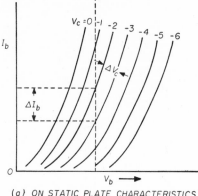

(a) ON STATIC PLATE CHARACTERISTICS

g_m = mutual transconductance in μmhos

r_p = dynamic plate resistance in ohms

μ = voltage amplification factor, dimensionless

The mutual transconductance, g_m, is a measure of the degree of control that the grid voltage exerts on the plate current. Suppose that an incremental change, ΔV_c, is made in the grid voltage while the plate voltage, V_b, is held constant. This causes an incremental change, ΔI_b, in plate current as shown in figure 8.15. The ratio of this incremental change in plate current to the incremental change in grid voltage, as ΔV_c approaches zero, is the *mutual transconductance*, g_m. That is,

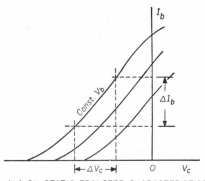

(b) ON STATIC TRANSFER CHARACTERISTICS

Figure 8.15. Evaluation of g_m.

$$g_m = \lim_{\Delta V_c \to 0} \left(\frac{\Delta I_b}{\Delta V_c}\right)_{V_b = \text{const.}} = \left(\frac{dI_b}{dV_c}\right)_{V_b = \text{const.}} \quad (8.6)$$
$$= \frac{\partial I_b}{\partial V_c}$$

The partial derivative symbol used in the last equation indicates that the derivative is taken with V_b assumed constant.

The *voltage amplification factor*, μ, is a measure of the relative effectiveness of the grid and plate voltages in controlling the plate current. Assume that the plate voltage is changed by an incremental amount ΔV_b and that the grid voltage is adjusted by an amount ΔV_c

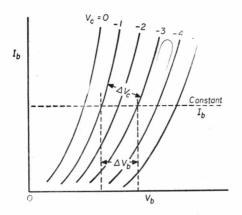

Figure 8.16. Evaluation of μ.

just sufficient to keep the plate current I_b constant. This is illustrated in figure 8.16. The ratio of the change in plate voltage to the change in grid voltage, as the change in grid voltage approaches zero, is the voltage amplification factor μ. That is,

$$\mu = -\lim_{\Delta V_c \to 0} \left(\frac{\Delta V_b}{\Delta V_c}\right)_{I_b = \text{const.}} = -\left(\frac{dV_b}{dV_c}\right)_{I_b = \text{const.}} = -\frac{\partial V_b}{\partial V_c} \quad (8.7)$$

The minus sign is included because a positive increment in plate voltage is offset by a negative increment in grid voltage. The voltage amplification is defined as a positive constant.

The *dynamic plate resistance*, r_p, is the reciprocal of the slope of the static plate characteristics. That is,

$$r_p = \lim_{\Delta I_b \to 0} \left(\frac{\Delta V_b}{\Delta I_b}\right)_{V_c = \text{const.}} = \left(\frac{dV_b}{dI_b}\right)_{V_c = \text{const.}} = \frac{\partial V_b}{\partial I_b} \quad (8.8)$$

The interrelationship between the three variational coefficients is readily established. Because the plate current is a function of both the plate and grid voltages, this fact can be expressed implicitly in the following way:

$$I_b = f(V_b, V_c)$$

The differential of the function is

$$dI_b = \frac{\partial I_b}{\partial V_b} dV_b + \frac{\partial I_b}{\partial V_c} dV_c$$

However, it has been shown that

$$r_p = \frac{\partial V_b}{\partial I_b} \quad \text{and} \quad g_m = \frac{\partial I_b}{\partial V_c}$$

Hence, the differential of the implicit function is

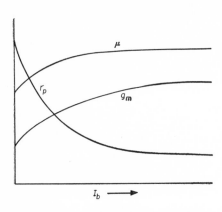

$$dI_b = \frac{dV_b}{r_p} + g_m\, dV_c \quad (8.9)$$

If the plate current is assumed to be constant then $dI_b = 0$ and equation (8.9) reduces to

$$-\frac{dV_b}{dV_c} = g_m r_p$$

or

$$\mu = g_m r_p \quad (8.10)$$

This is the desired result.

Figure 8.17. Effect of plate current on the variational coefficients of a triode.

Because the static plate characteristics of triodes are never straight lines and are never exactly parallel or equally spaced, the three-triode coefficients may vary considerably from their rated and published values. Figure 8.17 indicates how they depend upon plate current.

8.8. Disadvantages of triodes

Purely because of the geometrical arrangement of the three electrodes, a triode possesses interelectrode capacitances (see chapter 10). However, with three electrodes there are three capacitances, as follows:

C_{pk} = plate-to-cathode capacitance

C_{gk} = grid-to-cathode capacitance

C_{gp} = grid-to-plate capacitance

These capacitances are shown schematically in figure 8.18. Of the three, C_{gp} is of the greatest interest at the moment because it acts as a coupling element between the grid and plate circuits. Although it cannot be proven conveniently at this point, the relatively large value of C_{gp} common to most triodes imposes a fundamental limitation upon the operation of such tubes as high frequency amplifiers.

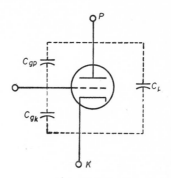

It can also be shown that the size of C_{gp} sets an upper limit upon the voltage amplification factor, μ, of the tube. The reason for this is that a large grid voltage change in a high μ tube will cause a large change in

Figure 8.18. Interelectrode capacities in a triode.

plate voltage. The plate voltage change is coupled back into the grid circuit by C_{gp} and can, under certain conditions, produce an undesirably unstable circuit.

Finally, the plate current in the tube depends upon both the plate

Table 17
CONSTANTS OF VACUUM TRIODES

Tube Type	μ	r_p k-ohms	g_m μmhos	C_{gk} $\mu\mu$f	C_{gp} $\mu\mu$f	C_{pk} $\mu\mu$f	Comments
1LE3	14.5	19	760	1.7	1.7	3.0	Receiving
2C40	36		4,850	2.1	1.3	0.05	Lighthouse
6C4	17	7.7	2,200	1.8	1.6	1.3	Miniature
6J4	55	4.5	12,000	5.5	4.0	0.24	Miniature
6J5	20	7.7	2,600	3.4	3.4	3.6	Receiving
9002	25	12.5	2,000	1.2	1.4	1.1	Midget
2C39	100		17,000	6.5	1.95	.035	Lighthouse
2C43	48		8,000	2.9	1.7	.05	Lighthouse
100TH	40		5,500	2.9	2.0	0.4	Transmitting
811	160		5,500		5.5	5.5	0.6	Transmitting

and grid voltages. The plate voltage change opposes the grid change, effectively reducing the amplification factor of the tube. Hence, it is generally desirable to find some method of isolating the plate so that plate current is nearly independent of the plate voltage. If this can be achieved, very large values of μ can be realized.

These three undesirable characteristics of triodes were successfully corrected by inserting a second grid in the tube. The resulting vacuum tube, which has four electrodes, is called a *tetrode*. It is discussed in the next section.

Representative values of triode capacitances, together with values for μ, r_p, and g_m are given in table 17.

8.9. Tetrodes

A tetrode is a vacuum tube having four electrodes: a cathode, control grid, and plate, with a *screen* or *shield* grid interposed between the plate and control grid. This is illustrated in figure 8.19. This construction splits the grid-to-plate capacitance into two components in series as follows:

$$C_{ps} = \text{plate-to-screen capacitance}$$
$$C_{gs} = \text{grid-to-screen capacitance}$$

In the ideal case, the screen is held at a fixed potential with respect to the cathode by means of a constant voltage supply. Thus, regardless of how much the plate voltage varies, the fact that the screen potential is constant shields the control grid from the plate voltage fluctuations. Of course, perfect isolation can never be achieved, but this seemingly simple insertion of a second grid reduces the grid-to-plate capacitance to a value of the order of 1/500th or less of its original value.

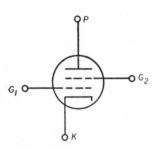

Figure 8.19. Circuit symbol for a tetrode: G_1 = control grid; G_2 = screen grid.

Because the screen effectively shields the space charge from the attracting effect of the plate voltage, the plate current is almost independent of the plate voltage. As a result, it is possible to achieve voltage amplification factors of the order of 1000, a sizable increase over that possible with triodes.

The plate cannot supply the accelerating field for the electrons in the space charge cloud; this function is assumed by the screen. Thus, the screen voltage is kept positive with respect to the cathode. Some of the electrons attracted by the screen hit wires in the screen grid and cause an appreciable screen current to exist. However, most of the electrons pass through openings in the screen grid and go on to the plate. What transpires thereafter depends mainly upon the magnitudes of the plate and screen voltages as explained in later paragraphs.

The circuit connections required to measure the static plate characteristics of a tetrode are shown in figure 8.20. Suppose that the

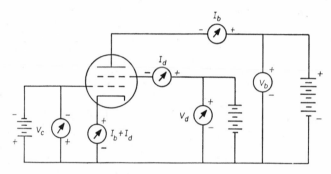

Figure 8.20. Circuit connections to measure the characteristics of a tetrode.

control grid voltage is fixed at some negative value while the screen voltage is held at a positive level. Then assume that the plate voltage is increased from zero and the plate current is plotted as a function of the plate voltage. The results are shown in figure 8.21.

The total cathode current in a tetrode is the sum of the plate and screen currents, and this is virtually constant for fixed values of control grid and screen grid voltages. It does not depend upon the plate voltage. However, the *division* of this total current between plate and screen will obviously depend upon the relative potentials between the two electrodes. A very small plate current will flow even when the plate voltage is zero, because electrons accelerated by the screen that pass through openings in the screen have enough energy to overcome the decelerating field between the screen and plate and appear as plate current.

As the plate current is increased above zero, the total cathode current remains relatively constant, but the plate current increases while the screen current decreases. Moreover, the electrons strike the plate with greater energy now because the magnitude of the decelerating field is reduced.

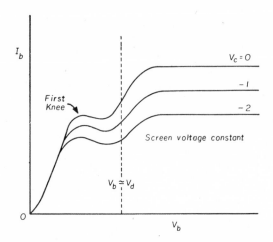

Figure 8.21. Static plate characteristics of a tetrode.

As the plate voltage continues to increase, the electrons eventually strike the plate with sufficient energy to produce secondary emission. The secondary electrons are accelerated toward the screen because of the direction of the electric field between the plate and screen. This secondary emission current subtracts from the primary electron current causing the *net* plate current to decrease. Over a small range, as the plate voltage increases, the primary electrons strike the plate with more energy and produce more secondary electrons, thereby decreasing the total plate current even more. This process continues until the plate voltage approaches and exceeds the screen voltage. When this occurs, the direction of the electric field between the plate and screen reverses and the secondary electrons are attracted back toward the plate. The plate current increases and eventually, for large values of plate voltage, becomes nearly independent of the plate voltage.

The obvious nonlinearity in the tetrode characteristics, apparent in figure 8.21, places a severe limitation upon the useful range of operation. As a result, tetrodes have been largely replaced by *pentodes* and *beam power tubes*, which are discussed in the next two sections.

8.10. Pentodes

The difficulties caused by secondary emission from the plate of a tetrode are largely overcome by the addition of a third grid to the tube as shown in figure 8.22. This new electrode is located between the plate and screen grid. Because the purpose of this new grid is to suppress secondary emission effects, it is called the *suppressor grid*. The resulting tube has five electrodes and is called a *pentode*.

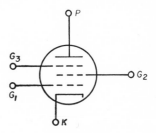

Figure 8.22. Circuit symbol for a pentode: G_1 = control grid; G_2 = screen grid; G_3 = suppressor grid.

Suppression of secondary emission effects is normally achieved by connecting the suppressor to the cathode. This makes the screen-cathode and screen-suppressor voltages equal. As a result, electrons accelerated from the cathode by the screen are decelerated by a corresponding amount after passing through the screen. Electrons arrive at the suppressor with nearly zero velocity. They are then under the attracting influence of the plate and are again accelerated. When they strike the plate, secondary emission may occur, but the secondary electrons are attracted back to the plate and do not subtract from the plate current. The resulting static plate characteristics of a pentode then appear as shown in figure 8.23. It is clear that the double knee and dip appearing in the tetrode characteristics have been eliminated.

The shielding of the control grid from the plate is improved by the insertion of the suppressor grid. The grid-to-plate capacitance is reduced to about one half that of a corresponding tetrode, while the voltage amplification factor, μ, is nearly doubled. Some of the constants of representative pentodes are summarized in table 18.

The rounding of the *knee* of the pentode characteristic is undesirable because it acts to limit the maximum range of linear operation of the tube. The rounding is caused[9] mainly by the dispersion of the electrons around the suppressor grid wires.

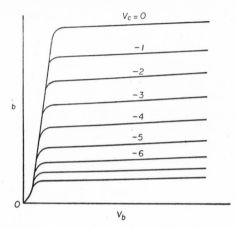

Figure 8.23. Static plate characteristics of a pentode.

Because the screen is located directly in the electron stream and is positive, a relatively large screen current exists. This reduces the plate current and is an unwanted power loss.

Both of the foregoing disadvantages are largely eliminated in the *beam power tube* discussed in section 8.12.

Table 18
CONSTANTS OF VACUUM PENTODES

Tube Type	g_m μmhos	r_p k-ohms	C_i $\mu\mu$f	C_{gp} $\mu\mu$f	C_0 $\mu\mu$f	Comments
1T4	750	800	3.6	0.01	7.5	Remote CO; min.
1L4	1025	350	3.6	0.008	7.5	Sharp CO; min.
6AB7	5000	700	8.0	0.015	5.0	Remote CO
6AC7	9000	750	11.0	0.015	5.0	Sharp CO
6AG7	7700	100	12.5	0.06	7.5	Sharp CO
6AK5	4300	420	4.0	0.02	2.8	Sharp CO
6SK7	2000	800	6.0	0.003	7.0	Remote CO
2E24	3200		8.5	0.11	6.5	Beam pentode
4E27	2800		12.0	0.06	6.5	Beam pentode

[9] O. H. Schade, "Beam Power Tubes," *Proc. I.R.E.*, Vol. 26, 1936, pp. 137–181.

8.11. Pentode energy level diagram

Pentode operation can be visualized in a general way through the use of the usual electronic energy level diagram. A typical case is shown in figure 8.24 in which all electrode potentials are adjusted for conventional operation.

An electron emitted with sufficient energy to overcome the small potential energy hill, caused by the space charge and control grid,

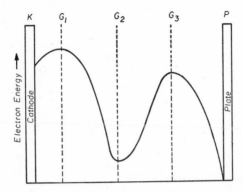

Figure 8.24. Electronic energy level diagram in a pentode under normal operating conditions.

is attracted by the screen and falls down the other side of the hill. The kinetic energy acquired by the electron in the process is sufficient to permit it to overcome the energy hill introduced by the suppressor. It then falls to the plate. Secondary electrons emitted from the plate are not emitted with sufficient energy to overcome the potential energy hill between the plate and suppressor, so they fall back to the plate.

8.12. Beam power tubes[10]

The distinguishing structural characteristics of beam power tubes are shown in figure 8.25. The screen and control grids are spirally wound and accurately aligned so that the screen wires are shaded by the control grid wires. This causes the electrons to travel from

---

[10] *Ibid.*

cathode to plate in layers, passing through and between screen grid wires. The screen current is very low because few electrons strike screen grid wires. Thus, one disadvantage of the pentode is overcome.

Beam power tubes can be made as pentodes or tetrodes. In the tetrode construction there is no suppressor grid. However, the same effect is achieved by the high density space charge in the screen-plate region. The charge density is so great that the repelling force it

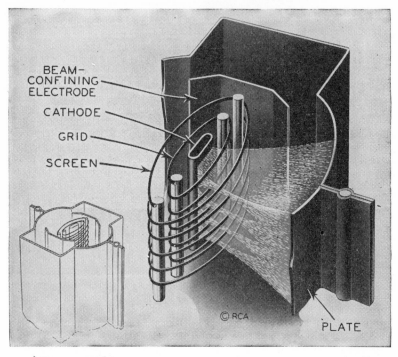

BEAM—
CONFINING
ELECTRODE

CATHODE

GRID

SCREEN

© RCA

PLATE

Figure 8.25. Beam power tube construction. (Courtesy R.C.A.)

exerts at the surface of the plate is large enough to cause secondary electrons to return to the plate. Thus, the electron beam replaces the suppressor grid. In this tetrode construction, *beam-forming* plates are used as shown in figure 8.25. These plates are at cathode potential and assist in producing the electron beam. They also prevent secondary electrons from leaving the plate and going to the screen over a path outside the beam.

In beam pentodes, an actual suppressor grid is used instead of relying upon the electron beam.

Typical characteristic curves for a beam power tube are shown in figure 8.26. The *knee* is less rounded than for a pentode and the

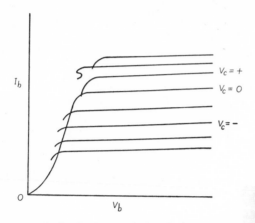

Figure 8.26. Static characteristics of a beam power tube.

linear range of operation is extended. The double-valued nature of the plate current in the region of the *knee* has been analyzed elsewhere.[11]

8.13. Other thermionic vacuum tubes

Space limitations on electronic equipment and the desire for special tubes designed for optimum performance in particular applications have led to the development of many special purpose tubes. Multi-unit tubes typify this trend. In these types two or more separate tubes are combined into a single envelope. Several of the many possibilities include

(1) dual diode = two diodes
(2) twin triode = two triodes
(3) duplex-diode triode = two diodes + one triode
(4) duplex-diode pentode = two diodes + one pentode

[11] B. Salzberg, A. V. Haeff, "Effects of Space Charge in the Grid-Anode Region of Vacuum Tubes," *RCA Rev.*, Vol. 2, 1938, pp. 336–374.

The characteristics of the individual tube elements are essentially the same as if the tubes were isolated in separate envelopes.

Another unique case involving special construction is the *variable mu* or *remote cut-off* tube. Such tubes may be triodes or pentodes in which the control grids are spirally wound with nonuniform spacing between turns. This results in the remote cut-off characteristic shown in figure 8.27. The conventional *sharp* cut-off characteristic is shown on the same figure for comparative purposes. Because of the curvature in the transfer characteristic of the remote cut-off tube, the μ and g_m can be varied over a wide range of values by changing the grid voltage.

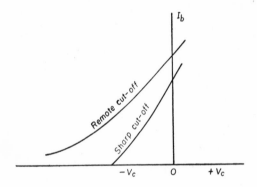

Figure 8.27. Static transfer characteristics of remote and sharp cut-off tubes.

There are many other special purpose tubes of unusual construction. *Mixers* and *converters* have as many as five grids. *Electron-ray tubes* combine a triode and fluorescent target inside a single envelope. There are, in addition, many special-purpose tubes such as the *resnatron*, *graphecon*, *phasitron*, *image orthicon*, *klystron*, and *photomultiplier* that cannot be discussed here because of space limitations.

8.14. Mechanical factors affecting tube reproducibility

Most engineers have had the experience of designing and building a laboratory model of some particular equipment that functions very well after careful adjustments on the bench. However, if ten copies are made, it might turn out that only a fraction of the equipment would operate as well as the original. The tubes are promptly blamed for this difficulty. The accusation may be well founded because there are considerable variations in electrical characteristics from tube to tube.

Instead of simply blaming the tube manufacturer, it is better to understand some of his problems. They are not simple. For example, in a high transconductance pentode the variation in the electrical characteristics of the tube is largely determined by three factors:

(1) cathode-to-control grid space
(2) diameter of the grid wires
(3) winding pitch of the control grid wires

For a tube such as the type 5654 pentode, the nominal cathode-to-control grid spacing is only 0.00325 ± 0.00075 in. This is a very difficult tolerance to hold when the electrodes are spaced so closely together. If the spacing varies over this entire range about the nominal center value, the transconductance of the tube will vary from 4600 to 5800 μmhos. This gives some indication of the very difficult manufacturing problems involved if the tube characteristics must be held within small limits and the tubes are to be produced without excessive rejections.

The control grid of the type 5654 pentode is an ellipsoidal, helical winding of 0.001-in. diameter, gold plated, tungsten wire wound 206 turns to the inch. A slight distortion in one turn may affect the cut-off characteristics of the tube without noticeably changing the mutual transconductance.

The screen grid of the type 5654 pentode is wound 160 turns to the inch using the same kind of wire as that used for the control grid. It is wound in the opposite sense to the control grid to minimize *shadowing* effects. This shadowing, plus the fact that the screen is closer to the cathode than to the plate, cause the tube-to-tube variation in screen current to be larger than the plate current variation.

Within reasonable tolerances, the plate and suppressor spacings are relatively unimportant in their effects upon the characteristics of the tube.

Mica is generally used in receiving-type tubes for mechanical support and electrode spacing. Hence, these parts must be manufactured to very close tolerances. For example, the holes in the mica spacers for the control and screen grid side rod supports are held to ±0.00025 in. The same tolerance is applied to the hole in the mica cathode support.

The fit of the cathode into its support is very important. If it fits too loosely, the cathode vibrates excessively and causes a time variation in tube perveance leading to *microphonics*. If it fits too tightly, the ends of the cathode are cooled excessively, reducing emission and plate current. It might also cause excessive bowing and mechanical strain.

All in all, it is clear that the tube designer and manufacturer have many difficult problems in purely mechanical aspects of producing tubes in quantity with consistent electrical characteristics and without an excessive rejection rate.

From this very brief discussion it should be abundantly clear that mechanical problems in electronic equipment are very important. The study of electrical engineering is obviously more than a study of electrical phenomena and should include the elements of mechanics, thermodynamics, and strength of materials, to name only a few relating just to vacuum tube design. There is no clear line of demarcation between the activities of electrical, mechanical, metallurgical, chemical, or other types of engineers.

8.15. Other factors affecting tube reproducibility

Most receiving-type tubes use indirectly-heated, oxide-coated cathodes. They are prepared by spraying a mixture of barium and strontium carbonates plus a nitrocellulose binder on a nickel sleeve. While the tube is being evacuated, voltages are applied to the tube and the carbonates are reduced to oxides. Ideally, the cathode is then brought up to peak emission by an aging process involving special thermal treatment.

The foregoing is an overly brief account of a long chain of delicate processes. Impurities in any of the cathode materials can be introduced at many points and they have a marked effect upon the emission characteristics. Inconsistencies in the heater winding, cathode emitting surface, and the fit of the cathode support all affect the cathode temperature, which, in turn, can affect various electrical characteristics of the tube.

Tube components such as grids, plates, sleeves, mica supports, and so on, are generally manufactured nearly automatically and their tolerances can be held rather accurately. Assembly of these parts into complete tubes is often done by humans, rather than machines, each worker being subject to human error and frailty. They may distort the electrode alignment, bend a turn in a grid wire, contaminate a cathode, or rub emitting material onto a grid. Though many such defective units are rejected by inspectors, the inspectors are also human and capable of error.

Altogether, it is estimated that over 800 separate manufacturing steps are required in the production of a modern vacuum tube. It is not surprising that random variations in these 800 steps cause variations in the characteristics of tubes.

8.16. Cathode ray tubes

A schematic view of a *cathode ray tube*, abbreviated CRT, is shown in figure 8.28. The tube consists of three main parts:

(1) electron gun
(2) deflecting system
(3) phosphorescent screen

The *electron gun* contains a thermionic cathode to supply electrons, a control grid, and a focusing anode. These three elements operate together in much the same manner as a conventional triode. However, the focusing anode has a small hole in it so that only those electrons making a small angle with the axis of the tube go through

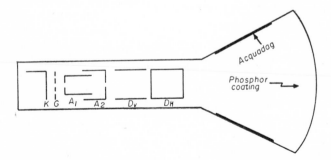

Figure 8.28. Cathode ray tube (CRT): K = cathode; G = intensity grid; A_1 = focusing anode; A_2 = accelerating anode; D_v = vertical deflecting plates; D_H = horizontal deflecting plates.

the hole. The remainder are collected by the focusing anode. Thus, the electrons emerge from the hole in the anode in a narrow, pencil-like beam. This electron beam constitutes the *cathode rays*. The beam is further focused by electrostatic lenses or by an axial magnetic field. It is then acted upon by the second anode, A_2, which accelerates the electrons to high energy levels.

When the intense beam of electrons strikes the phosphor coated screen, three important things occur, as follows:

(1) Some of the phosphor atoms are excited by the electronic impacts. When they regain their unexcited state they release photons of visible light. Thus, the point of impact of the electron beam appears as a spot of light.

(2) Secondary emission from the phosphor screen occurs. The secondary electrons travel over to the *acquadag* coating on the walls of the tube and are removed. On the average, the number of secondary electrons is equal to, or slightly greater than, the number of primary electrons. As a result, the phosphor remains electrically neutral or acquires a slightly positive charge.

(3) Some of the energy of the incident electron beam appears as heat. Thus, prolonged exposure of one part of the screen to the electron beam will cause a burned spot to appear.

The intensity of the light emitted by the phosphor-coated screen is controlled by the number of atoms excited each second. This can be varied by varying the density of electrons in the electron beam. This is readily accomplished by varying the voltage on the control grid in the electron gun.

The spot of light can be made to occupy any point on the face of the screen by properly deflecting the electron beam away from its normally axial position. There are two methods of achieving this deflection, as follows:

(1) *Electrostatic deflection*—The electron beam is passed between two pairs of parallel plates as shown in figure 8.28. One pair controls the sidewise motion and the other the vertical motion of the beam. An electric field is established between each pair of plates and it can be shown[12] that the deflection of the screen is approximately a linear function of the voltage between the plates.

---

[12] See for example, J. D. Ryder, *Electronic Engineering Principles*, Englewood Cliffs, N. J.: Prentice-Hall, Inc., 1947, chap. 3.

(2) *Magnetic deflection*—Two pairs of coils are used to produce magnetic fields at right angles to one another and perpendicular to the electron beam. It is easily shown[12] that the deflection of the electron beam is nearly a linear function of the current in the deflecting coils.

PROBLEMS

8.1. Equation (8.1) is an expression for the space charge limited current in a diode. Using the static characteristics of a 6AL5 diode, complete a table of values for I_b vs. V_b. Take at least eight values for each.

8.2. From the data tabulated above, plot I_b vs. V_b on log-log graph paper. Determine the exponent in the space charge equation and the value of the perveance from this graph.

8.3. Calculate the perveance of a parallel plane diode if the electrodes are 1 cm apart and the cathode is a rectangle measuring 1 cm by 0.1 cm.

8.4. Compute the perveance of a cylindrical diode having a cathode 2 cm long, 1 mm in diameter, and a plate 2 cm in diameter.

8.5. Recompute problem 8.4 using a plate 1 cm in diameter.

8.6. A cylindrical diode is to be designed to provide a plate current of 10 ma when the plate voltage is 100 volts. Compute the plate radius. What is the largest cathode radius possible with your design?

8.7. Figure 8.4 shows the electrical circuit used to measure the diode characteristics. Does the voltmeter actually read the desired voltage? If not, how much error is involved?

8.8. At the beginning of section 8.2 it is stated that some electrons are thermionically emitted from a solid with more energy than other electrons. Explain why this is so.

8.9. Figure 8.11 shows the circuit used to measure the static plate characteristics of a triode. What instrument readings will be in error here and what is the extent of the error? Assume the voltmeter resistances to be 100,000 ohms and the ammeter resistance to be 0.1 ohm. The plate current is 10 ma, the plate voltage is 100 volts, and the grid voltage is −10 volts.

8.10. Suppose the ammeter in figure 8.11 is replaced by a short circuit. Then the ammeter is placed directly in series with the source of plate potential. What instrument errors are involved now and how important are they? Use the numerical values given in problem 8.9.

8.11. The equation for the plate current through a triode is given in equation (8.4). Using the method given in problems 8.1 and 8.2 for a diode, calculate the perveance of a 6J5 triode. Use the static plate characteristic curves supplied by the manufacturer.

8.12. Using the static plate characteristics, construct the static transfer characteristics of a 6J5 triode, corresponding to values of plate voltage of 120, 160, and 200 volts.

8.13. From the static characteristics of a 6J5 triode, evaluate μ, r_p, and g_m when the tube is operated in the region near $I_b = 10$ ma and $V_b = 200$ volts. How do these values compare with those published by the tube manufacturer?

8.14. Repeat problem 8.12 for a 6SK7 pentode and comment upon the results relative to those obtained for the 6J5 triode.

8.15. Repeat problem 8.13 for a 6SK7 pentode.

8.16. Construct an approximate energy level diagram for a tetrode with all potentials except the plate voltage fixed. Show three different cases for the plate voltage:

(1) zero plate voltage

(2) plate voltage equal to screen voltage

(3) plate voltage larger than the screen voltage

Discuss these curves and relate them to the static characteristics of a tetrode.

8.17. Figure 8.29 shows the deflecting system of an electrostatically deflected CRT. It is assumed that the electric field between the deflecting plates does not fringe. Assume that the electrons enter the field of the deflecting plates with a velocity v. Derive the equation

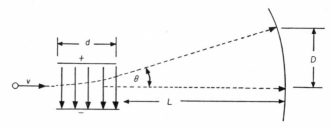

Figure 8.29. D = deflection; V_d = deflection voltage; S = distance between plates; L = drift space; d = length of plates; v = electron velocity.

for the deflection of the electron beam from the center of the CRT screen. You may assume that the angle θ is so small that $\sin \theta = \theta$.

8.18. The electron achieves its velocity in problem 8.17 by an accelerating field that gives it a particular kinetic energy. Suppose the electron falls through a difference in potential of 1500 volts; what is its velocity?

8.19. Suppose the electron in problem 8.18 passes through a deflecting system like that shown in figure 8.29. What will happen to the deflection if the accelerating voltage is doubled to 3000 volts? What will happen if the deflection voltage is doubled?

9

GASEOUS CONDUCTION AND GAS TUBES

A *gas tube* is an electronic device consisting of two or more electrodes enclosed in a container with a gas. The gas is usually at a low pressure. The literature covering gas tubes and the fundamental processes involved in the conduction of electricity through gases is vast and absorbing. It is not a simple subject and it cannot be covered in very much detail here. There are a number of excellent books on conduction in gases[1-3] and the reader interested in further details of this field should refer to them.

As far as this book is concerned, the main interest involves the terminal characteristics of gas tubes rather than the various structural forms that have evolved. Thus, this chapter presents a brief discussion of electrical conduction through gases. The various main tube types are then listed and classified according to the gas discharge essential to the operation of the tube. The current-voltage characteristics of the main tube types are then described. Readers interested in structural details of these tubes should refer to the handbooks and application aids published by the tube manufacturers.

[1] F. A. Maxfield, R. R. Benedict, *Theory of Gaseous Conduction and Electronics*, New York: McGraw-Hill Book Co., Inc., 1941.

[2] L. B. Loeb, *Fundamental Processes of Electrical Discharges in Gases*, New York: John Wiley & Sons, Inc., 1939.

[3] J. D. Cobine, *Gaseous Conductors*, New York: McGraw-Hill Book Co., Inc., 1941.

9.1. Excitation and ionization

From the comments in chapter 3 it will be recalled that the electrons in an atom are normally in the lowest possible energy levels. This is another way of saying that the electrons are in the closest permissible orbits to the nucleus. It is possible to give extra energy to some of the electrons so that they take up positions in specified outer orbits, which correspond to higher energy levels. When the dynamic array of electrons in the atom is altered in this way, the atom is said to be *excited*. A discrete amount of energy is necessary to excite an atom because there are discrete energy differences between permitted energy levels.

An atom will remain in an excited state for only a small fraction of a microsecond (1×10^{-6} second). Under certain conditions the excited electron then reverts back to a lower energy level and the excess energy is emitted as a photon of light. If it reverts back to its original energy level before excitation, the photon energy will be exactly equal to the energy absorbed when the electron was initially excited.

An atom may also be excited into a *metastable state*. In this condition an electron is excited to a higher than normal energy level, but according to selection rules based upon quantum theory, it cannot revert back to a lower level by emitting a photon. As a result, one of two things might occur:

(1) The atom might collide with another particle, give up the required amount of energy and return to the normal state.

(2) The metastable atom might absorb the proper amount of energy by collision with other particles or from radiation. This might raise the electron to a higher energy level from which it can return to the normal state by emitting a photon.

If sufficient energy is given one of the outermost orbital electrons in an atom, the electron may be sufficiently energetic to completely escape from the attraction of the nucleus. The atom is then said to be *ionized*. This is the simple, or ordinary ionization process. When a positive ion and an electron recombine to form a neutral atom, the excess energy of the electron is released as a photon of light.

Ionization also results from some two-step processes. Atoms are first excited into metastable states and are subsequently ionized.

The energy necessary to produce excitation or ionization of a gas atom or molecule may be supplied in several ways. However, in most commercial gas tubes, high speed electrons serve as the ionizing agent. This action is obtained only under certain special conditions and some of the influencing factors are discussed in this chapter.

9.2. Mean free path

Consider the case of an electron in a pure molecular or atomic gas. Suppose that a fairly weak electric field is produced in the gas. The electron is forced to move in response to this field. However, it soon bumps into one of the thermally agitated molecules or atoms of the gas and rebounds as shown in figure 9.1. The process continues as the

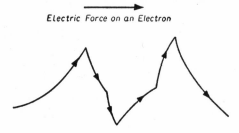

Electric Force on an Electron

Figure 9.1. Electron path in a gas.

electron drifts through the gas. Over a total distance of travel, L, let n_c denote the number of collisions. The *mean free path* (MFP) of the electron in this gas is defined as the average distance between collisions. This is clearly,

$$\lambda_e = \text{MFP of electron} = \frac{L}{n_c} \tag{9.1}$$

The number of collisions occurring over the distance L can be shown[4] to be

$$n_c = \frac{\pi d^2}{4} Ln \tag{9.2}$$

where d = diameter of the molecules or atoms, n = number of gas atoms or molecules per meter^3. Hence, the mean free path of electrons in pure gases is

---

[4] Maxfield and Benedict, *op. cit.*, p. 110–111.

$$\lambda_e = \frac{4}{\pi d^2 n} \tag{9.3}$$

It can also be shown that the mean free path of a molecule of the gas moving in the gas is

$$\lambda_m = \text{MFP molecule} = \frac{\lambda_e}{4\sqrt{2}} \tag{9.4}$$

It is important to know how the mean free path depends upon pressure and temperature. According to a well known[5] relationship,

$$P = nkT \tag{9.5}$$

where P = gas pressure in newtons/meter^2, k = Boltzmann's constant, T = temperature in °K, n = number of molecules or atoms per meter^3. Substitute this relationship into the equation for the mean free path of an electron. The result is

$$\lambda_e = \frac{4kT}{\pi d^2 P} \tag{9.6}$$

From this you can see that the mean free path increases as the temperature increases and the pressure decreases.

The mean free path of the gas molecule or atom, λ_m, is generally measured at standard conditions of temperature and pressure. Once λ_m is known, the electronic mean free path can be calculated from equation (9.4). Then equation (9.6) can be used to convert the value to any desired combination of temperature and pressure.

Let λ_1 denote the mean free path at a pressure P_1 and temperature T_1. That is,

$$\lambda_1 = \frac{kT_1}{\sqrt{2}\pi d^2 P_1} \tag{9.7}$$

At any other temperature T_2 and pressure P_2 we have

$$\lambda_2 = \frac{kT_2}{\sqrt{2}\pi d^2 P_2} \tag{9.8}$$

Take the ratio of the last two equations and solve for the unknown mean free path λ_2. That is,

$$\lambda_2 = \lambda_1 \frac{P_1}{P_2} \frac{T_2}{T_1} \tag{9.9}$$

Thus, if the mean free path λ_1 is known at T_1 and P_1, it can be cal-

[5] *Ibid:* p. 89.

culated at any other temperature and pressure. Representative values for the mean free path λ_m are given in table 19.

The general concept of mean free path and a knowledge of the factors influencing it are necessary to understand the properties of gas tubes.

Table 19

MEAN FREE PATHS OF GAS ATOMS OR MOLECULES

(At 0°C and 1 Standard Atmosphere)

Gas	MFP in meters
H_2	11.16×10^{-8}
He	17.65×10^{-8}
Ne	12.53×10^{-8}
N_2	5.96×10^{-8}
Hg	8.32×10^{-8}
Xe	3.58×10^{-8}

1 standard atmosphere = 1.01325×10^5 newtons/meter²

9.3. Collisions and their consequences

Consider the case of electrons moving through a pure gas as a result of an applied electric field. Both the electrons and the gas atoms or molecules will have kinetic energy. The kinetic energy of the electrons is the sum of the energies received from thermal and electrical sources. The kinetic energy of the gas atoms is thermal in origin. Let

W_k (gas) = average kinetic energy of the gas atoms

W_k (electron) = average electronic kinetic energy

The total energy of the two particles before collision is

W_T (before collision) = W_k (gas) + W_k (electron)

If the total kinetic energy of the two particles is the same after collision as before collision, it is called an *elastic* collision. That is, for an *elastic* collision,

W_T (before collision) = W_T (after collision)

Even though the total energy of the system is conserved and remains constant, the kinetic energy of each particle involved in the collision will change. Because the electron mass m is very much less than the mass M of the gas atom or molecule, the electron gives up a small fraction of its kinetic energy to the gas atom. This fraction is approximately

$$\text{fraction of } K.E. \qquad f \doteq 2.66 \frac{m}{M} \frac{\text{electron mass}}{\text{gas atom mass}} \qquad (9.10)$$

This is a very small number.

Now suppose that the electric field intensity is increased so that the kinetic energy of the electron is increased. Eventually this energy will become equal to or greater than the excitation or ionization energy of the gas atom or molecule. In some collisions it may transpire that a whole quanta of energy will be transferred from the electron to the atom, increasing its internal energy and producing excitation or ionization. In such a case the kinetic energy of the electron is reduced by the amount of the absorbed quanta of energy. The total kinetic energy of the system is not conserved and the collision is said to be *inelastic*. In this case,

$$W_T \text{ (before collision) } \neq W_T \text{ (after collision)}$$

However, we can write an equality as follows:

$$W_T \text{ (before collision) } = W_T \text{ (after collision) } + W_e \qquad (9.11)$$

where W_e = excitation or ionization energy.

It develops that not every electron having a kinetic energy equal to or greater than an excitation or ionization energy produces an inelastic collision. Not more than two or three out of every thousand collisions are actually inelastic when the electron energy exceeds the excitation or ionization energy.

The *probability* of an inelastic collision is practically zero when the electron kinetic energy exactly equals the ionizing or exciting energy. This probability increases almost linearly with the electronic kinetic energy reaching a maximum when it is approximately equal to twice the ionization or excitation energy. Thereafter, the probability of collision decreases as the electronic kinetic energy increases.

Under certain conditions it is clear that ionizing collisions can be produced and this results in the generation of positive gas ions. These ions are also accelerated by the electric field and collide with gas atoms. However, because the mass of the gas ion and atom are essentially the same, the ion loses about half its kinetic energy in an *elastic* collision. Thus, the ion energy is always quite small because at every collision it gives up half the energy acquired from the electric field between collisions. As a result, the positive ions seldom acquire enough energy to produce inelastic collisions and their effect in this connection is generally neglected.

9.4. Gas discharges

The inevitable presence of cosmic rays and minute traces of radio-active material causes all gases, including the air around us, to contain ions and electrons. The electrons may exist in the free state only momentarily before forming a negative ion, but whether or not this occurs depends partially upon the nature of the gas. In the case of the inert gases such as helium, argon, krypton, neon, and xenon, the electrons remain free and do not form negative ions. This is one of the reasons for using inert gases in commercial gas tubes.

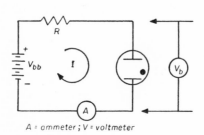

A = ommeter ; V = voltmeter

Figure 9.2. Circuit to determine the current-voltage characteristics of a cold cathode gas tube.

Suppose that an inert gas is included in the cold cathode gas tube shown in figure 9.2. As the voltage across the tube is initially increased above zero, the free ions and electrons are attracted to opposite electrodes and a very small current is produced in the tube. As long as the ions and electrons are produced in the gas by cosmic rays or other agencies more rapidly than they are removed by the electric field in the tube, the electric current increases linearly as a function of the applied voltage. This corresponds to region O-A in figure 9.3. A point is soon reached, however, where the electrons and ions are removed as rapidly as they are formed. The current can no longer increase, the tube is *saturated*, and the region A-B in figure 9.3 is obtained.

As the voltage difference across the tube is increased beyond the point B in figure 9.3, some ionization is produced by collision of electrons with gas atoms. This causes the anode current to increase along an approximately exponential curve as the anode voltage in-.

creases. This is called the region of the *Townsend discharge*.[6,7] If the source of electrons is removed, the current through the tube dies out because there are no electrons available to produce current or ionization. Hence, a Townsend discharge does not maintain itself.

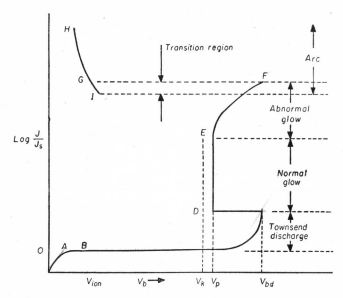

Figure 9.3. Current-voltage characteristic of a gaseous discharge:[8] V_{bd} = breakdown voltage; V_k = cathode drop; $V_p - V_k$ = plasma drop; J = anode current density; J_s = saturation current density.

When the voltage across the tube exceeds V_{bd}, the *breakdown potential*, current is maintained through the tube even if the original ionizing agency is removed. This is a self-sustaining *glow discharge*. It occurs when the voltage across the tube is many times larger than the ionization potential of the gas.

This is called a *glow discharge* because of a softly luminous glow

[6] Townsend and Tizard, *Proc. Roy. Soc.*, Vol. A87, 1912, p. 357; Vol. A38, 1913, p. 336.

[7] J. S. Townsend, *Nature*, Vol. 62, 1900, p. 340; *Phil. Mag.*, Vol. 1, 1901, p. 198; *Phil. Mag.*, Vol. 3, 1902, p. 557; Vol. 6, 1903, pp. 389, 598; Vol. 8, 1904, p. 738.

[8] After M.I.T. Staff, *Applied Electronics*, New York: John Wiley & Sons, Inc., 1943, p. 148, Fig. 13.

that appears at the cathode surface. The current density in this cathode glow tends to remain constant; added current requirements are met by the glow spreading until it eventually covers the whole cathode. This situation obtains at point E in figure 9.3. The region from D to E on this curve is called the region of *normal glow*.

As the supply voltage, V_{bb}, is increased further beyond the point E, the current density in the cathode glow increases. The tube current increases, but not as rapidly as the supply voltage. Thus, an increase in V_{bb} is not offset by an equal drop across R and the voltage across the tube rises. This is the *abnormal glow* region, E-F, shown on figure 9.3.

As point F on the curve of figure 9.3 is approached, the cathode glow begins to concentrate into a *cathode spot*. Suddenly, at point F, the tube breaks down into a sustained *arc discharge*. The discharge takes place between the cathode spot and the anode. This corresponds to the region I-H on figure 9.3. The voltage drop across the tube is of the order of the ionization potential of the gas; typical values of ionization potential are given in table 20. In many cases the voltage drop across the tube is less than the ionization potential of the gas. Neither the exact mechanism involved in the formation of the arc nor the cause of the overlapping transition region are completely understood. However, it is believed that double step ionization processes play an important part in the arc discharge.

Each of these types of gas discharges, Townsend, glow, and arc, are discussed in more detail in the following sections.

Table 20

IONIZATION POTENTIALS OF VARIOUS GASES[9]

Gas	First Ionization Potential in eV
Helium	24.58
Neon	21.56
Argon	15.76
Krypton	13.94
Xenon	12.08
Mercury	10.38

[9] Adapted with permission from Henry Semat, *Introduction to Atomic Physics*, Rev. Ed., New York. Rinehart and Co., Inc., 1946, Table XI, pp. 228–230.

9.5. Townsend discharge[10]

Consider the case of two parallel, plane electrodes immersed in a gas at a pressure P as shown in figure 9.4a. A voltage difference V_b is impressed across the plates. The electric field intensity in the gas is $E = V_b/d$.

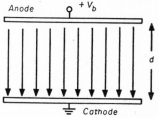

Anode $+V_b$

d

Cathode

(a) PARALLEL PLANE GAS TUBE

Now suppose that by some unspecified method, free electrons are introduced at the cathode surface. These electrons are accelerated toward the anode by the electric field. Every now and then the electrons collide with thermally agitated neutral gas atoms or molecules. Up to about point B in figure 9.4b the collisions are all elastic because the electrons never acquire ionizing energies.

For small values of the voltage difference V_b, electrons are introduced at the cathode faster than they are removed by the electric field. As the voltage difference is increased, the electrons are

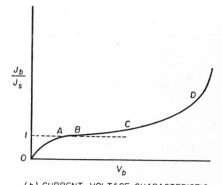

(b) CURRENT-VOLTAGE CHARACTERISTIC

Figure 9.4. Device and characteristic associated with a Townsend discharge.

removed more and more rapidly causing the current density at the anode, J_b, to increase more or less linearly. Some curvature in the curve of figure 9.4b exists in this region because of space charge effects.

At some point between A and B on the curve of figure 9.4b, the voltage difference is large enough to remove the electrons as rapidly as they are introduced at the cathode. The resulting value for the anode current density is called the *saturation current density* J_s.

---

[10] L. B. Loeb, *op. cit.*, chap. 8, 9.

As the voltage difference across the tube becomes even larger, electrons acquire ionizing energies following numerous elastic colli-‍sions with gas atoms. When this occurs, every now and then an electron will have an inelastic *ionizing collision* with a gas atom, producing another electron and a positive ion. This increases the current through the tube by increasing the number of electrons arriving at the anode. The essential ideas are illustrated in figure 9.5.

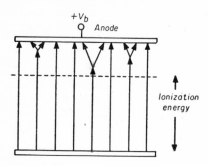

Figure 9.5. Showing increase in anode current as a result of electrons ionizing gas atoms, producing more electrons.

The branched lines in figure 9.5 indicate electrons having inelastic ionizing collisions. You will observe that not all of the electrons have ionizing collisions even though they all have ionizing energy by the time they cross the dotted line in figure 9.5. The *probability* of inelastic collision increases as the electron energy increases, so that there are more ionizing collisions near the anode than there are near the dotted line.

Operation according to the approximate picture given in figure 9.5 would correspond roughly to point C on the current-voltage characteristic of figure 9.4b.

Now suppose that the voltage difference across the tube is several times larger than the ionization potential of the gas. This is shown in figure 9.6 where the anode voltage is more than three times larger than the ionization potential.

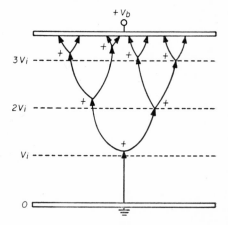

Figure 9.6. Showing extensive increase in current for large voltage drop across the tube.

Events associated with one *very* hypothetical electron released at the cathode are shown in figure 9.6. This electron is accelerated toward the plate and after numerous elastic collisions, acquires ionizing energy. It eventually makes an ionizing collision with a gas atom, producing an additional electron and a positive gas ion. Now the *two* electrons are accelerated, rapidly gaining ionizing energy again. Following inelastic collisions with gas atoms we then have four electrons and two more positive ions. In the example shown, eight electrons finally arrive at the plate, or anode, all being associated with the one primary electron originally released at the cathode.

Not every electron released at the cathode will be as efficient as the one in this example. However, the discussion does serve to illustrate the idea of a rapid increase in current as the electrode voltage difference is increased.

The positive gas ions do *not* contribute any further ionization by collision processes. This was explained in section 9.3.

From this rather oversimplified discussion it is apparent that the anode current density is essentially an exponential function of the interelectrode spacing. This is true if the electric field intensity E and gas pressure P are held constant. This was first noted by Townsend and he expressed the idea for parallel, plane electrodes as

$$J_b = J_s \epsilon^{\alpha d} \tag{9.12}$$

where d = electrode spacing in meters, J_s = saturation current density, J_b = anode current density, α = average number of electron-ion pairs formed per meter of movement of the primary electron. The constant, α, is called the *first Townsend coefficient*. It varies with the electric field intensity as you might expect.

Unfortunately, equation (9.12) does not always fit the experimental data. The most noticeable deviations occur when the ratio of the electric field intensity to the gas pressure is fairly large. The actual measured ionization current is larger than that predicted by equation (9.12).

A more accurate equation for the Townsend discharge current for parallel plane electrodes is[11]

$$J_b = J_s \frac{\epsilon^{\alpha d}}{1 - \beta(\epsilon^{\alpha d} - 1)} \tag{9.13}$$

where β = *second Townsend coefficient*. Loeb[12] lists seven different

[11] *Ibid:* p. 378.
[12] *Ibid:* pp. 402–406.

possible causes of the second Townsend coefficient. He observes that, in all likelihood, all seven may be operative to a greater or lesser extent under various conditions. No one theory seems able to explain *all* observed phenomena.

However, it does appear that the more important contributions to the second Townsend coefficient in most cases arise from electron emission from the cathode. This emission may result from either of two different actions:

(1) Secondary emission produced by positive ion bombardment of the cathode.

(2) Photoelectric emission of electrons.

Photons are produced in the gas by electron-ion recombinations or even more complicated processes. Some of these photons pass through the gas, strike the cathode, and cause photoemission.

Actually, about all that we can say about the second Townsend coefficient is that it measures the number of electrons produced by *secondary effects* resulting from the passage of a single primary electron through the interelectrode space.

9.6. Condition for a sustained discharge

The Townsend discharge will not maintain itself. If the source producing the electrons at the cathode is removed, the discharge dies out and the current through the tube becomes zero. However, from the discussion in the preceding section we can readily establish an approximate equation as the condition for the discharge to become self-sustaining.

Each primary electron produces $\epsilon^{\alpha d}$ electrons at the anode. This represents $(\epsilon^{\alpha d} - 1)$ *new* electrons resulting from $(\epsilon^{\alpha d} - 1)$ collisions. Hence $(\epsilon^{\alpha d} - 1)$ positive ions are created by each *primary* electron. These positive ions create β secondary electrons as a result of all of the factors contributing to the second Townsend coefficient. Hence, if

$$N_s = \text{number of secondary electrons produced}$$
$$\text{by the sum of all actions of positive ions}$$
$$\text{resulting from one primary electron}$$

then $$N_s = \beta(\epsilon^{\alpha d} - 1) \qquad (9.14)$$

In the Townsend discharge, N_s is always a number less than unity. That is, on the average, one primary electron does not produce a whole secondary electron through secondary phenomena associated with the action of the positive ions. The discharge cannot possibly sustain itself until the primary electron is completely regenerated by secondary effects. So, the discharge will become selfsustaining only when one primary electron produces one secondary electron by secondary effects, making $N_s = 1$. Hence, for a sustained discharge,

$$N_s \geq 1$$

or
$$\beta(\epsilon^{\alpha d} - 1) \geq 1$$

This leads to the condition that

$$\epsilon^{\alpha d} \geq \frac{1 + \beta}{\beta} \tag{9.15}$$

for a sustained discharge.

The condition for a sustained discharge is *not* coincident with the breakdown voltage, V_{bd}. Rather, it corresponds to the voltage across the tube when the sustained, normal glow discharge is present. The equation for the breakdown voltage is an exceedingly complicated problem and is not treated here.

9.7. Glow discharge

Once the condition for a sustained discharge is met, the tube breaks down into a *glow discharge*. It is called a glow discharge because the tube becomes luminous approximately as shown in figure 9.7a.

For the discharge to be self-sustained, the second Townsend coefficient must have a value such that

$$\epsilon^{\alpha d} \geq \frac{1 + \beta}{\beta}$$

Although the second Townsend coefficient was discussed in a general way earlier, it is necessary now to know the factor that is most important in sustaining the discharge. Loeb[13] demonstrates that the photoelectric effect is negligible in the glow discharge. He shows that *secondary emission* produced by positive ion bombardment of the cathode is the fundamental action involved in the production of the second Townsend coefficient.

If the discharge is established in a long, narrow, cylindrical tube,

---

[13] *Ibid:* pp. 568–569.

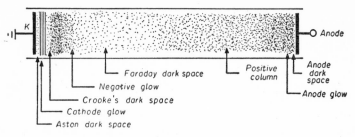

Aston dark space
Cathode glow
Crooke's dark space
Negative glow
Faraday dark space
Positive column
Anode dark space
Anode glow

(a) PHYSICAL APPEARANCE OF A GLOW DISCHARGE

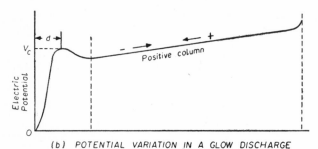

(b) POTENTIAL VARIATION IN A GLOW DISCHARGE

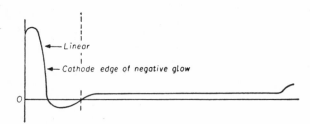

Linear
Cathode edge of negative glow

(c) ELECTRIC FIELD INTENSITY IN THE DISCHARGE

Figure 9.7. Characteristics of a glow discharge.

it exhibits various regions of comparative darkness and lightness as shown in figure 9.7a. Each of these regions is marked on the figure with the name most commonly associated with it. Figure 9.7b and 9.7c show the variations in electric potential and electric field intensity as functions of the distance along the discharge.

Although there are a number of regions shown in figure 9.7a, there are really four main parts of the discharge, as follows:

(1) Crooke's dark space
(2) Negative glow

the anode edge of the negative glow are attracted toward the anode
by the small accelerating field shown in figure 9.7c. After moving
some distance, they acquire additional kinetic energy and can produce
ionizing and exciting collisions. Once again the gas becomes luminous
in this region called the *positive column*.

The positive column contains slightly more positive ions than
electrons. The difference in charge densities is generally so small that
the region is often considered to be virtually neutral. The electric
field intensity in this region is very small as shown in figure 9.7c.
Because there are no appreciable space charge effects, the charges
move in an essentially random manner with only a slight orientation
caused by the weak electric field. This causes the electrons to drift
slowly to the anode while the positive ions drift slowly toward the
Crooke's dark space.

9.8. Some other aspects of glow discharges

The difference in potential between the cathode edge of the negative glow and the cathode is called the *cathode fall*, V_c. This term is
identified in figure 9.7b. It should be clear from the discussion preceding this that the cathode fall must have a particular value to
sustain the discharge. For a sustained discharge the positive ions
must acquire sufficient kinetic energy from the cathode fall to produce
secondary emission of electrons from the cathode. This process obviously depends upon the cathode material, which controls the work
function, and the gas, which controls the properties of the positive
ions. Thus, as you might expect, the cathode fall is critically dependent upon the gas and cathode material. Typical values for the
cathode fall are given in table 21.

The current through the discharge is given approximately by

$$I_b = A \frac{\mu_p(1 + \beta)}{\pi d^3} V_c^2 \tag{9.24}$$

where A = area of the cathode covered by glow, μ_p = mobility of
the positive ions, $d \doteq$ distance covered by the cathode fall, V_c =
cathode fall, β = second Townsend coefficient. The current density
J_c at the cathode surface is

$$J_c = \frac{I_b}{A} = \frac{\mu_p(1 + \beta)}{\pi d^3} V_c^2 \tag{9.25}$$

In the region of operation corresponding to the *normal glow* discharge, it is observed that the cathode fall V_c and fall distance d remain constant as the discharge current I_b varies over rather wide limits.

Table 21

DATA CONCERNING THE CATHODE FALL V_c[14]

(For the Normal Glow Discharge)

CATHODE MATERIAL	GAS							
	AIR		N$_2$		H$_2$		ARGON	
	V_c	d	V_c	d	V_c	d	V_c	d
Copper..........	370	0.23	208	....	214	0.8	130	....
Aluminum.......	229	0.25	180	0.31	170	0.72	100	0.29
Iron............	269	0.52	215	0.42	250	0.9	165	0.33
Platinum	277	....	216	....	276	1.0	131	....

(V_c in volts; d in mm at a pressure of 1 mm of Hg)

This requires the current density J_c in the glow to remain constant. This would be possible only if the area A of the glow changes. It is observed experimentally that this does occur. As I_b increases, A increases so that J_c remains constant. The normal glow region is shown in figure 9.3.

Eventually, for some value of discharge current, the glow covers the entire cathode area and A can no longer increase. Now as the current is increased beyond this point, the current density at the cathode must increase. This is called the *abnormal glow* region as shown on figure 9.3. The increase in current density is accompanied by an increase in the cathode fall V_c and a change in the fall distance d. The cathode fall can be increased only by increasing the total potential difference V_b from anode-to-cathode. Thus, the voltage drop across the discharge increases as the discharge current increases in the abnormal glow region.

There are many, many other extremely interesting aspects of glow discharges not covered here. Positive column striations, plasma oscillations, and the Aston dark space are samples. The reference to Loeb's work should be consulted for further information.

---

[14] L. B. Loeb, *op. cit.*, Tables XXXVI, XXXIX, with permission.

9.9. Arc discharge

In the abnormal glow region of the complete gas discharge characteristic, the voltage across the discharge increases as the discharge current increases. This produces a rapid rise in the power input to the discharge from the source of electric potential. Because most of the potential drop occurs in the cathode fall, a large part of this power input is supplied to the cathode by the energetic positive ions. This causes the temperature of the cathode to rise. As the cathode temperature increases and as the discharge current continues to increase, the cathode glow begins to concentrate into a spot. Suddenly, the tube breaks down into a sustained *arc discharge*. The cathode glow concentrates into a very brilliant spot. This occurs at point *F* on the curve of figure 9.3.

The fundamental distinction between the glow and arc discharges arises from the difference in cathode fall potentials. For a glow discharge the cathode fall is of the order of 200 to 300 volts, while it is only 10 to 20 volts in an arc discharge. It seems clear that some new phenomenon must occur in the arc discharge that was not present in the glow discharge.

For cathode materials such as carbon and tungsten, having high boiling temperatures, it seems fairly certain that this new phenomenon is *thermionic emission of electrons from the cathode spot*. The cathode spot temperatures are very high; the spot temperature for tungsten is about 3300°K, while it is nearly 3600°K for carbon. These temperatures are high enough to produce an appreciable electron emission that proves adequate to sustain the discharge. Calculations based upon this assumption closely correspond to experimental observations.

The secondary emission produced by positive ion bombardment is very small compared to the thermionic emission current. The positive ions no longer produce the necessary electrons directly; instead they provide energy to heat the cathode and this results in electron emission. As a result, the cathode fall can drop to quite low values, well below those necessary to sustain a glow discharge by secondary emission alone.

Arc discharges can also be produced with mercury and copper cathodes. These materials boil at such low temperatures that it does not seem possible that thermionic emission could be important. However, this is an extremely complicated phenomenon and it is not at all completely understood.

The potential variation along an arc discharge is shown in figure 9.8. In the positive column of a glow discharge the electrons acquire enough energy from the field to ionize atoms or molecules when they collide with an electron. The action in the positive column of an arc discharge is somewhat different. Here it appears that the neutral

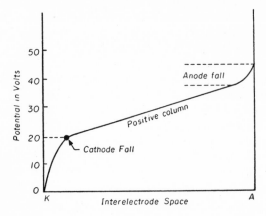

Figure 9.8. Potential variation along an arc discharge path.

gas atoms or molecules receive continuing additions of kinetic energy by elastic collisions with numerous electrons. Ultimately, the neutral particle acquires sufficient energy to undergo ionizing collisions with other neutral gas atoms or molecules.

9.10. Classification of gas tubes

In the preceding discussion it was shown that there are three distinctly different types of gas discharges:

> (1) Townsend discharge
> (2) normal glow discharge
> (3) arc discharge

Practical gas tubes are most conveniently classified and discussed by identifying the type of discharge fundamental to their operation. Representative tube types are given in the following outline:

(1) Townsend discharge
    (a) gas phototubes
    (b) Geiger tubes
(2) Glow discharge
    (a) voltage regulator tubes
    (b) cold cathode triodes (starter anode **types)**
    (c) neon glow tubes
(3) Arc discharge
    (a) phanotrons and mercury pool diodes
    (b) excitrons
    (c) tungar tubes
    (d) ignitrons
    (e) thyratrons
    (f) strobotrons

The remainder of this chapter is devoted to a discussion of the essential characteristics of these tubes. Only main tube types are discussed in any detail.

9.11. Gas phototubes

A gas phototube consists of a *photoemissive* cathode and an anode placed in an enclosure with an inert gas at low pressure. The electrical circuit symbol for a gas phototube is shown in figure 9.9. It is the same as the symbol used for the vacuum phototube except that a black dot is included to signify the presence of gas. This is the standard convention used to distinguish gas tubes from vacuum tubes on electrical circuit diagrams.

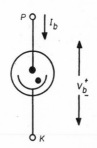

Figure 9.9. Circuit symbol for a gas phototube.

The current-voltage characteristics of a gas phototube are shown in figure 9.10 with the light intensity in *lumens* as the family parameter. In the region of the Townsend discharge a given illumination of the cathode will produce a larger tube current than would be obtained if the tube were evacuated. This effect is called *gas amplification*.

Up to a voltage V_i, the characteristics are essentially the same as those of a corresponding vacuum phototube. The electronic energies are below the ionization potential of the gas so that electron collisions with gas atoms are elastic. However, when the voltage across the tube exceeds V_i, the accelerating field inside the tube is sufficient to raise the energies of the electrons to ionizing values. Beyond this voltage a typical Townsend discharge characteristic is obtained. The ionization resulting from this discharge is the cause of the gas amplification effect.

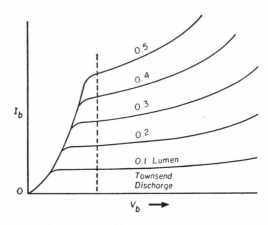

Figure 9.10. Current-voltage characteristics of a gas phototube.

, The operating voltage of the tube must be low enough to prevent the formation of a glow discharge. This is necessary because the intense positive ion bombardment of the cathode might be sufficient to sputter the emitting material off of the cathode. However, if the operating voltage of the tube is kept below a safe maximum value, but well above the lower limit V_i, gas amplification factors of the order of four or more can be obtained. This is a very considerable increase in sensitivity over a corresponding vacuum phototube.

Despite the advantages of gas amplification, a gas phototube has two major limitations not common to vacuum tube types. It is clear from figure 9.10 that the spacings between successive curves are not equal at the high voltages necessary for gas amplification. As a result, the tube current is not a linear function of the light intensity on the cathode and this is undesirable. The second limitation is caused by the fact that there is a time lag between the instant that the light intensity changes and the instant when the ionization process establishes the new equilibrium current. Techniques have been established to compensate for this effect so that it is not quite as serious as it might seem.

Gas phototubes are widely used in photoelectric control systems and in the reproduction of sound-on-film recordings.

9.12. Voltage regulator tubes

The normal glow discharge exhibits a nearly constant voltage drop across the tube over a wide range of tube currents. This effect is widely used in glow discharge *voltage regulator* tubes. The tube consists of two cold electrodes immersed in an inert gas at low pressure. The circuit symbol is shown in figure 9.11. The current-voltage characteristic is simply the glow discharge region from figure 9.3. Of course, the Townsend discharge region is also included, but the tube is never operated in this mode and when the curve is plotted on a linear current scale it is scarcely discernible, as shown in figure 9.12.

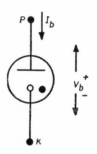

Figure 9.11. Circuit symbol for a cold cathode glow discharge tube.

The name *voltage-regulator* tube derives from the fact that the voltage across a glow discharge is nearly in-

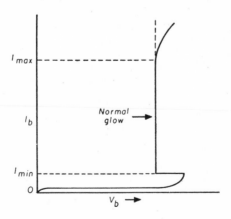

Figure 9.12. Current-voltage characteristic of a glow discharge tube.

dependent of the current through it over a specified range of operation. *Voltage regulation* is defined as follows:

$$\text{Voltage regulation} = \frac{V \text{ (no load)} - V \text{ (rated load)}}{V \text{ (rated load)}}$$

$$= \frac{V \text{ (no load)}}{V \text{ (rated load)}} - 1$$

In a glow discharge tube the *no load* and *rated load* voltages are nearly
equal so that the voltage regulation is
almost zero, where zero indicates perfect
regulation.

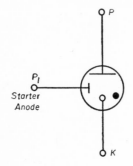

Figure 9.13. Starter anode gas triode.

Commercial voltage-regulator tubes are
designed to operate with specified voltage drops such as 75, 90, 105, and 150
volts.

A modification of the basic glow discharge diode is the *starter anode gas
triode* shown schematically in figure 9.13.
The tube is designed so that a glow discharge is easily initiated between the
third electrode, called the *starter anode,*
and the cathode. This discharge supplies the positive ions which
makes it easier to start the main discharge. The reader should refer to the manufacturer's handbook for operating data. The type
OA4-G is a representative tube type.

9.13. Thermionic arc discharge diodes

Arc discharge diodes are subdivided according to the type of cathode
used. The two most important types are
    (1) thermionic cathode
    (2) mercury pool cathode
Hot cathode (thermionic) arc discharge diodes are called *phanotrons.* In commercial tubes the cathode heating is generally provided
by a heater element rather than by positive ion bombardment.
Phanotrons are indicated schematically by the circuit symbol shown
in figure 9.14. The current-voltage characteristic of figure 9.15 is
typical of that observed for phanotrons. This is essentially the arc
discharge region of figure 9.3, except that the current has been plotted

on a linear scale in the present case. Oxide-coated cathodes are nearly always used in phanotrons to achieve large emission currents at

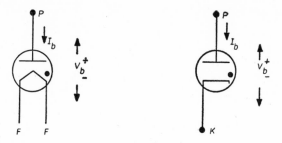

Figure 9.14. Circuit symbols for phanotrons: (a) directly heated; (b) indirectly heated.

relatively low cathode temperatures. The coating may be applied directly to the heater wires or on the surface of an indirectly-heated element. The indirectly-heated con-struction is generally used when very large emission currents are required because larger cathode emitting sur-faces can be obtained in this way.

The structural form of thermionic cathodes used in gas tubes is influenced by a number of practical factors that make them appear very different from the cathodes used in vacuum tubes. Readers interested in this should refer elsewhere.[15,16]

The gas in a phanotron may be one of the inert types or the vapor of a few drops of mercury. According to table 20 (page 292), the ionization potential of mercury is less than that of the in-ert gases. Thus, the voltage drop across mercury vapor tubes is less than that

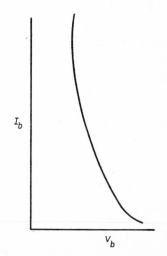

Figure 9.15. Current-voltage characteristic of an arc dis-charge diode.

[15] M.I.T. Staff, *Applied Electronics*, New York: John Wiley & Sons, Inc., 1943, pp. 212–216.

[16] A. W. Hull, "Gas Filled Thermionic Tubes," *Trans. A.I.E.E.*, Vol. 47, 1928, pp. 753–763.

across other tube types. Because of this, and for reasons apparent only from an analysis of actual circuits, the operating efficiency of mercury vapor tubes exceeds that of tubes filled with one of the inert gases. However, the characteristics of mercury vapor tubes undergo variations when the ambient temperature changes. Inert gas tubes are not appreciably affected. Hence, when extreme temperature conditions are encountered and stability of characteristics is important, the tubes containing inert gases are more suitable.

Once the arc is initiated in a phanotron, the positive ions that are produced bombard the cathode. This becomes a serious problem if the energies of the ions are very large because the cathode coating could be sputtered off. Fortunately, it has been found[16] that this type of cathode damage can be largely avoided if the voltage across the tube is kept below a certain critical value. Because this voltage is larger than the ionization potential of the gas in the tube, oxide-coated cathodes can be used in gas tubes without being harmed.

In operating a phanotron it is important that the cathode reach its operating temperature before the voltage source V_{bb} is connected across the series combination of tube and load resistance. Unless this precaution is observed, the emitted current may be less than the rated value, the voltage drop (IR) through the load resistance will be small, and the voltage across the tube, $V_{bb} - IR$, may exceed the recommended maximum safe value. Cathode destruction by energetic positive ion bombardment would then result.

An external load resistance R must always be inserted in series with an arc discharge tube and the source of voltage, V_{bb}. Because the tube is essentially a constant voltage device it is roughly equivalent to a voltage source with zero internal resistance. If the supply voltage V_{bb} exceeds that of the equivalent battery or voltage source representing the tube, then the tube effectively short circuits the voltage source V_{bb}. The tube would burn out from an excessive current demand. Thus, some external resistance must always be connected in series with the tube to limit the current to a safe value.

9.14. Mercury pool diodes

Another type of gas diode uses a *mercury pool cathode* which acts as a source of electrons and supplies the mercury vapor needed for ionization. There does not appear to be any evidence to suggest that electrons are emitted from the cathode by thermionic means or as a result of secondary emission produced by positive ion bombardment. The actual mechanism involved is not well understood.

When the tube is conducting, the arc discharge takes place between a bright *cathode spot* on the mercury pool and the anode. The emission of electrons takes place from this spot. Enormous emission currents are obtained, far in excess of anything possible thermionically at the temperatures that are reported for the cathode spots. The maximum current per spot averages about thirty to forty amperes[17] and more spots form as the current demand increases. The maximum possible emission current appears to be virtually unlimited.

The voltage drop across a mercury pool diode is somewhat larger than that across a mercury phanotron. This arises from the fact that the voltage drop across the tube supplies the energy to produce electron emission by providing the positive ions with the necessary kinetic energy. In a phanotron, a separate heater supply is provided to furnish this energy.

The thermionic cathode of a phanotron stands as an ever ready source of electrons as long as it is hot. An arc discharge will form whenever the proper anode voltage is supplied. However, the cathode spot in a mercury pool tube supplies the ionizing electrons and the spot is formed only during a discharge. It is not there when the tube is not conducting and the tube is not self-starting as a result. Thus, an auxiliary *starting electrode* is necessary to initiate a small discharge and cathode spot that will then permit the formation of the main discharge.

These tubes are often made with several anodes, perhaps as many as sixteen or eighteen. In such construction, successive anodes are progressively made positive as a function of time and the voltage is removed from the other anodes. Thus, the arc shifts from one anode to another in succession.

The current-voltage characteristic of mercury pool tubes is essentially the same as the phanotron characteristic. Both are arc-discharge devices and should exhibit similar characteristics.

The temperature of the cathode spot has been estimated to be about 200°C. This is high enough to cause rapid evaporation of mercury and some bubbling and splashing. To prevent any of this

---

[17] E. D. McArthur, *Electronics and Electron Tubes*, New York: John Wiley & Sons, Inc., 1936, p. 137.

mercury from being deposited on the anode or other essential parts of the tube, rather intricate systems of baffles are used. The characteristics and drawings published by tube manufacturers should be consulted for more details.

One disadvantage of mercury pool diodes should be mentioned. About three amperes of current must be drawn from a cathode spot to sustain a discharge. The spot must be maintained because it is the source of the electrons. However, because the required anode current may fall below this value, it is customary to use *keep alive* electrodes to provide the minimum current from the spot necessary to insure its continued existence.

In operation, the anode-to-cathode voltage of the tube is usually alternating above and below zero volts. Normally, conduction is desired only when the anode is positive with respect to the cathode. If the tube conducts on the negative swing of the anode voltage, the tube is said to *arc back*. This is very undesirable. Some of the causes of arc back are listed below:

(1) high gas pressure caused by temperature
(2) some mercury might be splashed onto the anode and an effective cathode spot may form on it
(3) oxide evaporating from a hot cathode might deposit on an anode

In multiple anode construction, arc back between two or more anodes may occur. Factors like these greatly influence the structural form of commercial tubes.

9.15. Ignitrons

A mercury pool diode will not conduct until a cathode spot is formed. In a diode the spot is produced by a mechanical adjustment of the starter anode. However, it has been shown[18] that a cathode spot can be initiated by producing current in a special *igniter* electrode that is mechanically fixed in position. Starting the arc is then an all-electric process, not requiring mechanical adjustment.

The *igniter* electrode must be a semiconductor, highly refractory, and nonwetting when immersed in mercury. It is often made of

---

[18] J. Slepian, L. R. Ludwig, "A New Method of Initiating the Cathode of an Arc," *Trans. A.I.E.E.*, Vol. 52, 1933, p. 693.

silicon carbide. Because the igniter is not wet by the mercury, the mercury forms a meniscus about the electrode as shown in figure 9.16. When current is passed through the igniter and into the cathode, a cathode spot is formed at the meniscus in a few microseconds. The exact mechanism involved in the production of this spot is not completely understood. Once the spot is formed, the main discharge can occur if the anode voltage has the proper value. This tube, with its special igniter electrode, is called an *ignitron*. It is indicated on electrical circuit diagrams by the symbol shown in figure 9.17.

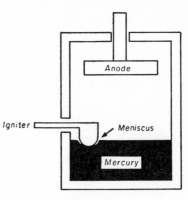

Figure 9.16. Ignitron.

The instant of tube conduction is controlled by the time when the igniter produces the cathode spot. Because of this controlled firing time, an ignitron is a gas *control tube*.

The current-voltage characteristics of an ignitron are the same as for a corresponding mercury pool diode if it is understood that the instant of firing is controlled by the igniter circuit.

Finally, because the igniter provides the cathode spot at any desired instant, ignitrons do not require *keep alive* electrodes.

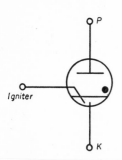

Figure 9.17. Ignitron circuit symbol.

9.16. Thyratrons

Suppose that a grid is inserted between the anode and cathode of a phanotron. If this grid is made sufficiently negative with respect to the thermionic cathode, it will shield the cathode and the emitted electrons from the accelerating field produced by the anode. Consequently, an arc discharge will not form because the electrons cannot acquire enough energy to produce ionizing collisions. However, as the grid voltage is gradually and progressively made less negative, the strength of its repelling force on the electrons is reduced. At some particular value of grid voltage, a few high-energy electrons will overcome the repulsion of the grid and pass through the openings in the grid into the grid-to-plate space. This is a region of strong accelerating field and these electrons rapidly acquire ionizing energy. The positive ions resulting from ionizing collisions are attracted to the negative grid and partially neutralize its repelling effects on the emitted electrons. This permits more electrons to pass the grid and contribute to the ionization. The process is cumulative and, in a matter of a few microseconds, an arc discharge is produced between the anode and cathode. The effect of the grid is completely neutralized by a positive ion *grid sheath*.

Once the arc is established, the grid no longer has the ability to control the current through the tube. This is so because every line of electric flux from the grid terminates on a positive ion in the grid sheath. The grid is completely neutralized. If the grid voltage is made more negative, it simply attracts more positive ions and remains electrically neutralized. Thus, the grid can control the time of tube conduction by *preventing* the formation of an arc. However, once conduction is established, the grid loses control. Control can be regained only by extinguishing the arc and this is possible only by reducing the plate voltage below the ionization potential of the gas long enough for the tube to de-ionize completely. Once the tube is de-ionized, the grid can regain control if it is sufficiently negative.

Grid control *can* be regained if the grid is made extremely negative. When operated in this manner the grid removes the positive ions more rapidly than they are being created in the discharge. Thus, the grid sheath is destroyed and the grid can begin to exert control and ultimately halt the discharge. Such operation would damage the tube if repeated because an excessive grid current exists during the process.

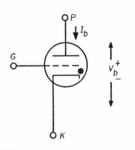

Figure 9.18. Thyratron circuit symbol.

Gas triodes operated according to the preceding principles are called *thyratrons*. The tube is marked on electrical circuit diagrams by the symbol shown in figure 9.18. While both the ignitron and the thyratron are gas-control tubes, they operate in exactly reverse ways. In a thyratron, the grid *prevents* arc formation until the desired moment; in an ignitron the igniter *initiates* the arc at the specified time.

The grid current in a thyratron is negligible as long as the tube is nonconducting. However, when the arc forms, a large grid current is produced because positive ions are attracted to the grid. To avoid damaging the tube, a current-limiting resistor is usually placed in series with the grid.

The value of grid voltage that just prevents arc formation, for a given anode voltage, is called the *critical grid voltage*. A plot of this voltage against the plate voltage is called the *firing characteristic* of the tube. A typical example of such a characteristic is shown in

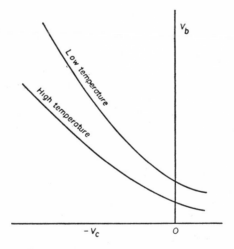

Figure 9.19. Firing characteristics of a mercury-vapor thyratron.

figure 9.19. This figure also shows that the characteristics for mercury vapor tubes are dependent upon temperature. When this variation with temperature cannot be tolerated, hydrogen thyratrons are often used.

The current-voltage characteristic of a thyratron is essentially the same as that of a corresponding phanotron if it is understood that the instant of firing is controlled by the grid, or more exactly, by the relationship between the grid and plate voltages.

There are other types of thyratrons with particular advantages in specialized applications. In particular, shield-grid thyratrons and positive-grid thyratrons are of interest. The manufacturer's handbooks should be consulted for further information.

PROBLEMS

9.1. Compute the minimum velocity an electron must have to ionize a mercury atom. How far would the electron have to travel through an electric field of 10,000 volts/meter to acquire this energy? When the positive mercury ion recombines with a free electron, what will be the frequency of the emitted photon? What will be the color of this light?

9.2. Repeat problem 9.1 in its entirety for the case of neon.

9.3. With the results of the preceding problems in mind, make some statements concerning the relationship between the number of ionizing collisions in neon and mercury vapor tubes of the same physical dimensions and having the same gas pressure. If the same current is desired under similar modes of operation from the two tubes, what probable relationship will exist between the tube voltages?

9.4. An electron in a mercury atom has two metastable energy levels at 4.66 and 5.46 eV. If such atoms exist in quantity in a given mercury vapor tube, compute the minimum electronic velocities required to produce ionization in each type of metastable atom.

9.5. Compute the velocity of a mercury ion after it falls through a potential difference of 10 volts. The atomic weight of mercury is 200.6. Assume the mercury atoms are singly ionized.

9.6. Compute the velocity of an electron after it falls through a potential difference of 10 volts. Compare this figure with that obtained in problem 9.5.

9.7. Calculate the density of gas atoms in a container if the gas is at a pressure of 10^{-4} mm of mercury and a temperature of 273°K. Note: The pressure in newtons/meter^2 = (pressure in mm of Hg) $\times$ $(1.013 \times 10^5)/760$.

9.8. The collision diameter of an atom of the gas in problem 9.7 is 2.5×10^{-10} meter. Compute the molecular and electronic mean free paths. Use the temperature and pressure specified in problem 9.7.

9.9. The plate and cathode of a vacuum diode are spaced 1.25 cm apart. Some residual molecular nitrogen (N_2) gas is present in the tube after evacuation. What is the maximum permissible gas pressure after evacuation at a gas temperature of 325°K if the electronic mean free path is not to be less than ten times the electrode separation?

9.10. The saturation current density in a vacuum phototube is 0.3×10^{-2} amp/meter². Air at a pressure of 1 mm of Hg is introduced and the first Townsend coefficient is measured under specified conditions of voltage and electrode spacing. If $\alpha = 120$ and $d = 2$ cm, calculate the current density at the anode.

9.11. A gas phototube is to have a gas amplification factor of 5. Calculate the value required for the first Townsend coefficient if the electrode spacing is 0.5 cm.

9.12. A particular gas and electrode combination are to be used in a glow discharge tube. It is known that $\alpha = 150$, $\beta = 0.0005$. What electrode separation is required to sustain the discharge?

9.13. In a voltage-regulator tube, $\alpha = 120$ and $d = 0.5$ cm. The problem is to choose the cathode material and this is determined in part by the second Townsend coefficient. Calculate the minimum value for β. Why does this affect the selection of the cathode material?

9.14. Calculate the ratio of the electron current density to the positive ion current density in the positive column of a hydrogen glow discharge. Clearly specify any assumptions you might make.

9.15. A glow discharge is established between copper electrodes in molecular nitrogen at a pressure of 1 mm of Hg. Calculate the kinetic energy of the positive nitrogen ions striking the cathode. Repeat for aluminum electrodes.

$$KE = \frac{1}{2} m v^2$$

$$\sqrt{\frac{2\,KE}{m}} = \sqrt{v^2}$$

10

INSULATORS AND CAPACITORS

Up to this point in the book we have been concerned almost exclusively with electrical *conduction processes;* the study has included electrical conduction in metals, semiconductors, vacuum, and gases. In this chapter we examine the structure and properties of materials variously called *insulators, nonconductors,* and *dielectrics.* Ideally, these materials do not conduct electricity in the usual sense at all. In perfect *insulators* there is no actual motion or transport of *free* charge. Thus, the electrical resistivity of such ideal insulators would be infinite.

In actual practice there is always some departure from this idealized, perfect insulator. Some electrical charge does pass through the material when an electric field is applied. We shall see how this *leakage current* arises in insulating materials.

The resistivity of a good, practical insulator is of the order of 10^{15} ohm-cm. The resistivity of a good metallic conductor is of the order of 10^{-6} ohm-cm. Because of this enormous difference of 21 orders of magnitude, it is reasonable to expect the physical structure of insulators to be very different from the physical structure of metals.

The chapter opens with a brief discussion of the chemical structure of some of the various types of insulating materials. The mechanism of leakage current is analyzed. The ideas of *polarization* and *dielectric constant* are then introduced so that the properties of capacitors may be presented. The chapter closes with a very brief discussion of ferroelectricity.

10.1. Insulators

The various types of solids were listed and briefly described in section 5.1 of chapter 5. If your recollection of this material is vague, you should reread section 5.1 before proceeding further with this chapter.

Insulators are materials that do not have any *free* charge, neither ions, electrons, nor holes. Thus, electrical conduction in the usual sense is impossible. The energy level diagram for an insulator might have the form shown in figure 10.1. This is identical to the diagram for an intrinsic semiconductor except that the width of the forbidden zone is so great that electrons cannot be excited from the valence band into the conduction band except at very high temperatures. At ordinary temperatures the material is an insulator because it has neither free electrons nor holes.

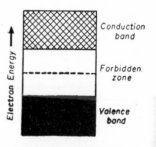

Figure 10.1. Energy-level diagram for an insulator.

Clearly, metals cannot be insulators because they always have free charges available for conduction. Covalent solids of the germanium and silicon type may or may not conduct. Hence, they may be conductors or insulators, depending upon the temperature.

The *ionic solids*, such as sodium chloride, are excellent insulators under ordinary conditions. Although every atom in the solid is ionized and constitutes a charged body, the ions are rigidly bound in position. They are not free to move under the influence of an electric field and electrical conduction is impossible.

The forces holding the ions together in the crystalline form assumed by an ionic solid can be computed from Coulomb's Law. This was given in chapter 1, as follows:

$$F = \frac{q_1 q_2}{4\pi\epsilon r^2} \quad \text{(in scalar form)} \tag{10.1}$$

where q_1 = charge on one ion = $+e$, q_2 = charge on the other ion = $-e$, r = distance between ions, ϵ = dielectric constant, a property of the medium separating the ions. Ordinarily the ions of the solid are separated by air or vacuum and the dielectric constant is denoted by ϵ_0. However, when an ionic solid is immersed in water, ϵ increases to about $78\epsilon_0$. As a result, the force of attraction between ions is so drastically reduced that the ions are released from their rigidly bound positions in the crystal and are free to wander about. In other words, the solid dissolves in the water. The resulting solution is an excellent conductor because it contains a plentiful supply of free ions of both signs. Clearly, moisture must be avoided when ionic solids are used as insulators.

From this very brief discussion you can see that solids arising from covalent bonding of atoms would be the best insulators as a general rule because

    (1) there are no free charges in such solids

    (2) the covalent bond is not electrostatic, does not follow Coulomb's Law, and is not weakened by moisture penetration

Materials of this type may be either organic or inorganic, but the organic types are much more numerous. The next few sections are devoted to short descriptions of these materials.

10.2. Organic compounds[1]

You may recall from chapter 5 that carbon forms covalent bonds with many other elements. Materials containing carbon in this form are called *organic compounds* and they far outnumber inorganic compounds in known variety.

The simplest of all organic compounds is *methane*, CH_4. The molecular structure of methane is shown in figure 10.2. The covalent bonding of the hydrogen atoms to the carbon atom is clearly indicated in a schematic manner in this figure. The carbon-hydrogen covalent bond is quite strong; the bond energy is taken to be about 3.8 eV.

The *homologs* of methane result from the successive additions of CH_2 groups. The first homolog is *ethane*, C_2H_6, which is methane plus one added CH_2 group. This molecular structure is shown schematically in figure 10.3.

Methane and ethane are both gases. The homologs remain gaseous until the fifth carbon atom is added. Between 5 and 20 carbon atoms

---

[1] The discussion from here through section 10.6 is largely paraphrased with permission from *The Westinghouse Engineer*, May, 1954; "Fundamentals of Electrical Insulation," J. Swiss, T. W. Dakin, pp. 114–124.

in the molecule produce a liquid compound. Molecules containing more than 20 carbon atoms form solids when aggregated. Thus, the physical character and many of the properties of the material gradually change as the molecular weight increases.

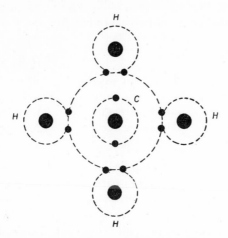

Figure 10.2. Molecular structure of methane, CH_4, the simplest organic compound.

The properties of the *solid* compounds continue to change as the molecular weight increases. In particular, as the molecular weight increases, the softening temperature increases, the mechanical

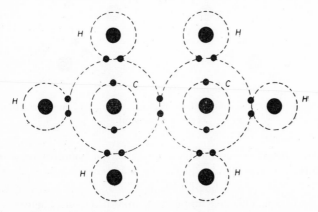

Figure 10.3. Ethane, C_2H_6, first homolog of methane.

strength increases, and the solubility decreases. From the standpoint of electrical insulation requirements, these changes are all in the right direction. This partially explains why electrical insulating materials generally have very high molecular weights.

The extent of the changes caused by variations in molecular weight may be inferred from a comparison of paraffin wax and polyethylene, as follows:

Paraffin Wax		*Polyethylene*
20–40	Molecular weight	4000-6000
60°C	Softening temp.	113°C
Poor	Mech. strength	Very tough
Readily	Dissolves in benzene	Not appreciably

Methane and its homologs are called *saturated* compounds because all bonds are made up of electron-pairs; the combination is essentially complete and there are no electrons left over. In *unsaturated* compounds, such as *ethylene*, bonding is accomplished by two or three electron pairs and at least one pair is left over. This is shown in figure

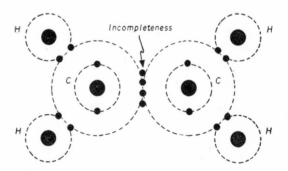

Figure 10.4. Ethylene, $CH_2{=}CH_2$, as an example of an unsaturated organic compound.

10.4. As a result of the incompleteness of the bonding, unsaturated compounds can undergo further bonding because one unused electron can enter into a paired bond with an electron from another unsaturated molecule. This has important practical consequences in the formation of *polymers* as discussed in the next section.

10.3. Formation of polymers

The very large molecules having molecular weights ranging from one hundred to several thousand are called *polymers*. The molecular weights of the *low polymers* are in the hundreds; gasoline and motor oil are familiar examples. *High polymers*, such as cotton and plexiglas, have molecular weights in the thousands.

A polymer is a chemical unit in which a given chemical structure occurs repeatedly. A *monomer* is the simplest unit from which a *polymer* can be formed. For example, polyethylene, which is a high polymer, is formed from the monomer ethylene. A schematic representation of polyethylene is shown in figure 10.5 and you can readily see how this is formed from the ethylene molecule shown in figure 10.4.

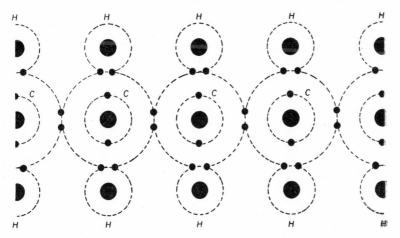

Figure 10.5. Polyethylene molecule, $-(CH_2)-(CH_2)-_{1000}$; showing how polyethylene forms from the repeated additions of the monomer ethylene.

From the geometric standpoint it seems fairly clear that the successive additions of the monomer could cause the polymer to form in either two or three dimensions. This would be determined by the character of the monomer. Polymers such as polyethylene, which form in two dimensions, have a threadlike molecular structure. They generally dissolve in particular solvents and are fusible. They are often called *thermoplastic resins*. Both polyethylene and polystyrene are of this type. When the molecules form in three dimensions the resulting solid is insoluble, infusible, and is said to be *thermosetting*. Glycerol is a three-dimensional polymer.

Organic polymers are usually classified according to the nature of the groups in the chain. Four of the more common groups are

(1) purely hydrocarbon
(2) amide groups
(3) ester groups
(4) epoxy groups

The arrangement of atoms in each of these groups is shown schematically in figure 10.6. The chemical symbols associated with these groups are also shown in the figure. Each bar between the letter symbols for the atoms signifies one covalent bond. You will observe the occurrence of a double covalent bond between oxygen and carbon in the amide and ester groups.

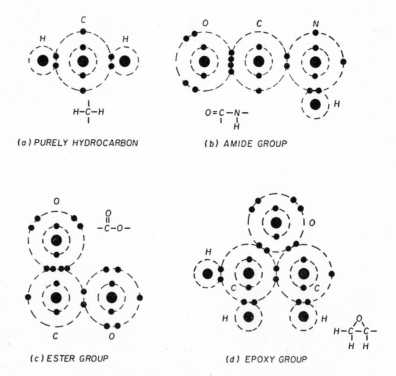

(a) PURELY HYDROCARBON   (b) AMIDE GROUP

(c) ESTER GROUP   (d) EPOXY GROUP

Figure 10.6. Groups common in organic polymers.

10.4. Organic high polymers

Organic high polymers may occur naturally or they may be synthetic. The structural parts of all living things, such as bone, muscle, nerve fiber, skin, and hair in animals and cellulose in plants are polymeric in form. Shellac is a natural polyester type of polymer with a molecular weight of about 900. It is secreted by the lac insect.

Synthetic high polymers may be roughly divided into three types: *rubber*, *fiber*, and *plastic*. They differ in degree, not in kind, because they are all essentially the same thing, having the same molecular structure. The difference arises from the difference in the relative strength of the forces between the molecular chains forming the solid. The distinctions come about as follows:

    (1) rubber—The forces of attraction between the large molecules are quite small so that the molecular chains do not form into regular geometrical arrays or lattices

    (2) fibers—The interchain forces are quite strong so that the chains fit into a regular geometrical array

    (3) plastic—intermediate between rubber and fiber

In many instances the same material is used as rubber, fiber or plastic. For example, polyethylene may be used as a rubber wire covering, for plastic food containers, or as a fiber in certain acid resistant materials.

There are many other organic insulating materials that include the following:

    (1) reactive solventless resins—such as Fosterite and the polyester and epoxy types

    (2) varnishes and wire enamels—including the alkyd type and phenolic type varnishes together with the silicones

    (3) perhalocarbons—hydrocarbons with hydrogen completely replaced by a halogen such as fluorine, bromine, iodine, and so on. Teflon (polytetrafluoroethylene) is one type.

10.5. Inorganic high polymers

Many of the inorganic insulating materials occur naturally. They are high polymers like the organic compounds and they have chain or net structures formed through covalent bonds. However, the bonds between chains or nets appear to be ionic or polar rather than covalent in inorganic high polymers. *Mica* and *asbestos* are the names connected with the two most common groups of inorganic, high polymer, insulating materials.

Micas are compounds of hydrogen, potassium, ferrous iron, and alkali metals. The two types in most common use in electrical insulation are described as follows:

(1) muscovite (white mica): $H_2KAl_3(SiO_4)_3$

(2) phlogopite (amber mica): $H_2KMg_3Al(SiO_4)_3$

Muscovite is the harder of the two, but it can be used only at temperatures up to about 500°C; phlogopite can be used at temperatures up to 800°C.

Asbestos is the name given to a group of silicates that contain magnesium, calcium, aluminum, and iron. Asbestos, unlike mica, is not a particularly good insulator because it tends to absorb water. This is a serious defect in an insulating material as we shall see later.

10.6. Ionic conduction in insulators

Electric current arising from the motion of electrons through insulators appears to be negligible because the physical structure of insulators does not normally permit the existence of free electrons. As a result, most of the unwanted current, or *leakage current*, in insulators is believed to arise from *ionic motion*. If it were not for this ion current, the insulator might be virtually perfect. In this section we shall see how this ion current is produced.

Practically all inorganic insulating materials, except glass, are *ionic crystals*. All of the atoms of such materials are ionized. Ordinarily they do not contribute to electrical conduction because they are rather

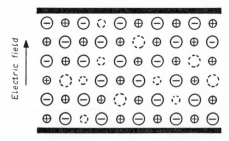

Figure 10.7. Imperfections in the form of lattice vacancies in an ionic crystal.

rigidly fixed in position within the crystal. However, there are always some imperfections, in the form of lattice vacancies, present in nearly any ionic crystal. This is illustrated by the two-dimensional sketch of the sodium chloride crystal shown in figure 10.7.

The sodium ions are physically smaller than the chlorine ions as shown in the sketch. When an electric field is impressed across a solid of this type, the smaller sodium ions can diffuse slowly through the crystal by successively jumping from one lattice vacancy to another; this gives the solid a small conductivity or a high resistivity.

As the temperature of the crystal increases, there is an increasing probability of crystal imperfections appearing. This tends to decrease the resistivity. At the same time, the thermal vibration of the sodium ions increases their mobility because they more frequently acquire sufficient kinetic energy to jump into an adjoining crystal lattice vacancy. This causes a further decrease in the resistivity. This negative temperature coefficient of resistance is characteristic of virtually all insulating materials.

Organic insulating materials are held together by covalent bonds, rather than by ionic forces. As a result, their resistivities are reduced from infinity almost entirely because of impurities, oxidation, or other degradation of the material.

When ionic compounds are present as impurities in organic materials, ionic conduction is possible when the compound dissociates. Thus, water absorbed by such insulation will cause a decrease in resistivity. Such insulation would be strongly affected by atmospheric humidity.

Table 22
VOLUME RESISTIVITIES OF SOME COMMON INSULATING MATERIALS

Material	Resistivity ohm-cm 25°C	Material	Resistivity ohm-cm 25°C
Cellulose acetate....	1×10^{10}	Paraffin wax........	1×10^{16}
Ebonite...........	2×10^{15}	Polyethylene........	1×10^{15}
Glass, Corning 707 ..	1.5×10^{11}	Polyisobutylene.....	1×10^{16}
Glass, Corning 790 ..	5.2×10^{9}	Polystyrene.........	1×10^{17}
Lucite............	1×10^{15}	Shellac............	1×10^{16}
Plexiglas..........	1×10^{15}	Teflon.............	1×10^{16}
Mica..............	5×10^{13}		

The resistance of organic materials varies over a wide range because it depends upon the purity of the material, the local atmosphere, and its previous history. Nevertheless, typical values for the resistivity of various insulating materials can be given. The general orders of magnitude for several materials are given in table 22.

10.7. Dipoles

Consider the case of two equal and opposite electric charges, $+e$ and $-e$, separated by a distance d in vacuum as shown in figure 10.8.

Figure 10.8. An electric dipole of moment $p = ed$.

This pair of electric charges constitutes an *electric dipole;* this was explained in section 1.7 of chapter 1. The *electric moment, p,* of the dipole is defined in equation (1.19) as

$$p = qd \quad \text{coulomb-meters} \qquad (10.2)$$

where q = dipole charge, d = distance between charges directed from the negative charge toward the positive charge. In the example shown in figure 10.8 the electric moment of the dipole is

$$p = ed \qquad (10.3)$$

A somewhat different case is shown in figure 10.9. This is a schematic representation of a helium atom. Here there are two electric dipole moments of equal magnitude and opposite direction. Hence, the *net* dipole moment is zero.

Figure 10.9. Dipoles in a helium atom.

Now suppose that the helium atom is placed in an electric field as shown in figure 10.10. The positive nucleus is displaced in one direction by the electric field; the orbital electrons are displaced in the opposite direction. This changes the dipole moments so that they are no longer exactly equal in magnitude. The atom now has a *net* dipole moment produced by the action of the electric field on the electrons and nucleus. This is called an *induced electronic dipole*. The net dipole moment, or induced electronic dipole disappears when the electric field is removed.

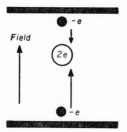 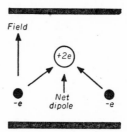

Figure 10.10. Induced dipole in helium for two extreme orientations of the electric field.

There are many, many dipoles formed between the ions making up an ionic solid. However, the *net* dipole moment of such a solid is zero because the atoms are symmetrically arranged under normal conditions. This symmetry causes a dipole in one direction to be exactly offset by another dipole in the opposite direction.

Now, if an electric field is impressed across an ionic solid the ions of opposite polarity are displaced in opposite directions. This results in a net electric dipole moment. This is called an *ionic dipole* moment because it is produced by ions. It is an induced dipole because it is caused by the electric field and disappears when the electric field is removed.

Molecular dipoles appear occasionally. These are molecules that possess a net dipole moment under normal conditions. Such molecules are generally unsymmetrical. These are the *polar* molecules discussed briefly in chapter 5. HCl is a typical example of a polar molecule and it is shown schematically in figure 5.4.

Polar molecules arise from the combination of two unlike elements where

(1) one element has a nearly completed outer electronic shell,

(2) the other element has a deficiency in the outer electronic shell. As a result, the element with the nearly completed outer shell tends to pull electrons away from the atom with the deficiency in the outer

shell. The molecule is then unsymmetric with the charge distributed so that one end of the molecule is relatively positive while the other end is relatively negative. Such molecules exhibit a net dipole moment.

10.8. Polarization and dielectric constant

Consider the case shown in figure 10.11. Here we have a pair of parallel metal plates separated by a distance d in vacuum. A potential

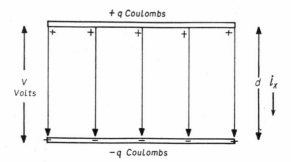

Figure 10.11. Charged plates in vacuum.

difference of V volts is established between the plates. The electric field intensity between the plates is then

$$E = \frac{V}{d}\,\mathbf{i}_x$$

The field intensity is directed in the sense shown by the lines in figure 10.11. The field produces lines of dielectric flux ψ and the flux density is given by

$$D = \epsilon_0 E = \text{electric flux density} \qquad (10.4)$$

The lines of flux are shown in figure 10.11, originating from positive charges and terminating on negative charges.

Now suppose that some insulating material is inserted between the two metal plates as shown in figure 10.12. Because of its physical structure this insulating material will contain some electric dipoles of some type. The electric field produced by the potential difference exerts forces on these dipoles causing them to rotate and align themselves with the electric field as shown in figure 10.12. As you can see from the figure, new lines of flux are set up within the material between the aligned dipoles and terminating on *additional* charges on the metal plates. The *new* value for the electric flux density can now be written as

$$\begin{pmatrix} \text{total flux} \\ \text{density} \end{pmatrix} = \begin{pmatrix} \text{flux density} \\ \text{in vacuum} \end{pmatrix} + \begin{pmatrix} \text{flux density} \\ \text{from dipoles} \end{pmatrix}$$

or
$$D = \epsilon_0 E + P \tag{10.5}$$

The quantity P, which is the flux density added by the aligned dipoles is defined as the *dielectric polarization*.

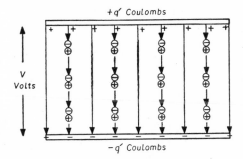

+q′ Coulombs

V
Volts

−q′ Coulombs

Figure 10.12. Action of dipoles to increase the flux density in the region between plates.

In the preceding paragraph we spoke of dipoles rotating when the electric field was applied. Actually, all of the dipoles in the material may be induced and present only when the electric field is applied. However, it is convenient to picture the insulator as being full of dipoles randomly oriented under normal conditions. When an electric field is applied, we assume that it causes the dipoles to rotate until they come into alignment with the electric field.

Suppose that the material between the plates in figure 10.12 contains a total of N dipoles. Assume that the electric moment of each dipole is p. Hence, the total dipole moment is

$$p_T = Np = \text{coulomb-meters}$$

If v denotes the volume of the insulating material, then the *dipole moment per unit volume* is

$$P = \frac{Np}{v} = \text{coulomb/meter}^2 \tag{10.6}$$

The units here, which are *coulombs per meter²* are the units of electric flux density. Hence, the P in equation (10.6) is the *polarization* defined earlier. Thus, the *polarization is the dipole moment per unit volume.*

The equation for the total dielectric flux was given in a previous equation as

$$D \triangleq \epsilon_0 E + P$$

where ϵ_0 = dielectric constant of vacuum. Now define a new term, ϵ, to be the *dielectric constant of the material between plates.* It is defined by the following equation:

$$D = \epsilon E \tag{10.7}$$

where ϵ = dielectric constant of the material between plates. Therefore, we can write

$$\epsilon E = \epsilon_0 E + P \tag{10.8}$$

Divide through by the electric field intensity.

$$\epsilon = \epsilon_0 + \frac{P}{E} \quad \text{farads/meter} \tag{10.9}$$

As long as the polarization and electric field intensity are parallel, and this is usually the case, then the dielectric constant, ϵ, of the material is greater than that of vacuum. It is also clear from this equation that materials containing a high density of dipoles will have a large polarization and a large dielectric constant.

Divide equation (10.9) through by ϵ_0. The result is

$$k_r = 1 + \frac{P}{D} \quad \text{(dimensionless)} \tag{10.10}$$

Table 23
RELATIVE DIELECTRIC CONSTANTS

Material	State	k_r	Material	State	k_r
Glass.........	solid	3.9–5.6	Steatite.......	solid	5.9
Isolantite......	solid	3.8	Pyranol.......	liquid	5.3
Mica..........	solid	5.45	Oil...........	liquid	2.2
Polyethylene...	solid	2.25	Water.........	liquid	78
Polystyrene....	solid	2.55	Air..........	gas	1.00059
Quartz........	solid	3.9	CO_2...........	gas	1.000985
Paper.........	solid	3.5	H_2............	gas	1.000264

where $k_r = \epsilon/\epsilon_0$. The dimensionless constant k_r is called the *relative dielectric* constant. As long as the electric flux density and polarization are parallel, the relative dielectric constant is always greater than unity. For vacuum, the relative dielectric constant is equal to unity, of course. Some typical values for the relative dielectric constant are given in table 23.

10.9. Capacitance

In figure 10.11 shown previously, a charge of $+q$ coulombs is produced on one plate in vacuum, and a charge of $-q$ coulombs on the other plate when a potential difference of V volts is established. If the potential difference is doubled it is found that the number of charges on each metal plate doubles. It appears that the ratio of the charge q to the potential difference V is a constant of the system. This constant is defined as the *capacitance* C. That is,

$$C = \frac{q}{V} \quad \text{coulombs/volt} \tag{10.11}$$

A physical structure having capacitance is called a *capacitor*, or less frequently now, a *condenser*. The unit of capacitance is the *farad*, where

$$1 \text{ farad} = 1 \text{ coulomb/1 volt} \tag{10.12}$$

The farad is too large a unit for most commercial capacitors so that decimal fractions are generally used as follows:

$$1 \ \mu f \ = 1 \text{ microfarad} = 10^{-6} \text{ farad}$$
$$1 \ \mu\mu f = 1 \text{ micro-microfarad} = 10^{-12} \text{ farad}$$

When some insulating material is included between the plates of a capacitor, the situation depicted in figure 10.12 results. The dipoles in the material rotate by an amount sufficient to bring them into alignment with the electric field. In so doing they produce new lines of flux, and induce additional charges on the capacitor plates. This causes the total accumulated charge q' on each plate to be larger than the charge for the vacuum case even though the potential difference remains the same. Let

$$q_i = \text{induced charge}$$
$$q' = q + q_i \tag{10.13}$$

The new value for the capacitance is

$$C' = \frac{q'}{V} = \frac{q + q_i}{V} \tag{10.14}$$

This capacitance is larger than that obtained with vacuum between the plates.

You can easily see that the extent of the increase in capacitance is controlled by the character of the insulating material between plates. The capacitance increases as the density of dipoles increases because this raises the number of induced charges.

The ratio of the capacitance obtained with some insulating material between plates to the capacitance with vacuum insulation is the relative dielectric constant k_r. That is,

$$k_r = \frac{C'}{C} = \frac{q + q_i}{q} = 1 + \frac{q_i}{q} \tag{10.15}$$

10.10. Capacitor construction

Before we can understand why capacitors are manufactured in particular forms we must determine how the capacitance depends upon physical dimensions.

You will recall from section 10.9 that the dielectric constant is a measure of the amount of charge induced on the plates of a capacitor by the electric field in the insulator. It was also shown in section 10.8 that the dielectric constant is a measure of the dielectric polarization. The dielectric constant increases in direct proportion to the increase in induced charge. We find then that the dielectric constant can be defined as follows:

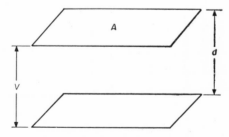

Figure 10.13. Parallel plate capacitor.

$\epsilon =$ charge induced on 1 meter² of capacitor plates
by an electric field intensity of 1 volt/meter

Hence, in the case of a vacuum insulator, 8.854×10^{-12} coulomb is induced on one square meter of metal plate by an electric field having an intensity of one volt per meter. When any other insulating material is used the induced charge will be larger.

Suppose that we have a capacitor consisting of parallel plates A meters in area and separated by a distance of d meters. If the voltage difference between plates is V volts, the situation shown in figure 10.13 exists. The electric field intensity in the insulating material is, in scalar form,

$$E = \frac{V}{d}$$

neglecting fringing effects near the edge of the plates. Hence, the total electric charge accumulated on the plates of the capacitor is

$$Q = \epsilon A E = \epsilon A \frac{V}{d} \qquad (10.16)$$

However, the charge can also be computed from the equation defining capacitance to be

$$Q = CV \qquad (10.17)$$

Equate (10.16) and (10.17) and solve for the capacitance. The result is

$$C = \epsilon \frac{A}{d} \qquad (10.18)$$

This is the desired result. You can see that the capacitance is
(1) linearly dependent upon the dielectric constant

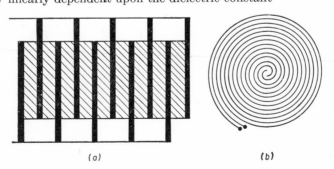

(a)   (b)

Figure 10.14. Two types of capacitors: (a) multiple plate, sandwich construction; (b) rolled paper, or electrolytic type.

(2) directly proportional to the area of the plates

(3) inversely proportional to the distance between plates

Evidently, if a large capacitance is desired, the insulating material should have a large dielectric constant, large plate areas are used, and the separation between plates is small. With these facts in mind, the structural forms of practical capacitors, such as those shown in figure 10.14, are readily understood.

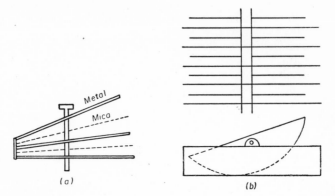

Figure 10.15. Two types of variable capacitors: (a) small variable capacitor; variable d and ϵ; (b) rotary variable capacitor; variable A.

There are many instances where variable capacitors are required. Obviously, the capacitance will vary as A, ϵ, or d are changed. All three methods can be used, though variations in A and d are most common. Two types of commercial variable capacitors are shown in figure 10.15.

10.11. Frequency dependence of dielectric constant

We have seen that the relative dielectric constant of insulating materials is governed by the number of dipoles within the material. This is so because the number of dipoles controls the increase in induced charge over the charge on the plates when a vacuum insulator is used.

If we apply a constant voltage to the plates of a capacitor, the induced charge is a maximum because all of the dipoles are oriented in the direction of the electric field. Hence, the relative dielectric constant has its largest value.

Now suppose that we apply an alternating voltage to the capacitor plates in place of the constant voltage. This alternating voltage is assumed to follow a sinusoidal variation as a function of time as shown in figure 10.16. It is alternately positive and negative. When the

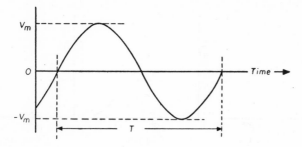

Figure 10.16. Alternating voltage: T = period; $f = 1/T$ = frequency.

voltage alternates in this manner, the dipoles must rotate periodically so that they stay aligned with the electric field intensity in the insulation. As the frequency of this voltage is increased, the polarization has less and less time to form. That is, when the electric field reverses, the dipole orientation must reverse. However, if the field is alternating very rapidly, it might reverse so quickly that the dipoles do not have a chance to fully rotate before the direction of the field again reverses. Thus, the polarization is incomplete, fewer charges are induced on the capacitor plates, and the relative dielectric constant decreases from the value recorded with a constant voltage applied.

We have seen that there are generally three different types of dipoles, leading to three different types of polarization, as follows:

(1) electronic polarization arising from electronic dipoles

(2) ionic polarization arising from ionic dipoles

(3) molecular polarization arising from molecular dipoles

Because of the small size and mass of the electrons, electronic polarization is essentially complete at all frequencies from zero, through visible light and up into the ultraviolet part of the spectrum. Thus, there is no evidence of a drop in electronic polarization. This is shown in figure 10.17.

Ionic polarization involves the motion of much more massive and much larger particles than electrons. As a result, ionic polarization becomes less than complete in the near infrared part of the spectrum as shown in figure 10.17. The polarization is incomplete at these frequencies because the ionic dipoles are so massive that they cannot rotate fast enough to keep up with the rapidly reversing electric field. Thus, they lag behind the field and the net polarization is reduced.

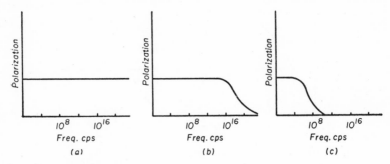

Figure 10.17. Effect of frequency on polarization: (a) electronic polarization; (b) ionic polarization; (c) dipole polarization.

Dipole polarization involving the rotation of entire molecules drops off rapidly in the radio frequencies as shown in figure 10.17. This is expected because they are very much larger and more massive than ions and cannot rotate as rapidly.

From this very brief discussion it is clear that the total dielectric constant of an insulating material should decrease as the frequency of the applied electric field increases. The general character of the curve appears as shown in figure 10.18.

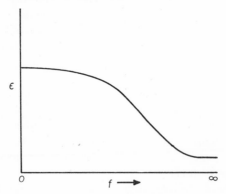

Figure 10.18. Effect of frequency on total dielectric constant.

This effect is confirmed experimentally. For example, the relative dielectric constant of water at zero frequency is 78; it is reduced to only 2 at frequencies of 10^{14} to 10^{15} cycles per second.

10.12. Electrets

Electrets are a particular class of substances that may show *permanent* electric moments. They are produced by solidifying mixtures of certain organic waxes in a strong electric field. Some of the wax molecules carry permanent dipole moments. These are oriented by the electric field and then held to this orientation when the wax solidifies. The resulting solid exhibits a permanent electric dipole moment.

For further details the reader is referred to an excellent summary by Gutman.[2]

10.13. Ferroelectricity

Certain types of crystalline insulators, or *dielectrics*, exhibit *spontaneous* electric dipole moments. Such crystals are said to be *ferroelectric*. These crystals are classified into three natural groups as follows:

(1) barium titanate and related crystals
(2) Rochelle salts and associated isomorphous salts
(3) potassium dihydrogen phosphate and associated isomorphous salts

Barium titanate ($BaTiO_3$) has the simplest form of any crystal exhibiting the ferroelectric effect. As a result, it has received the greatest attention and is generally the best understood.

The crystal structure of barium titanate is shown in figure 10.19. This shows one unit of a three-dimensional *ionic* crystal. The structure is essentially cubic with the various ions arranged as follows:

(1) doubly-charged positive barium ions (Ba^{++}) at the cube corners; eight ions in all for a total of sixteen positive electronic charges
(2) doubly-charged negative oxygen ions (O^{--}) in the centers of the cube faces; six ions in all for a total of twelve negative electronic charges

---

[2] F. Gutman, *Rev. Mod. Phys.*, Vol. 20, 1948, p. 457.

(3) quadruple-charged positive titanium ion (Ti^{++++}) at the cube
center; one ion for a total of four positive electronic charges

Of the twelve negative electronic charges associated with the oxygen ions, four form ionic bonds with the quadruple charged positive
titanium ion. The remaining eight negative electronic charges form
ionic bonds with eight of the positive electronic charges associated
with the barium ions. The remaining eight positive electronic charges

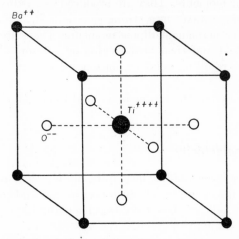

Figure 10.19. A unit from barium titanate, $BaTiO_3$, crystal; this
is called the Perovskite structure. (After Kittel, *Introduction to Solid
State Physics*, New York: John Wiley & Sons, Inc., 1953, p. 116, Fig.
7.1.)

associated with the barium ions, one for each ion, bond this crystal
unit to successive units to form a three-dimensional crystal. Although
this may be a rather drastic oversimplification, you can see that the
electric field about the titanium ion is primarily the contribution of
the oxygen ions. The barium ions produce a very slight effect.

Kittel[3] shows that this particular type of crystal structure is favor-
ably disposed toward the formation of spontaneous electric dipole
moments. The relationship between the titanium and oxygen ions
seems most important, especially the oxygen ions in line with the
titanium ions and parallel to the displacement of the titanium ion.

[3] Charles Kittel, *Introduction to Solid State Physics*, New York: John Wiley &
Sons, Inc., 1953, p. 114.

Because of the unusual character of this crystalline form, the electric field intensity in the neighborhood of the titanium ion is very much larger than it would be in an ordinary body-centered cubic. Thus, a small shift in the position of the central titanium ion causes a large increase in the net dipole moment. If a strong electric field is applied to the crystal, a point is eventually reached where the displacement, and the local electric fields created by the polarization, increase faster than the elastic restoring forces on the ions. This ultimately leads to a shift in the symmetry of the ionic positions and a permanent dipole moment is created in the crystal. The crystal is then ferroelectric.

10.14. Hysteresis in barium titanate

Suppose that we are experimentally taking data to plot some dependent variable y as a function of some independent variable x. We first increase x from 0 to x_m, then decrease it back to 0, then to $-x_m$, and finally back to x_m. When we plot our data for y we find that it has the general form shown in figure 10.20.

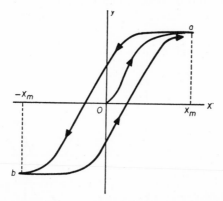

Figure 10.20. General character of the hysteresis effect.

After the initial increase in x we find that a continuous loop, *aba*, is traced out as x is varied over the range from x_m to $-x_m$. This enclosed curve, such as that shown in figure 10.20, is called a *hysteresis loop*. This characteristic of a different curve for increasing and decreasing values of the independent variable is called *hysteresis*.

One of the most striking practical effects associated with barium titanate crystals is their hysteresis loops. In this case:

(1) The independent variable, corresponding to x, is the *applied* electric field intensity E produced inside the crystal.

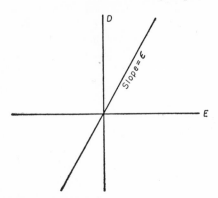

(2) The dependent variable, corresponding to y, is the *dielectric flux density* D, where $D = \epsilon E$.

In ordinary dielectric materials the dielectric constant ϵ is essentially constant under conditions of constant temperature and slowly varying electric field intensities. Hence, a plot of D versus E for such materials yields a straight line as shown in figure 10.21. This is indicative of a constant value for the dielectric constant ϵ.

Figure 10.21. Dielectric flux vs. electric field intensity in a linear dielectric.

However, the unusual structure of barium titanate yields polarization and dielectric constants that depend upon the applied electric field intensity. If we obtain data to plot the dielectric flux density D as a function of the electric field intensity E we get a hysteresis loop of the form shown in figure 10.22.

In figure 10.22 you can see that if we reduce the applied electric field intensity to zero, the flux in the dielectric is not zero, but has a value D_s. This is the flux produced by spontaneous polarization arising from a shift in the positions of the ions within the crystal. It is necessary to apply an opposing field of $-E_c$ volts/

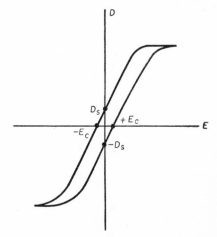

Figure 10.22. Hysteresis loop for barium titanate.

meter to reduce the dielectric flux density to zero. This value of electric field intensity is called the *coercive force*.

The existence of hysteresis in barium titanate has more than mere academic importance. Because of this characteristic, ferroelectric ele-

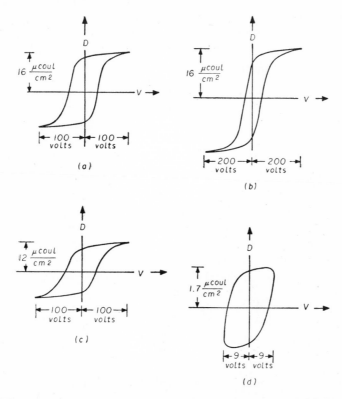

Figure 10.23. Hysteresis loops of barium titanate crystals: (a) 60 cps loop for 100 volts peak applied voltage; 0.0045 inch thick crystal; (b) 60 cps loop for 200 volts peak applied voltage; 0.0035 inch thick crystal; (c) 6000 cps loop for 100 volts peak applied voltage; 0.0045 inch thick crystal—compare with (a) to see the effect of frequency; (d) 60 cps loop for 9 volts peak applied voltage; 0.0035 inch thick crystal—compare with (b) to see the effect of applied voltage. (After J. R. Anderson, "Ferroelectric Materials as Storage Elements for Digital Computers and Switching Systems," *Elec. and Comm.*, No. 1, January 1953, pp. 395–401, Figs. 2 and 3.

ments may enjoy a wide field of application as storage or memory units in electronic computers and possibly in certain types of amplifier and switching circuits.

The hysteresis loops obtained when the electric field intensity is a sinusoidal function of time differ somewhat from those obtained with a slowly varying, essentially constant field. These *dynamic* hysteresis loops are shown for a few cases in figure 10.23.

10.15. Current through capacitors

Capacitance was defined at an earlier point as follows:

$$C = \frac{q}{V} = \text{capacitance in farads}$$

where q = charge in coulombs, V = potential difference in volts. Thus, the charge accumulated on the plates of a capacitor is given by

$$q = CV \tag{10.19}$$

The capacitance is normally independent of time and may be considered to be a constant in the discussion that follows. Hence, as long as the potential difference between the plates of the capacitor is constant, the charge on the capacitor is constant. Because there is no time rate of change of electric charge, the capacitor does not conduct electric current.

Now suppose that the applied potential difference does depend upon time. This will make the electric charge accumulated on the plates depend upon time. Hence,

$$V = v(t) = \text{voltage that is time dependent}$$
$$q = q(t) = \text{accumulated electric charge}$$

So,
$$q(t) = Cv(t) \tag{10.20}$$

Differentiate equation (10.20) with respect to time.

$$\frac{dq}{dt} = C\frac{dv}{dt} + v\frac{dC}{dt}$$

Because the capacitance is assumed to be time invariant, or constant, $dC/dt = 0$. Hence,

$$\frac{dq}{dt} = C\frac{dv}{dt} \tag{10.21}$$

However, the time derivative of electric charge is the definition of electric current i so that

$$i = C \frac{dv}{dt} = \text{current through capacitor} \qquad (10.22)$$

It is important to note that this current is produced in the capacitor without charge motion in the insulating material between the condenser plates. Not even dipole motion need be involved because the dielectric material in the capacitor could be vacuum. The electric current comes about through the time rate of change of charge accumulation on the capacitor plates. Thus, there will be a time rate of change of electric charge at the capacitor terminals and this constitutes the current computed from equation (10.22).

Of course, the dielectric normally contains dipoles and dipole rotation normally results when an electric field is applied. However, this effect is accommodated in the value assigned to the capacitance and does not alter our general picture of the mechanism of current in the capacitor.

Equation (10.22) can be expressed somewhat differently as follows:

$$dv = \frac{1}{C} i \, dt$$

Integrate both sides of the equation.

$$v = \frac{1}{C} \int i \, dt = \frac{q}{C} \qquad (10.23)$$

This states that the voltage across a capacitor is proportional to the instantaneous charge on the plates of the capacitor, or to the integral

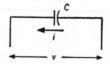

Figure 10.24. Capacitor relationships.

of the current through the capacitor. The factors involved in equations (10.22) and (10.23) are shown in figure 10.24, which also shows the electrical circuit symbol for a capacitor.

10.16. Capacitor circuit relationships

The behavior of connected circuits of many capacitors may be computed using the two simple relationships for single capacitors given in the preceding section. For example, consider the case of *parallel*

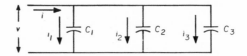

Figure 10.25. Parallel connection of capacitors.

connected capacitors as shown in figure 10.25. For each of the three capacitors we can write

$$i_1 = C_1 \frac{dv}{dt}$$

$$i_2 = C_2 \frac{dv}{dt}$$

$$i_3 = C_3 \frac{dv}{dt}$$

From equation (5.31) of chapter 5 we know that

$$i = i_1 + i_2 + i_3$$

Hence, it is clear that

$$i = (C_1 + C_2 + C_3) \frac{dv}{dt} \qquad (10.24)$$

We would like to replace these three capacitors by a single capacitor C that would draw the same current i from the voltage source v. That is,

$$i = C \frac{dv}{dt} \qquad (10.25)$$

From a term-by-term comparison of equations (10.24) and (10.25) you can see that this equivalent capacitance is

$$C = C_1 + C_2 + C_3 \qquad (10.26)$$

In other words, a single capacitor of capacitance equal to the sum of all paralleled capacitances behaves in precisely the same manner as the paralleled capacitances. Putting it another way, the total capacitance of the paralleled capacitors is equal to the sum of the individual capacitances.

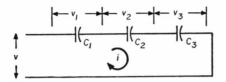

Figure 10.26. Capacitors in series.

When capacitors are connected in series, as shown in figure 10.26, a somewhat different result is obtained. In the case shown in figure 10.26 we know that

$$v_1 = \frac{1}{C_1} \int i \, dt \qquad v_2 = \frac{1}{C_2} \int i \, dt \qquad v_3 = \frac{1}{C_3} \int i \, dt$$

However, from equation (5.29) we can write

$$v = v_1 + v_2 + v_3$$

Substitute the equations for the three capacitor voltages and the result is

$$v = \left(\frac{1}{C_1} + \frac{1}{C_2} + \frac{1}{C_3} \right) \int i \, dt \qquad (10.27)$$

The equation for the single capacitor that is equivalent to this series combination is

$$v = \frac{1}{C} \int i \, dt$$

Hence,

$$\frac{1}{C} = \frac{1}{C_1} + \frac{1}{C_2} + \frac{1}{C_3} \qquad (10.28)$$

or

$$C = \frac{1}{\dfrac{1}{C_1} + \dfrac{1}{C_2} + \dfrac{1}{C_3}} \qquad (10.29)$$

Thus, the effective capacitance of series-connected capacitors is equal to the reciprocal of the sum of the reciprocals of the individual capacitances. When only two capacitors are involved, the total equivalent capacitance is

$$C = \frac{1}{\dfrac{1}{C_1} + \dfrac{1}{C_2}} = \frac{C_1 C_2}{C_1 + C_2} \qquad (10.30)$$

A capacitor stores electrostatic energy in much the same way that a spring stores mechanical potential energy. The energy stored in a capacitor is readily computed from the general relationship given in equation (10.31) below:

$$W = \text{energy} = \int (\text{power})\, dt \qquad (10.31)$$

or, in a more symbolic form,

$$W = \int P\, dt = \int vi\, dt$$

However, in a capacitor,

$$i = C\frac{dv}{dt}$$

so that

$$W = C \int v\, dv = \tfrac{1}{2}Cv^2 \qquad (10.32)$$

The electrostatic potential energy stored in the dielectric of the capacitor can also be computed from

$$W = \tfrac{1}{2}\frac{q^2}{C} \qquad (10.33)$$

PROBLEMS

10.1. A sheet of polystyrene is inserted between two thin aluminum electrodes. The electrodes measure 5 cm by 5 cm and are spaced 1 mm apart. Calculate the resistance of the conduction path between electrodes and the capacitance of the system. Draw an equivalent electric circuit of the system showing the arrangement of the resistance and capacitance just calculated.

10.2. A parallel-plate, mica-dielectric capacitor measures 2 cm by 2 cm with an electrode spacing of 1 mm. Calculate the capacitance and the leakage resistance.

10.3. Two long tubular electrodes are arranged coaxially with one another. The radius of the inside conductor is a and the radius of the outer conductor is b. Derive the equation for the capacitance of a length L of the structure. Neglect field fringing effects.

10.4. Compute the charge densities on the plates of the capacitors in problems 10.1 and 10.2 with a potential difference of 50 volts. Repeat for a potential difference of 10 volts.

10.5. Calculate the dipole moment per unit volume in water with an electric field strength of 1000 volts/cm.

10.6. Repeat problem 10.5 for polystyrene.

10.7. A potential of 100 volts is applied to a capacitor of 0.01 μf. Compute the charge accumulation on the plates.

10.8. How would you expect the dielectric constant of a material to depend upon temperature? Explain your answer in detail.

10.9. The potential difference across a capacitor is given by $v = V_m \sin \omega t$. Derive the equation for the current through the capacitor. Make sketches of the voltage and current as functions of time, showing their correct time relationships.

10.10. Repeat problem 10.9 for a potential difference of $v = V_1 + V_m \sin \omega t$. What do you conclude from problems 10.9 and 10.10?

10.11. The current through a capacitor is given by $i = I_m \sin \omega t$. Derive the equation for the voltage across the capacitor. Sketch the voltage and current in their proper time relationships.

10.12. Calculate the total equivalent capacitance of two capacitors of 8 μf and 16 μf connected (a) in parallel, (b) in series.

10.13. Repeat problem 10.12 for three capacitors of 4 $\mu\mu f$, 10 $\mu\mu f$, and 16 $\mu\mu f$.

10.14. A constant voltage of 115 volts is applied across a 16 μf capacitor. Calculate the energy stored in the capacitor.

10.15. A capacitor of 4 μf is connected in series with two capacitors of 8 μf and 10 μf which are in parallel with each other. Calculate the total equivalent capacitance of the circuit.

11

MAGNETIC PROPERTIES
OF MATTER

In chapter 2 we very briefly discussed the magnetic field and how it is established by moving charges or by an electric current. Such a field may be produced in vacuum, gas, liquid, or solid materials. The effects produced by this magnetic field are very important in engineering and science. Whatever these effects may be, they are dependent upon the characteristics of the material. Thus, in this chapter we shall examine the structural characteristics of various materials as they affect the *magnetic* properties of materials.

There is some correspondence in terminology and approach between the magnetic and dielectric properties of matter. You may find it helpful to read through sections of chapter 10 while studying this chapter.

11.1. Magnetic moment

The general conception of a magnetic field was introduced in sections 2.4 and 2.5 of chapter 2. It was observed in chapter 2 that a magnetic force field is produced about a magnet so that any other magnet in the vicinity experiences a force. We can examine the properties of this force field by moving a magnet of pole strength P throughout the region and measuring the magnitude and direction of the force exerted on the magnet by the field.

Let F signify the vector force exerted on the north pole of the magnet. The strength of the north pole is taken to be P. The pole strength of the south pole is also P units, but the force is in the opposite direction. The *magnetic field strength* or *magnetic field intensity* H can be defined in terms of these factors as follows:

$$H = \text{magnetic field intensity}$$

$$= \frac{\text{force on a north pole}}{\text{pole strength}}$$

or
$$H = \frac{F}{P} \tag{11.1}$$

In other words, the magnetic field intensity can be defined as the force per unit north pole.

Now suppose that a small and very thin bar magnet is located in a uniform magnetic field of intensity H as shown in figure 11.1. Let P denote the strength of the north and south poles of the magnet. Assume the distance between poles, the length of the magnet, to be d. This is a *magnetic dipole* and closely corresponds in form to the electric dipole discussed in chapter 10.

According to equation (11.1), the field exerts a force of magnitude $F = PH$ on each end of the magnet, but the forces are in opposite directions as shown in figure 11.1. The total *torque* T acting on the magnet

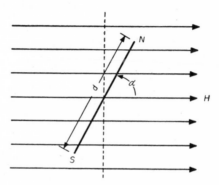

Figure 11.1. Thin bar magnet in a uniform magnetic field.

is the sum of the two torques produced by the two forces at the ends of the magnet. That is

$$T = T_N + T_S = F\frac{d}{2}\sin\alpha + F\frac{d}{2}\sin\alpha$$

$$= Fd\sin\alpha$$

Solve equation (11.1) for the force F and substitute the result into the equation for the torque. This yields

$$T = (Pd)H\sin\alpha \tag{11.2}$$

The two forces producing this torque constitute a *couple*. The *magnetic moment* of this couple is defined as the product of the pole strength and the interpolar distance. That is,

$$m = \text{magnetic moment}$$

$$m = Pd \qquad (11.3)$$

Combine equations (11.2) and (11.3) and the result is

$$T = mH \sin \alpha \qquad (11.4)$$

From an examination of figure 11.1 you can see that the torque acts in such a manner that it aligns the dipole so that it is parallel to the magnetic field when the torque is zero.

It is often necessary to know the magnetic moment of a circular plane current in a uniform magnetic field. You will remember that the electrons in an atom revolve about the nucleus and spin on their axes. In each case they correspond rather closely to circular plane currents. It is extremely important for us to know how they interact with an applied magnetic field. We shall determine this by considering the case of a plane current in a uniform magnetic field.

The general problem is shown in figure 11.2. This shows a perfectly square current element d meters on a side, carrying a current I, and located in a magnetic field of flux density B. For the purposes of this calculation it is assumed that the square can rotate about the z axis *only*. The plane of the square is inclined with respect to the magnetic field so that the plane makes an angle α with respect to the y axis.

The equation for the force exerted by a magnetic field on a current-carrying conductor is given in equation (2.28) of chapter 2 as

$$F = IL \times B \qquad (11.5)$$

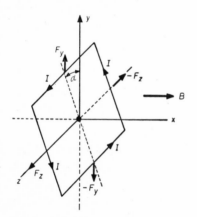

Figure 11.2. Square current element inclined at an angle with respect to a uniform magnetic field directed along the x axis; square free to rotate about the z axis.

Because the force depends upon the *cross product* of these two terms, it is clear that only the component of IL perpendicular to B produces any force. The conductors in the front and back have current elements with x and y components, but the y components produce forces in the $+z$ and $-z$ directions. However, the square cannot rotate about the vertical axis.

The x component is parallel to the magnetic field and does not produce any force.

The top and bottom conductors have only components of IL. The x displacement parallel to the magnetic field does not produce any force. However, the z components produce forces directed up and down as shown in figure 11.2. Hence,

$$F = \pm(Idi_z) \times Bi_x = \pm(BId)i_y \qquad (11.6)$$

These two forces are at right angles to lever arms so that a turning torque about the z axis of the square results. The total torque is

$$T = 2F \times \text{(lever arm)}i \qquad (11.7)$$

The lever arm in this case is

$$\text{lever arm} = \mp\left(\frac{d}{2}\sin\alpha\right) \qquad (11.8)$$

Hence, the total torque is

$$T = -(Id^2B)(\sin\alpha)i_y \times i_z$$

However, d^2 is the area A of the square. Hence, replacing B with $\mu_0 H$, the equation for the *magnitude* of the turning torque about the z axis is

$$T = (AI\mu_0)H\sin\alpha \qquad (11.9)$$

From a term-by-term comparison of this equation and equation (11.4) it is clear that the magnetic moment of the plane, square current is

$$m = AI\mu_0 = \text{magnetic moment of plane current} \qquad (11.10)$$

or $m = \text{(area)(current)}\mu_0 \qquad (11.11)$

The unit associated with the magnetic moment is the *weber-meter*.

The direction of the torque on the square current element is such that it acts to make the angle α zero. This results when the plane of the current element is perpendicular to the magnetic flux density.

Exactly the same result is obtained for a plane *circular* current. That is,

$$m\text{ (circular current)} = \text{(area)(current)}\mu_0 \qquad (11.12)$$

The area of a circular current element is πr^2, where r is the radius of the circle.

The purpose of this brief analysis was to show that both dipoles and plane current elements have magnetic moments. Thus, in much of the discussion that follows we shall assume that plane circular currents are accurately represented by *equivalent dipoles*. The dipoles are equivalent in the sense that we assign them magnetic moments equal to the magnetic moments of the circular currents they are assumed to represent.

11.2. Magnetic polarization

In the preceding section we saw that a circular current has a magnetic moment and could be replaced by an equivalent dipole of the same moment. Circular currents arise in all materials because of the circulation and spin of the electrons. Thus, all materials will contain these equivalent magnetic dipoles and the magnetic properties of the materials will be determined by the origin and behavior of the equivalent dipoles.

In discussing the magnetic properties of materials it is convenient to have a term that measures the amount of magnetization of the material in a total or gross way. A term called the *magnetic polarization*, M, is defined to serve this function. The magnetic polarization is defined as the *magnetic dipole moment per unit volume*. This corresponds exactly to the definition of electric polarization, P, given in chapter 10.

Suppose that a material contains n magnetic dipoles of strength P and interpolar distance d. The individual magnetic moments of the dipoles are each

$$m = Pd \quad \text{weber-meter} \tag{11.13}$$

Now suppose that all of the dipoles are aligned in the same direction. The total magnetic moment for the material is then

$$m_T = nPd \quad \text{weber-meter} \tag{11.14}$$

The magnetic polarization of the material is then

$$M = \frac{nPd}{V} \quad \text{weber/meter}^2 \tag{11.15}$$

where V = volume of material in meter^3.

Now picture a physical situation like that shown in figure 11.3. Here we have arranged a whole series of magnetic dipoles in a uniform geometric pattern with all dipole axes aligned in the same direction.

Faraday conceived the idea of representing a magnetic field, such as that produced by the dipoles in figure 11.3, by endless *lines of magnetic induction*. These lines of induction are conceived to flow out of north poles, into south poles, producing closed paths like those shown in figure 11.3.

The total number of lines of magnetic induction crossing a given area A at right angles is called the magnetic flux ϕ in that area and is measured in webers. The flux per unit area, or *flux density* is $B = (\phi/A)i$, measured in webers per meter².

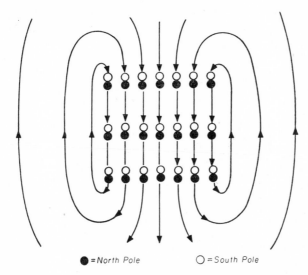

● = *North Pole*   ○ = *South Pole*

Figure 11.3. Lines of induction produced by a uniform geometric array of magnetic dipoles.

Suppose that we produce by some method a magnetic field in vacuum. The magnetic field intensity is H. This field will create a magnetic flux density B at any arbitrarily selected surface. If we double the field intensity, the flux density also doubles because B and H are related by the proportionality constant μ_0, the permeability of the medium. That is,

$$B_v = \mu_0 H \tag{11.16}$$

The flux density is subscripted with a v to denote this as the flux density produced *in vacuum* by the magnetic field intensity.

Now suppose that some material substance containing magnetic dipoles is placed within this field. Although the dipole distribution may have been random, the magnetic field aligns the dipoles parallel to the magnetic field. As a result, the dipoles produce the local magnetic field shown by the dotted lines in figure 11.4b.

The applied magnetic field and the local dipole magnetic field add vectorially at every point in space to produce the net flux distribution shown in figure 11.4c.

You will observe that the magnetic flux density within the material sample is larger than it had been for vacuum as shown by comparison between figures 11.4a and 11.4c. This is caused, of course, by the

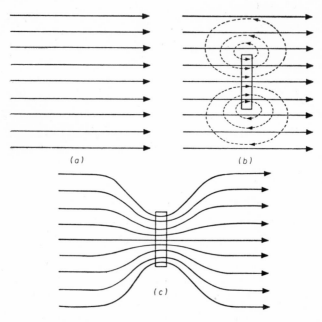

Figure 11.4. Effect of dipoles in a magnetic material on the flux distribution: (a) uniform field in vacuum; (b) dipole field, shown dotted, resulting from dipole alignment by magnetic field; (c) resulting field.

dipole alignment which produces the local dipole field. Thus, the total flux density within the magnetic material is the vector sum of the contributions arising from both the applied field and the induced dipole field. Hence, mathematically, the flux density within the material is

$$B = \mu_0 H + M \quad \text{webers/meter}^2 \qquad (11.18)$$

where $\mu_0 H$ = flux density in vacuum, M = magnetic polarization = flux density from the local dipole field. We will use equation (11.18) in the next section to discuss the various types of magnetic materials.

Later in the chapter we will discuss the origins of the magnetic dipoles in the various types of magnetic materials.

11.3. Permeability and types of magnetic materials

It was shown in the preceding section that the total flux density in a sample of material was equal to the vector sum of the flux density in vacuum and that resulting from the alignment of the magnetic dipoles. In other words,

$$B = \mu_0 H + M \qquad (11.19)$$

Now divide this equation through by the magnetic field intensity to obtain

$$\frac{B}{H} = \mu_0 + \frac{M}{H} \quad \text{henries/meter} \qquad (11.20)$$

The ratio of the magnetic flux density to the magnetic field intensity is a scalar if the two vectors are parallel. We will assume this to be so since it is generally a valid assumption. It is generally valid because the dipole field is generally aligned either parallel or antiparallel to the magnetic field intensity.

The scalar quantity that is the ratio of the flux density to the field intensity is defined as the *permeability* μ of the material. That is,

$$\mu \stackrel{\Delta}{=} \frac{B}{H} \quad \text{henries/meter} \qquad (11.21)$$

Hence, equation (11.20) can be written as

$$\mu = \mu_0 + \frac{M}{H} \quad \text{henries/meter} \qquad (11.22)$$

The vectors M and H are taken to be either parallel or antiparallel. The ratio is then a scalar quantity that could be either positive or negative. As a result, the permeability μ of the material can be either larger or smaller than μ_0, the permeability of vacuum.

The second term in equation (11.22) is defined as the *magnetic susceptibility* χ. That is,

$$\chi \stackrel{\Delta}{=} \frac{M}{H} \quad \text{henries/meter} \qquad (11.23)$$

so that the equation for the permeability of the material is

$$\mu = \mu_0 + \chi \tag{11.24}$$

or
$$\chi = \mu - \mu_0 \tag{11.25}$$

Thus, the susceptibility measures the increase in magnetic dipole moment.

From equation (11.22) it is evident that the permeability of any material will be controlled by two factors, as follows:

(1) the number of magnetic dipoles in the material; this determines the *magnitude* of the dipole polarization vector M

(2) the direction of the polarization vector M relative to H

Later in the chapter we shall examine the structure of various materials with respect to the two factors just listed.

The permeability of any material is generally expressed as the product of two factors as shown in equation (11.26):

$$\mu = k_m \mu_0 \tag{11.26}$$

where k_m = relative permeability (dimensionless). Consequently, the equation for the *relative permeability* is

$$k_m = 1 + \frac{\chi}{\mu_0} = 1 + \frac{M}{\mu_0 H} \tag{11.27}$$

You can easily see from this equation that the relative permeability can be greater or less than unity according to whether the polarization and field intensity are parallel or antiparallel.

It turns out that there are three different types of magnetic materials divided according to the value assigned to k_m. The distinctions are made as follows:

(1) *paramagnetic* materials—k_m slightly larger than 1; χ is $+$

(2) *ferromagnetic* materials—k_m much larger than 1; χ is $+$

(3) *diamagnetic* materials—k_m less than 1; χ is $-$

These differences arise from differences in atomic, molecular, and crystalline structure as we shall see later.

11.4. Curie temperature

The three types of magnetic materials were listed in the preceding section. Of the three types, only *ferromagnetic* materials exhibit a *spontaneous magnetic flux*. In other words, a ferromagnetic material possesses a net magnetic flux even when the applied magnetic field intensity is zero. This spontaneous flux arises from a directed orientation of the magnetic dipoles in the material even when the magnetic field is zero. We shall see a little later how this comes about. For the moment it is sufficient to say that some dipole alignment exists, thereby producing a spontaneous magnetization of the material.

As the temperature of the ferromagnetic material is increased, a point is eventually reached where the spontaneous magnetization disappears and the substance becomes *paramagnetic*. The temperature at which this occurs is called the *Curie temperature*. Some typical values for the Curie temperature are given in Table 24.

It was previously shown that the permeability can be expressed as

$$k_m = 1 + \frac{\chi}{\mu_0} = 1 + \frac{M}{\mu_0 H} \qquad (11.28)$$

As the temperature of the material is increased, the phantom particles tend to destroy the orientation of the dipoles. This acts to reduce the polarization M, causing a reduction in the susceptibility and relative permeability. This action becomes more pronounced at progressively higher temperatures until k_m drops to virtually unity at the Curie temperature. The resulting variation of relative permeability as a function of temperature is shown in figure 11.5.

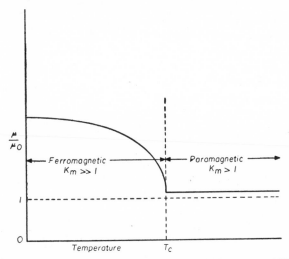

Figure 11.5. Temperature variation of the relative permeability of a ferromagnetic material, showing the Curie temperature T_c.

Above the Curie temperature the material is paramagnetic. The susceptibility continues to drop as the temperature is increased. This should be generally expected because of the disordering effects of the phantom particles at elevated temperatures. The decrease in susceptibility and relative permeability is continuous if there is no change in crystal structure. However, crystalline changes generally occur and produce sharp discontinuities in the curve of permeability as a function of temperature. There are variations in these curves, particularly for cobalt and nickel, that are not very well understood.

Table 24

CURIE TEMPERATURES

Material	Curie Temp. °K
Iron	1043
Nickel	1400
Cobalt	631

11.5. Atomic structure of ferromagnetic materials

A study of ferromagnetic materials is primarily a study of the origins of the magnetic polarization characteristic of such materials. Such a study must commence with an examination of the atomic structure of such materials and then proceed to the structure of the solid state. In this section we shall briefly discuss the atomic characteristics of ferromagnetic elements.

Iron is probably the most common ferromagnetic element. It has an atomic number of 26. From chapter 3 you will recall that this requires 26 orbital electrons and 26 nuclear protons. A rather detailed explanation of how these electrons are assigned to the various main shells and subshells was given in chapter 3. This culminated in table 4 wherein the electronic distributions for the first 46 elements are given. Reference to this table gives the distribution of electrons in iron atoms as shown schematically in figure 11.6. In this figure, n is the principal quantum number and l is the orbital quantum number.

In an iron atom the $n = 3$, $l = 2$ subshell is most important in the development of the ferromagnetic effect. This shell can accommodate 10 electrons as shown in table 4 for element number 29. However, in the case of iron there are only 6 electrons in this subshell so that it is only partially filled. Even though it is incompletely filled, the next subshell, corresponding to $n = 4$, $l = 0$, is completely filled with 2 electrons. While these outermost electrons become the *free* electrons involved in electronic conduction of electricity, the electrons in the incomplete $n = 3$, $l = 2$ subshell are closely related to the ferromagnetic effect.

You will recall from chapter 3 that electrons are assumed to spin about an axis like a top and that the spins are either parallel or antiparallel. Because of this spin the electrons have some of the properties of a circular current and should possess a magnetic moment. The magnetic moment cannot be calculated very easily because we know nothing about the size and shape of an electron or the way

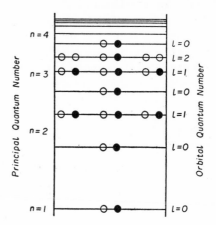

Figure 11.6. Distribution of the 26 electrons in an iron atom: + spins are shown by white circles, − spins by black circles.

the charge is distributed. To obtain agreement with experimental results the *spin magnetic moment* is assigned the value m_s, where

$$m_s = \frac{\mu_0 e h}{4 \pi m} \quad \text{weber-meter} \tag{11.29}$$

where e = charge on an electron in coulombs, μ_0 = permeability of vacuum in henry/meter, m = mass of an electron in kg, h = Planck's constant in joule-sec. The quantity given in equation (11.29) is called a *Bohr magneton*.

The total spin magnetic moment of an atom is computed as the sum of the individual spin magnetic moments. These spins are either parallel or antiparallel, so the spin moments either add or subtract from each other. In some materials the net spin magnetic moment is zero because there are equal numbers of electrons spinning in opposite directions. However, in an atom of iron the situation is rather different. The spin moments of the electrons in all of the shells cancel exactly except in the $n = 3$, $l = 2$ subshell. Here there are four uncompensated spins and the atom has a net magnetic spin moment of four Bohr magnetons.

This general idea is illustrated in figure 11.6. All electrons spinning in one direction are shown by white circles. All electrons spinning in the opposite direction are shown by black circles. You will observe in this figure that the spins in any subshell except $n = 3$, $l = 2$, are compensated by opposite spins. However, in the incomplete subshell there are four uncompensated spins and the atom exhibits a spontaneous magnetic moment or polarization equal to four Bohr magnetons.

Of course, in a free atom the motions of the electrons about their orbits constitute circular currents of definite magnetic moment. These moments definitely contribute to the total magnetic moment of the atom. Although this is an important effect in atoms and gases, it is *not* a large effect in solid materials as we shall see in a later section.

11.6. Electron distribution in solid ferromagnetic materials

When a number of isolated iron atoms are combined to form a solid crystal, the picture presented in the preceding section is altered somewhat. In the solid, the adjacent atoms influence the motion and distribution of one another's electrons. This interaction is quite pronounced in the $n = 3$, $l = 2$ subshell. The interactions are even more severe in the $n = 4$ subshells. Our problem now is to determine the extent of these effects on the net magnetic spin moment of the individual atoms. Nickel provides one illustration.

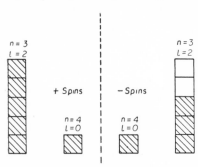

Figure 11.7. Electron distribution and spins in a nickel atom.[1]

In the nickel *atom* the various subshells are all filled up through $n = 3$, $l = 1$. Moreover, all spins are compensated so that the net magnetic spin moment up to this point is zero. However, there are two uncompensated spins in the $n = 3$, $l = 2$ subshell, whereas the

[1] After Bozorth, *Ferromagnetism*, New York: D. Van Nostrand Co., Inc., 1951, p. 436, Fig. 10-7.

two electrons in the $n = 4$, $l = 0$ subshell are fully compensated. This is illustrated in figure 11.7, which purports to show the number of electrons of different spin in the last two subshells. A cross-hatched square denotes one electron and the white squares represent electron vacancies. You can see from this that there are two uncompensated spins in the $n = 3$, $l = 2$ subshell and this leads to a spontaneous magnetic moment for the nickel atom equal to two Bohr magnetons.

When a large number of nickel atoms are combined into a solid crystal of nickel, it is impossible to associate these outer electrons with any one particular atom. This is so because the many atomic interactions produce an overlapping of the atomic shells. As a result, the $n = 3$, $l = 2$, and $n = 4$, $l = 0$ electrons tend to wander about the interatomic array in a more or less random manner. Momentarily they may enter an $n = 4$, $l = 0$ subshell of one atom and then move on to an $n = 3$, $l = 2$ subshell of another atom. As a result, the electronic distribution given for a single, isolated nickel atom no longer applies. Instead, the distribution shown in figure 11.8 applies. It appears to fit experimental observations.

In the case shown in figure 11.8 we find that there are only 0.6 uncompensated spins. Of course, there are electron vacancies of 0.7 in the $n = 4$, $l = 0$ subshell, but each compensates the other so that there is no net magnetic moment in this subshell. The total electron vacancy remains 2 units as you would expect if the atom is not to become ionized.

This diagram represents a *time average* of conditions. At any one instant an electron is either in or out of a subshell and there is no fractional division of electrons. However, because the electrons do move in

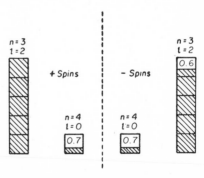

Figure 11.8. Electron distribution and spins in a nickel atom that is part of a nickel crystal. (After Bozorth.)

and out of these subshells, on the average they are occupied by the equivalent of a fraction of an electron. The figure is valid only for such an average representation. It is not correct at any one instant of time.

By comparing figures 11.7 and 11.8 you can see that the net spin magnetic moment has been reduced from 2.0 to 0.6 Bohr magneton. In other words, the reduction in the net spin magnetic moment per atom associated with crystallization causes a reduction in the magnetic polarization of the solid material below that of the aggregate polarization of the atoms.

For iron, a similar analysis shows a reduction of polarization from 4.0 to 2.2 Bohr magnetons.

11.7. Domains and crystal anisotropy

In 1907, Weiss proposed the theory that ferromagnetic materials are composed of large numbers of regions called *domains*. In each domain all of the magnetic dipoles are aligned parallel to one another. As a result, each domain can be characterized by its total magnetic

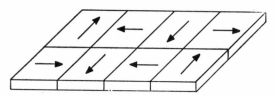

Figure 11.9. Schematic of domain structure of an unmagnetized sample of ferromagnetic material.

dipole moment. A given solid sample could then be represented somewhat as shown in figure 11.9. This shows the material divided into domains with the magnetic dipole moment shown vectorially. In an unmagnetized sample of ferromagnetic material the orientation of the domain magnetization vectors is perfectly random so that the net magnetization is zero.

The existence of these domains is well substantiated by experiment. Using special and refined techniques it is possible to see the domains in solid samples using an optical microscope with a magnification of about 200. Of course, they are never as regular in appearance as the highly idealized representation given in figure 11.9.

The magnetic dipole moment is a vector quantity. The magnetic moment of a domain is given by the *magnitude and direction* of the domain magnetization and by the volume of the domain. The *direc-*

tion of the magnetization is very important and it turns out that this depends upon the crystal structure of the solid material comprising the domain.

For example, iron solidifies in the body-centered cubic crystal form as shown in figure 11.10. Experimentally it is found that magnetization proceeds easily in one direction and less readily in others. The *easiest* direction is denoted 100, which signifies a direction perpendicular to a cube face. From figure 11.10 you can see that there are six

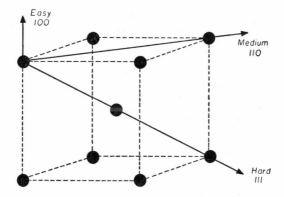

Figure 11.10. Crystal structure of iron, showing comparative ease of magnetization in different directions through the crystal.

directions corresponding to this. The next easiest direction is across a diagonal of a cube face; this is denoted as the 110 direction through the cube. The hardest direction for magnetization is diagonally through the cube, the 111 direction. This effect of different magnetic properties in different directions through the crystal is called *crystal anisotropy*.

In the case of the iron crystal there are six directions through a solid crystal corresponding to the *easy* 100 direction. Hence, in the absence of any other forces, an unmagnetized sample of iron will normally have one sixth of its domain magnetization vectors oriented in each of the six directions of easy magnetization.

A slightly different situation results with nickel. In this case, as shown in figure 11.11, the crystal is a face-centered cubic. The direction of *easy* magnetization is diagonally through the body of the crystal; this is the 111 direction. In a solid crystal there are eight possible 111 directions. Hence, an unmagnetized sample of nickel will normally have one eighth of its domain magnetization vectors oriented in each of eight directions of easy magnetization.

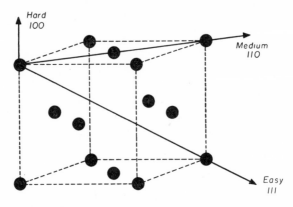

Figure 11.11. Crystal structure of nickel, showing comparative ease of magnetization in different directions through the crystal.

The reason for this anisotropy in the magnetic properties of crystals is not easily explained; it will not be attempted here. An atomic model has been proposed and the most complete investigation of it was made by Van Vleck.[2]

11.8. Further aspects of domain theory

In 1932, Bloch[3] showed that the boundary between domains is not abrupt on an atomic scale, but is spread over a region about 1000 atomic diameters in thickness. This region of transition between domains is called the *Bloch wall*. Consider the case shown schematically in figure 11.12. There are two adjoining domains in which the domain

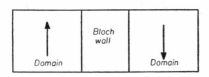

Figure 11.12. Bloch wall between adjoining domains.

[2] J. H. Van Vleck, "On the Anisotropy of Cubic Ferromagnetic Crystals," *Phys. Rev.*, Vol. 52, pp. 1178–1198.

[3] F. Bloch, "Theory of the Exchange Problem and of Residual Magnetism," *Z. Physik*, Vol. 74, pp. 295–335.

magnetization vectors are opposite in direction. The magnetization vector undergoes a gradual rotation through the Bloch wall.

The magnetic moment vector of a domain can be changed in either of two ways if we assume a constant temperature.

(1) The direction of the magnetization vector can be changed by *rotation*.

(2) The magnitude of the magnetization vector can be changed by changing the domain volume; this requires a *moving boundary*.

The properties of these two processes are shown in a highly schematic manner in figures 11.13 and 11.14.

In figure 11.13a, two adjacent domains are shown where there are no external forces applied. For convenience, the domain magnetization vectors are assumed to have the same magnitude and to be at

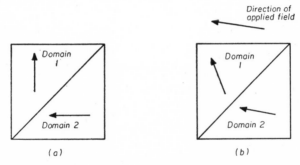

Figure 11.13. Rotation of magnetization vectors through the action of an applied magnetic field: (a) domain magnetization vectors; zero applied field: (b) change in direction of domain magnetization when a field is applied. (After Bozorth.)

right angles to one another. When an external magnetic field is applied as shown in figure 11.13b, the magnetization vectors rotate without change of magnitude. The greatest rotation occurs for that vector more nearly perpendicular to the applied magnetic field.

The two sketches shown in figure 11.14 illustrate the meaning of the *moving boundary*, showing how this changes the domain volume. The change in volume changes the total magnetization of each domain as shown in the figure by the different lengths associated with the vectors.

These changes in magnetization of the domains require the expenditure of energy; some of this energy may appear as heat. When heat is produced the action is *irreversible*. When heat is not evolved, the

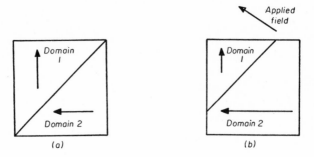

Figure 11.14. Change of domain volume by a moving boundary when a magnetic field is applied: (a) domain magnetization vectors, zero applied field; (b) change in domain volume when an external magnetic field is applied. (After Bozorth.)

action is *reversible*. Thus, the rotation of the magnetization vector or the change in domain volume may be either reversible or irreversible.

It might occur to you that we could change the magnitude of the domain magnetization by simply increasing the dipole moment, rather than by increasing the domain volume. However, it turns out that this requires tremendous magnetic field intensities, as high as the very highest known. It does not appear to be an important effect in most practical cases.

11.9. Magnetization curves

The permeability μ of a ferromagnetic material is not a true constant, but varies with the applied magnetic field intensity. As a result, there is a nonlinear relationship between the magnitudes of the flux density B and the magnetic field intensity H. If the nonlinearity was of a simple type the dependence of B upon H could be expressed mathematically. However, the nonlinearity is very complicated and depends upon many diverse factors. Therefore, the properties of ferromagnetic materials are usually given in graphical form by showing a plot of flux ϕ or flux density B as a function of the magnetic field intensity H. Such a graph is called a *magnetization curve*. A representative curve is shown in figure 11.15.

As the magnetic field intensity H is gradually increased from zero, the flux density B increases continuously. However, at a certain

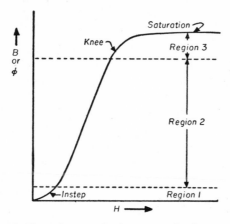

Figure 11.15. Normal magnetization curve of a ferromagnetic material.

rather indefinite point, further increases in magnetic field intensity H produce only very small changes in flux density B. Eventually there is no further change in flux density whatever, regardless of the increase in magnetic field intensity. This is called the *saturation* region of the magnetization curve and is shown on figure 11.15. The *knee* of the curve denotes the region of transition from the unsaturated to the saturated condition. In some materials the change is very abrupt, while it is very gradual in others.

A *normal* magnetization curve for a ferromagnetic material is obtained only under certain very special conditions, as follows:

(1) The material is initially unmagnetized.

(2) Data is obtained by continuously increasing the magnetic field intensity from zero without retracing any steps.

(3) The temperature is below the Curie point.

The domain theory is useful in explaining the origins of the magnetization curve. For small values of magnetic field intensity, corresponding to the region shown as the *instep* in figure 11.15, a reversible boundary displacement occurs in the domains. Those domains having magnetizations more nearly in line with the applied field enlarge at the expense of those domains having other orientations of magnetic moments. This was shown earlier in figure 11.14. The process is essentially reversible.

In region 2 of figure 11.15, as the magnetic field intensity increases, there is a continuing boundary displacement, but the process is irreversible.

In the region of the knee of the curve, a rotation of domain magnetization vectors takes place. The rotation is *not* gradual. The domain magnetization vectors rotate suddenly by either 90° or 180° and come into parallelism with the crystal axis most nearly coinciding with the direction of the applied field. There are no fractional rotations. Each rotation is complete by either 90° or 180° required for parallelism to the appropriate crystal face. The extent of the knee of the curve is determined by the magnetic field intensity required to produce rotation of all domain magnetization vectors.

Beyond the knee of the curve, as the applied magnetic field becomes stronger yet, the magnetization vectors of the domains gradually rotate and are brought more nearly into parallelism with the applied magnetic field. In doing this, the magnetization vectors are no longer parallel to a face of the crystal. When all of the domain magnetization vectors are aligned parallel to the applied magnetic field, the material is saturated.

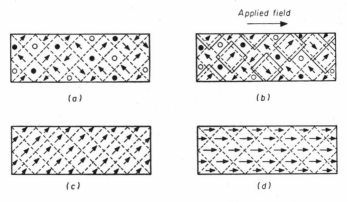

Applied field

(a)   (b)

(c)   (d)

Figure 11.16. Change of domain magnetization as a function of magnetic field intensity in iron: (a) unmagnetized; (b) partial magnetization; boundary displacement; (c) sudden rotations; complete at the end of the knee; (d) saturation complete.

These effects are shown in highly schematic form in figure 11.16. In these sketches the dotted lines represent the directions of the crystal axes and show the division of the material into domains. The arrows, circles, and dots show the direction of domain magnetization. These are always parallel to a crystal axis in iron. The black dots represent the tail end of in-going arrows while the circles represent the points of out-coming arrows. You will find it helpful to correlate these figures with the discussion of the magnetization curve.

11.10. Hysteresis

All ferromagnetic materials exhibit *hysteresis* to some extent. This effect, which was named by Ewing, is illustrated in figure 11.17. After the normal magnetization curve is traced out, if the magnetic field intensity is gradually reduced from the maximum value required to produce complete saturation, the flux density is reduced, but along

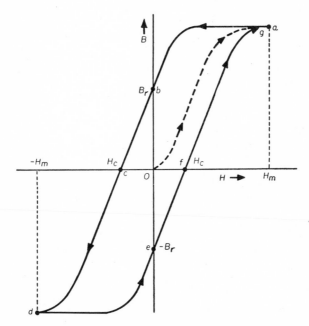

Figure 11.17. Hysteresis loop of a ferromagnetic material under static conditions.

a different path than it followed during the original increase. Thus, a new curve is traced out. If the magnetic field intensity is decreased to zero, reversed, increased to $-H_m$, part a-b-c-d of the curve in figure 11.17 is traced out. If H is then reduced to zero, reversed and increased to $+H_m$, path d-e-f-g is traced out. If this cycle of operation is repeated several times the curve eventually closes upon itself. The complete closed curve is called a *hysteresis loop*.

The magnetic processes involved in the production of the hysteresis loop are the same as those responsible for the normal magnetization curve. The same three regions and domain magnetization effects are present. As you might expect, the phenomenon is largely controlled by the irreversible boundary displacement occurring in region 2.

The vertical intercepts $\pm B_r$ in figure 11.17, corresponding to zero magnetic field intensity, are the values of the *residual flux density*. Hence, you can see that the sample remains magnetized after the magnetizing force is removed. The sample is then a *permanent magnet*. The horizontal intercepts $\pm H_c$ correspond to the values of field intensity required to reduce the flux density in the sample to zero. H_c is called the *coercive force*. Typical values for the coercive force and residual magnetism are given in table 25.

The area of the hysteresis loop is a measure of the energy expended in the irreversible boundary displacement of the domains. This is the principal energy loss. However, a small amount of energy is also lost in domain magnetization rotation. All of this lost energy appears as

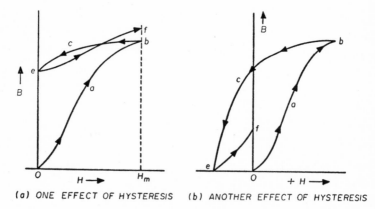

(a) ONE EFFECT OF HYSTERESIS   (b) ANOTHER EFFECT OF HYSTERESIS

Figure 11.18. Some effects of hysteresis.

heat and is called the *hysteresis loss*. Except in certain special cases it is desirable to make this loss as small as possible.

Some of the effects associated with hysteresis are shown in figure 11.18. In 11.18a the sample is initially unmagnetized. As the magnetic field intensity is increased the normal magnetization curve *o-a-b* is traced out. If the field intensity *H* is then reduced to zero, curve *b-c-e* is traced out. If *H* is then increased again to the same maximum value, curve *e-f* results.

In figure 11.18b the sample is initially unmagnetized. As the field intensity *H* is increased, the normal magnetization curve *o-a-b* is traced out. If *B* is reduced to zero, curve *b-c-e* is obtained. If the magnetic field intensity is returned to zero, some residual magnetism remains as curve *e-f* is traced out.

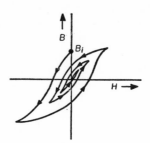

Figure 11.19. Method of demagnetizing an initially magnetized sample of material.

Table 25

SOME PROPERTIES OF FERROMAGNETIC MATERIALS

Material	Composition	Residual Magnetism webers/meter	Coercive Force amp-turns/meter
Carbon steel	98 % Fe 0.86% C 0.9 % Mn	0.95	3.6×10^3
Cobalt steel	52 % Fe 36 % Co 7 % W 3.5 % Cr 0.5 % Mn 0.7 % C	0.95	18×10^3
Alnico 5	51 % Fe 8 % Al 14 % Ni 24 % Co 3 % Cu	1.25	44×10^3

Suppose that a sample of ferromagnetic material is initially magnetized to some flux density B_i as shown in figure 11.19. The procedure required to demagnetize the sample is shown in the figure.

The hysteresis loops described so far were obtained under static conditions where only slowly varying magnetic field intensities were

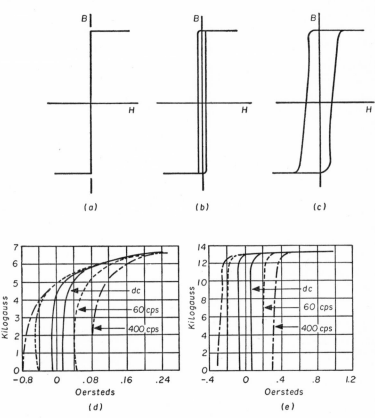

Figure 11.20. Dynamic hysteresis loops of various core materials used in magnetic amplifiers: (a) ideal hysteresis loop; (b) d-c hysteresis loop of 0.005 inch tape core of 65 permalloy; (c) dynamic hysteresis loop at 400 cps of 0.005 inch tape core of 65 permalloy; (d) hysteresis loops of 0.002 inch supermalloy; (e) hysteresis loops of 0.002 inch deltamax with magnetic anneal. (After H. W. Lord, "Dynamic Hysteresis Loops of Several Core Materials Employed in Magnetic Amplifiers," *Comm. and Elec.*, No. 5, March 1953, pp. 85–88, Figs. 1, 4, 8.)

used. When sinusoidally varying magnetic fields of various frequencies are used, the hysteresis loop increases in size and changes slightly in shape as shown in figure 11.20.

11.11. Magnetostriction

When a ferromagnetic sample is magnetized it turns out that its physical dimensions change slightly, by a few parts in a million. These changes are called *magnetostriction*. The change in length parallel to the direction of magnetization is called the *Joule magnetostriction;* this is the type of magnetostriction ordinarily specified.

The fractional change in length $\Delta d/d$ varies with different materials and with magnetic field intensity. For weak field intensities, iron expands in the direction of the magnetic field. At higher fields it contracts and eventually becomes shorter than it was before magnetization. This is illustrated in figure 11.21. However, cobalt undergoes a continual shortening as shown in figure 11.21.

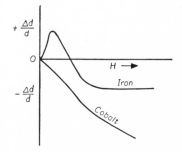

Magnetostriction is closely tied to the domain rotation that takes place in the region of the knee of the normal magnetization curve. There is no appreciable change in length up to that point. Moreover, when the sample is saturated so that all domain

Figure 11.21. Magnetostriction of iron and cobalt as a function of the magnetic field intensity. (After Bozorth.)

magnetization vectors are aligned, the maximum magnetostriction is obtained. Bozorth[5] proved that the change in dimensions of a single domain can be related to the change in direction of its magnetization by the following equation:

$$\left(\frac{\Delta d}{d}\right)_1 = \tfrac{3}{2}\left(\frac{\Delta d}{d}\right)_s (\cos^2 \theta - \tfrac{1}{3}) \qquad (11.31)$$

where $\left(\dfrac{\Delta d}{d}\right)_1$ = fractional change in length

---

[5] R. M. Bozorth, *Ferromagnetism*, New York: D. Van Nostrand, 1951, p. 812.

$$\left(\frac{\Delta d}{d}\right)_s = \text{fractional change in length at saturation}$$

θ = angle between the direction of magnetization and the direction in which the length is changed

For nickel, typical values for the fractional change in length at saturation range from 25 to 47 $\times$ 10^{-6}. Much smaller values are obtained for iron.

11.12. Grain orientation

There are many engineering applications in which the hysteresis loop should be nearly rectangular. The actual hysteresis loops of samples of *grain-oriented* materials approach the rectangular form rather closely.

A *grain* of a metal is composed of an array of cubic shaped crystals of the metal. Grain size varies over a wide range and the number of cubic crystals in the grain varies accordingly. All of the crystals within a given grain fit together like stacked blocks or cubes and are uniformly aligned within any one grain. However, where one grain is bounded by another, the crystals do not align exactly and the resulting imperfection is called the *grain boundary*.

Under ordinary conditions the cubes within any one grain have an arbitrary orientation with respect to the cubes of any other grain. Thus, on a large scale, the over-all effect is of a random orientation of crystals. This is illustrated in a crude manner in figure 11.22a. The grain boundaries are also shown and a small cube in each grain indicates the direction of orientation of all cubes within that grain.

In a previous discussion we found that cubic crystals are magnetically anisotropic. In iron and iron alloys, the preferred direction of magnetization is along one edge of the cube as shown by the arrows in figure 11.22, or perpendicular to a face.

In untreated alloys, such as the one shown in figure 11.22a, the random crystal orientation gives the material nondirectional and relatively poor magnetic properties. It has been found that by cold rolling and subsequent special heat treatments, the cubes can be *oriented in the rolling direction* as shown in figure 11.22b. The term *oriented* means that the cubes lie along one edge in the rolling direction; this is typical of present-day grain-oriented alloys. This results in a material of much improved magnetic characteristics with hysteresis loops of small area and almost rectangular shape. However, it exhibits this property only in the rolling direction and this directional characteristic of the material creates a number of manufacturing problems.

The ultimate in grain orientation is shown in figure 11.22c where the cubes lie flat on one face. Such a material will have three preferred magnetic directions, all at right angles to one another. This should remove the manufacturing problems encountered with current grain-oriented materials.

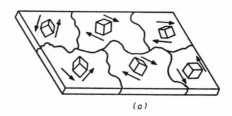

(a)

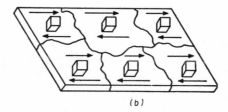

(b)

11.13. Diamagnetism

At the beginning of the discussion of *ferromagnetism* it was shown that the phenomenon arises from uncompensated electron spins that produce spin magnetic dipole moments. The spinning electron was conceived to resemble a circular current and thereby to be represented by an equivalent dipole. This was discussed in section 11.5, and is the source of the spin magnetic moment and the origin of ferromagnetism.

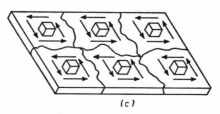

(c)

Figure 11.22. Cube orientation within grains. Arrows indicate best magnetic direction within the sheet: (a) random orientation; (b) grains oriented with cube edge in the rolling direction; (c) cubes sitting on one face—the ultimate goal. (After M. J. Bolton, "Orienting Grains in Transformer Steel," *G. E. Rev.*, May 1953, pp. 13–16.

While all electrons in all atoms exhibit spin magnetic dipole moments, at the same time they are traversing circular or elliptical orbits about the nucleus. Therefore, we should expect to find an orbital magnetic dipole moment associated with the orbital revolution of the electrons. In other words, the electron revolving in its orbit is treated as a circular current and its magnetic dipole moment can then be calculated. As a result, there are two magnetic dipole moments associated with each electron, one arising from electron spin and one arising from orbital motion.

Diamagnetism is closely associated with the orbital magnetic dipole moments of the electrons. Paramagnetism and ferromagnetism are most closely associated with magnetic dipole moments arising from electron spin.

The theory of diamagnetism originates with a paper published by Langevin in 1905. Langevin calculated the magnetic moment associated with an electron revolving in its orbit about the nucleus. This magnetic moment is the product of the equivalent current of the revolving electron and the area enclosed by the orbit. That is,

m_e = orbital magnetic dipole moment of an electron

or $m_e = \mu_0 A I_e$ (11.32)

where A = orbital area in meter², I_e = equivalent current of an orbital electron in amperes, μ_0 = magnetic permeability of vacuum in henry/meter.

The electron is not localized at a point, but is distributed on the average, uniformly around the orbit. If the radius of the assumed orbit is r, the circumference is $2\pi r$ and the concentration of charge per unit distance is

$$q = \frac{e}{2\pi r} \quad \text{coulombs/meter}$$ (11.33)

where e = charge on an electron in coulombs. The current is the product of the velocity of the charge and the charge concentration, or

$$I_e = vq = \frac{ve}{2\pi r} \quad \text{amp}$$ (11.34)

Hence, the dipole moment is

$$m_e = \mu_0 \pi r^2 \frac{ve}{2\pi r}$$

or $m_e = \frac{1}{2}\mu_0 ver \quad \text{weber-meter}$ (11.35)

Now suppose that a magnetic field of intensity H is established and directed perpendicular to the plane of the electron orbit as shown in figure 11.23. It can be shown that the magnetic field does *not* change the orbit. This is called the *Larmor theorem*. However, the magnetic field does exert a force F_m on the electron. In scalar form, this force is

$$F_m = \mu_0 H q v \sin \theta \qquad (11.36)$$

This equation was derived in chapter 2. In the case shown in figure 11.23,

$$q = e$$
$$\theta = 90° = \text{angle between } \boldsymbol{v} \text{ and } \boldsymbol{H}$$

Hence,

$$F_m = \mu_0 H e v \quad \text{newtons} \qquad (11.37)$$

This force must be offset by a change in the centrifugal force if other atomic forces are not to be upset. Because the centrifugal force is

$$F_c = \frac{mv^2}{r} \quad \text{newtons} \qquad (11.38)$$

then for equilibrium in the magnetic field

$$\Delta F_c = F_m \qquad (11.39)$$

where

$$\Delta F_c = \Delta \left(\frac{mv^2}{r} \right)_{r=\text{constant}}$$

Hence,

$$\Delta F_c = \frac{2mv\Delta v}{r} \quad \text{newtons} \qquad (11.40)$$

Therefore, establishing the equality given in (11.39) yields

$$\frac{2mv\Delta v}{r} = \mu_0 H e v \qquad (11.41)$$

Solve this for the change in electron velocity to obtain

$$\Delta v = \frac{\mu_0 H e r}{2m} \quad \text{meters/sec} \qquad (11.42)$$

The action of the magnetic field is such that Δv is positive in figure 11.23. In other words, the electron is speeded up. However, Δv is negative and the electron is slowed down if the direction of electron revolution is reversed.

The direction of the magnetic field set up by the electron in figure 11.23 is opposite to the direction of the applied magnetic field. The applied field increases the electron velocity, because Δv is positive, and this increases the magnetic field generated by the revolving electron in opposition to the applied field. Hence, the application of a magnetic field causes the electron to produce a field that opposes the action of the applied field.

Exactly the same result is obtained if the direction of electron rotation is reversed from that shown in figure 11.23. However, in this case the magnetic field associated with the electron is in the *same*

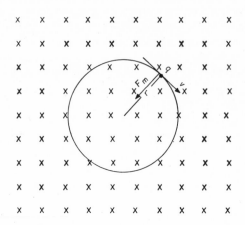

Figure 11.23. Orbital electron in a magnetic field perpendicular to the plane of the orbit.

direction as the applied field. The applied field causes a reduction in electron velocity, making Δv negative. This reduces the magnetic field of the orbital electron. As before, the action opposes that of the applied field.

The change in orbital magnetic moment associated with a change in velocity is

$$\Delta m_e = \tfrac{1}{2}\mu_0 \Delta ver \quad \text{weber-meter} \tag{11.43}$$

or, substituting equation (11.42) for the change in velocity,

$$\Delta m_e = \frac{(\mu_0 er)^2 H}{4m} \quad \text{weber-meter} \tag{11.44}$$

The *electronic susceptibility* associated with this moment is

$$\chi_e = -\frac{\Delta m_e}{H} \tag{11.45}$$

or
$$\chi_e = -\frac{\mu_0^2 e^2 r^2}{4m} \tag{11.46}$$

The minus sign signifies that the change in moment and applied magnetic field are in opposite directions. The negative susceptibility is the distinguishing characteristic of *diamagnetic* materials.

Of course, most atoms have many electrons and their orbits are oriented in all directions with respect to some applied magnetic field. Hence, to compute the diamagnetic susceptibility of the atom, it is necessary to total the moments of the electrons.

Clearly, all atoms will exhibit this diamagnetic property. However, all electrons also possess spin moments. Whenever the spin moments are completely compensated, the diamagnetic effect is all that remains and the material itself is diamagnetic. It seems clear that the inert gases should be diamagnetic because their atoms have an even number of electrons and all spins are fully compensated. The same remarks apply to positive alkali ions and negative halogen ions. Hence, ionic compounds such as sodium chloride (NaCl) are diamagnetic for the same reason. Most molecular compounds are also diamagnetic, and for the same reason. Antimony and bismuth are two other diamagnetic elements.

Diamagnetic materials have susceptibilities in the general range from -1×10^{-6} to -10×10^{-6}. These values are six or more orders of magnitude less than the susceptibilities of ferromagnetic materials. We conclude that the diamagnetic effect arising from electron orbital motion is much less than the ferromagnetic effect arising from uncompensated electron spins.

11.14. Paramagnetism

From the preceding discussion of diamagnetism it should be clear that *paramagnetism* falls somewhere between ferromagnetism and diamagnetism. It is obvious that it can occur only when there is an uncompensated electron. Accordingly, you would expect to find electronic paramagnetism in the following cases:

(1) Whenever an ion, atom, or a molecule has an odd number of electrons, the particle will be paramagnetic. In such a case the total spin cannot possibly be zero. Alkali metal atoms are typical examples.

(2) Whenever an inner shell of an atom is incomplete, there is a net spin moment and the atom is paramagnetic. The transition and rare-earth metals fit this category.

(3) When certain metal atoms are combined into a solid, the outer electrons become essentially free. It was shown by Pauli that a *gas* of free electrons has a weakly paramagnetic characteristic. Solid sodium exhibits this property.

11.15. Rowland's Law

It was shown previously that the magnetic flux density B and field intensity H are related by the permeability μ of the medium containing the flux. That is, in scalar form,

$$B = \mu H \qquad (11.47)$$

In the simple magnetic circuit shown in figure 11.24, a coil of N turns and carrying a current I produces a magnetic field intensity of NI ampere turns per meter of flux path. That is,

$$H = \frac{NI}{L} \quad \text{ampere-turns/meter} \qquad (11.48)$$

where L = length of the flux path in meters. The length of the flux path is shown by the dotted line in figure 11.24.

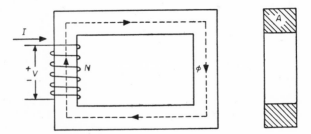

Figure 11.24. A simple magnetic circuit.

This magnetic field produces a flux ϕ in the material. If the cross-sectional area of the flux path is A, as shown in figure 11.24, the magnetic flux density is

$$B = \frac{\phi}{A} \qquad (11.49)$$

Now substitute equations (11.48) and (11.49) into equation (11.47). Solve for the flux, and the result can be written as

$$\phi = \frac{\mu A}{L} NI \tag{11.50}$$

The various terms in this equation are identified by the following names and symbols:

$$\mathcal{P} = \text{permeance of the flux path} = \mu \frac{A}{L} \tag{11.51}$$

$$\mathcal{F} = \text{magnetomotive force (mmf)} = NI \tag{11.52}$$

Hence, equation (11.50) can be written as

$$\phi = \mathcal{P}\mathcal{F} \tag{11.52}$$

This is called *Rowland's Law* for the magnetic circuit. It bears essentially the same relationship to magnetic circuits that Ohm's Law bears to electric circuits. The correspondence is more apparent if we define a new term, as follows:

$$\mathcal{R} = \frac{1}{\mathcal{P}} = \text{reluctance of the flux path} \tag{11.53}$$

Hence, Rowland's Law can also be written as

$$\phi = \frac{\mathcal{F}}{\mathcal{R}} \tag{11.54}$$

Ohm's Law for the electric circuit is

$$I = \frac{V}{R} \tag{11.55}$$

From a term-by-term comparison of the two equations you can see that:

(1) Magnetic flux corresponds to electric current.
(2) Magnetomotive force corresponds to electrical potential difference.
(3) Reluctance corresponds to electrical resistance.

Rowland's Law is the basic relationship required in the solution of magnetic circuits. Many practical magnetic circuits involve ferromagnetic materials so that the permeance of the flux path is a nonlinear function of the field intensity or magnetomotive force. Purely analytical solutions are virtually impossible under these conditions and resort is made to graphical analysis. This subject forms an important part of the study of electrical machinery.

11.16. Self inductance

Figure 11.25 shows a coil of N turns wound about one leg of a rectangular piece of magnetic material. A current I is caused to pass

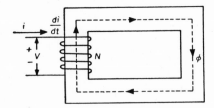

Figure 11.25. A simple inductance.

through the coil producing a flux ϕ in the magnetic material or *core*. The current is assumed to vary as a function of time and this produces a time variation in the flux.

From Rowland's Law we have the general relationship between magnetic flux and electrical current in the form

$$\phi = \mathscr{P}\mathscr{F} = \mathscr{P}NI \tag{11.56}$$

The time rate of change of flux is

$$\frac{d\phi}{dt} = N\left(\mathscr{P}\frac{dI}{dt} + I\frac{d\mathscr{P}}{dt}\right) \tag{11.57}$$

In some cases the permeance of the flux path is a constant, independent of time. In other cases it varies with time. However, for our purposes it is assumed that the permeance is time invariant so that its derivative with respect to time is zero. Hence, the time rate of change of flux is

$$\frac{d\phi}{dt} = N\mathscr{P}\frac{dI}{dt} \tag{11.58}$$

From the general law of magnetic induction derived in chapter 2 we have

$$V = N\frac{d\phi}{dt} \tag{11.59}$$

Substitute equation (11.58) for the time rate of change of flux and the resulting equation for the voltage drop across the coil is

$$V = (N^2\mathscr{P})\frac{dI}{dt} \tag{11.60}$$

The bracketed factor in equation (11.60) is defined as the *self inductance L* of the coil and material shown in figure 11.25. That is,

$$L \triangleq N^2 \mathcal{P} \tag{11.61}$$

Hence, the equation for the coil voltage can be written as

$$V = L \frac{dI}{dt} \tag{11.62}$$

This is a fundamental relationship in the field of electric circuit theory.

It is important to establish the proper relationship between the direction of the current through the coil and the relative polarity assigned to the potential difference across the coil. The situation shown in figure 11.25 is correct when the coil current is increasing so that dI/dt is positive. The following two statements can be made:

(1) *Increasing* current in an inductance is directed from a point of positive voltage to one of negative voltage; current is directed from + to −.

(2) *Decreasing* current in an inductance is directed from a point of negative voltage to one of positive voltage; current is directed from − to +.

It is helpful to examine the effect of an *inductor* as described by equation (11.62). The coil voltage is proportional to the time rate

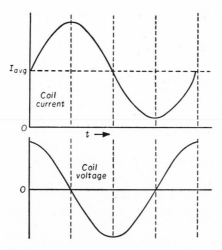

Figure 11.26. Voltage and current relationships in an inductor.

of change of current. If the current is increasing so that dI/dt is positive, the coil voltage is positive. If the current is decreasing, dI/dt is negative and the coil voltage is negative. The coil voltage produced by a sinusoidal current is shown in figure 11.26. The same coil voltage is obtained regardless of the value of I_{avg}.

The inductance can be defined in another way by rearranging the terms in equation (11.61) as follows:

$$L = N^2 \mathcal{P} = N^2 \frac{\phi}{\mathcal{F}} = N^2 \frac{\phi}{NI} \qquad (11.63)$$

or, finally,

$$L = \frac{N\phi}{I} = \frac{\lambda}{I} \qquad (11.64)$$

where $\lambda = N\phi =$ magnetic flux linkages.   (11.65)

In equation (11.64) inductance is defined as the *flux linkages per ampere* of electrical current. The symbol L used for inductance is associated with the L that is the first letter of the word *linkages*.

The energy stored in the magnetic field of an inductance is easily calculated. That is,

$$W = \text{energy stored in the inductor}$$

$$= \int (\text{power})\, dt = \int VI\, dt \qquad (11.66)$$

Substitute equation (11.62) for the voltage in (11.66).

$$W = \int LI \frac{dI}{dt}\, dt = \int LI\, dI$$

or $$W = \frac{1}{2} LI^2 \qquad (11.67)$$

11.17. Inductors as circuit elements

Some of the various symbols used to denote inductances, or inductors, on electrical circuit diagrams are shown in figure 11.27.

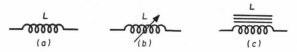

Figure 11.27. Circuit symbols for inductors.

A series connection of two inductors is shown in figure 11.28. Our problem is to determine how these two inductances combine to produce the total equivalent inductance of the circuit. The total voltage

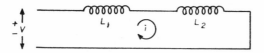

Figure 11.28. Series connection of two inductors.

across the two inductors is the sum of the two coil voltages. That is,

$$V = V_{L_1} + V_{L_2} \tag{11.68}$$

The same current is present in both coils so the two coil voltages are

$$V_{L_1} = L_1 \frac{di}{dt} \qquad V_{L_2} = L_2 \frac{di}{dt}$$

Hence, equation (11.68) can be written as

$$V = (L_1 + L_2) \frac{di}{dt} \tag{11.69}$$

The total inductance of the circuit is defined by the equation

$$V = L \frac{di}{dt} \tag{11.70}$$

Equate (11.70) to (11.69) and solve for the total inductance L.

$$L = L_1 + L_2 \tag{11.71}$$

Thus, the total inductance of a series combination of inductors is the sum of the separate inductances.

Two parallel connected inductors are shown in figure 11.29. The coil voltages are equal in this case so that

$$V = L_1 \frac{di_1}{dt} = L_2 \frac{di_2}{dt} \tag{11.72}$$

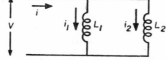

Figure 11.29. Parallel connected inductors.

Solve each of these equations for the time derivative of the current in each inductor. This gives

$$\frac{di_1}{dt} = \frac{V}{L_1} \quad \text{and} \quad \frac{di_2}{dt} = \frac{V}{L_2} \qquad (11.73)$$

Now, according to Kirchhoff's node law, the sum of the currents into a junction is equal to the sum of the currents out of the junction. Thus, in figure 11.29

$$i = i_1 + i_2 \qquad (11.74)$$

Take the derivative of both sides of this equation with respect to time.

$$\frac{di}{dt} = \frac{di_1}{dt} + \frac{di_2}{dt} \qquad (11.75)$$

Substitute equations (11.73) into (11.75) to obtain

$$\frac{di}{dt} = V\left(\frac{1}{L_1} + \frac{1}{L_2}\right) \qquad (11.76)$$

The total equivalent inductance of the parallel circuit is defined by

$$V = L\frac{di}{dt}$$

Solve this equation for di/dt.

$$\frac{di}{dt} = \frac{V}{L} \qquad (11.77)$$

Now equate (11.77) and (11.76), and solve the result for the total equivalent inductance L. The result is

$$L = \frac{1}{\dfrac{1}{L_1} + \dfrac{1}{L_2}} \qquad (11.78)$$

So, the total inductance of parallel connected coils is the reciprocal of the sum of the reciprocals of the individual coil inductances.

11.18. Mutual inductance

All of the discussion of inductance so far has been restricted to those cases involving single, isolated coils. Even when series and parallel connections were considered, it was assumed that the magnetic flux of one coil did not enter the flux path of any other coil. An arrangement of two coils is shown in figure 11.30 where the flux of each coil passes through the flux path of the other coil. This is a very common electrical principle embodied in practical devices called transformers.

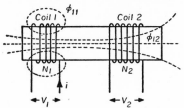

In figure 11.30 it is assumed that a current is present in coil 1 producing a flux ϕ_1. Some of this flux links the second coil and all of it links the first coil. In this situation we can define two different inductances by the following equations:

Figure 11.30. Two coils magnetically coupled through the mutual flux ϕ_{12}; flux paths are shown by dotted lines.

$$V_1 = L_1 \frac{di}{dt} \tag{11.79}$$

$$V_2 = L_{12} \frac{di}{dt} \tag{11.80}$$

where L_1 = self inductance of coil 1, L_{12} = *mutual* inductance between coil 1 and coil 2. It is clear from equation (11.80) that the mutual inductance relates the voltage across one coil to the current through the other coil.

The total magnetic flux ϕ_1 produced by coil 1 may be subdivided into two components as follows:

ϕ_{11} = flux produced by coil 1 linking *only* coil 1

ϕ_{12} = flux produced by coil 1 linking coil 2

= *mutual flux*

$\phi_1 = \phi_{11} + \phi_{12}$

The permeances of the paths associated with these fluxes are specified in the following way:

$\mathcal{P}_1$ = permeance of the path of ϕ_1

$\mathcal{P}_{11}$ = permeance associated with the path of ϕ_{11}

$\mathcal{P}_{12}$ = permeance associated with the path of ϕ_{12}

The total magnetomotive force is the product of the number of turns on coil 1 times the current through the coil. Thus, the magnetomotive force is $N_1 i$. By Rowland's Law we have

$$\phi_1 = N_1 i \mathcal{P}_1 = \phi_{11} + \phi_{12} \tag{11.81}$$

or $$\phi_{11} + \phi_{12} = N_1 i \mathcal{P}_{11} + N_1 i \mathcal{P}_{12} \tag{11.82}$$

Hence, the relationship between the permeances of the flux paths is

$$\mathcal{P}_1 = \mathcal{P}_{11} + \mathcal{P}_{12} \tag{11.83}$$

The *self inductance* L_1 of coil 1 is readily computed from equation (11.61) to be

$$L_1 = N_1^2 \mathcal{P}_1 = N_1^2 \mathcal{P}_{11} + N_1^2 \mathcal{P}_{12} \tag{11.84}$$

Hence, $$L_1 = L_{11} + N_1^2 \mathcal{P}_{12} \tag{11.85}$$

The calculation of the mutual inductance is a little less direct.

The flux linking coil 2 is ϕ_{12}. The magnetomotive force is $N_1 i$. The permeance of the flux path is $\mathcal{P}_{12}$. By Rowland's Law

$$\phi_{12} = N_1 i \mathcal{P}_{12} \tag{11.86}$$

The time rate of change of mutual flux is

$$\frac{d\phi_{12}}{dt} = N_1 \mathcal{P}_{12} \frac{di}{dt} \tag{11.87}$$

The voltage induced in coil 2 according to the law of induction is

$$V_2 = N_2 \frac{d\phi_{12}}{dt} = N_1 N_2 \mathcal{P}_{12} \frac{di}{dt} \tag{11.88}$$

Hence, from equation (11.80), the *mutual inductance* is

$$L_{12} = N_1 N_2 \mathcal{P}_{12} \tag{11.89}$$

Now combine equations (11.85) and (11.89) to obtain

$$L_1 = L_{11} + \frac{N_1}{N_2} L_{12} \tag{11.90}$$

It is a pretty simple matter to repeat the whole process for the case where coil 2 is energized with current and coil 1 is open circuited. It is left as an exercise for the reader to prove that

$$L_2 = L_{22} + \frac{N_2}{N_1} L_{21} \tag{11.91}$$

where $L_{21} = N_1 N_2 \mathcal{P}_{21}$ (11.92)

Ordinarily the permeance of the flux path is the same from coil 1 to coil 2 as it is from coil 2 to coil 1. Hence, usually $\mathcal{P}_{12} = \mathcal{P}_{21}$. This is not always true, but the exceptions are rare. Hence, we shall assume it to be true so that

$$L_{12} = L_{21} = M \tag{11.93}$$

Therefore, equations (11.90) and (11.91) become

$$L_1 = L_{11} + \frac{N_1}{N_2} M \tag{11.94}$$

$$L_2 = L_{22} + \frac{N_2}{N_1} M \tag{11.95}$$

Solve both of these equations for the mutual inductance M; multiply the results together and solve for M. This gives

$$M = \pm\sqrt{(L_1 - L_{11})(L_2 - L_{22})} \tag{11.96}$$

The circuit symbols used for mutual inductances and transformers are shown in figure 11.31. The circuit equations are obtained from

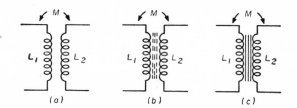

Figure 11.31. Circuit symbols for mutual inductances and transformers: (a) air core; (b) powdered-iron core; (c) iron core.

the defining equation for the mutual inductance given in equation (11.80). Thus,

$$V_2 = \pm M \frac{di_1}{dt} \quad \text{and} \quad V_1 = \pm M \frac{di_2}{dt} \tag{11.97}$$

The $\pm$ sign arises from the fact that the winding senses of the two coils can be the same or opposite to one another.

11.19. Coefficient of coupling

An equation for the mutual inductance M between two coils was derived in the preceding section and the result was given as

$$M = \pm\sqrt{(L_1 - L_{11})(L_2 - L_{22})}$$

Now suppose that all of the flux is mutual so that

$$\phi_1 = \phi_{12} \quad \text{and} \quad \phi_{11} = 0$$
$$\phi_2 = \phi_{21} \quad \text{and} \quad \phi_{22} = 0$$

This makes L_{11} and L_{22} zero, thereby making the mutual inductance have its largest possible value. In other words,

$$M_{max} = \pm\sqrt{L_1 L_2} \tag{11.98}$$

Although this is an idealized situation it is closely approximated in commercial transformers having ferromagnetic cores.

The ratio of the *actual* mutual inductance M to this theoretical maximum is called the *coefficient of coupling*, k. That is,

$$k = \pm\frac{M}{\sqrt{L_1 L_2}} \tag{11.99}$$

and so $$M = \pm k\sqrt{L_1 L_2} \tag{11.100}$$

Typical values for the coefficient of coupling range from 0.01 in radio frequency air-core transformers to figures in excess of 0.99 for iron-core transformers of special design.

PROBLEMS

11.1. Calculate the magnetic moment of a magnetic dipole having poles of strength 0.25×10^{-4} weber separated by a distance of 0.15 mm.

11.2. Calculate the torque on the dipole in problem 11.1 if it is located in a uniform magnetic field in vacuum. The strength of the field is 12 ampere-turns/meter. Assume the dipole axis makes an angle of 45° with the field intensity vector.

11.3. Calculate the magnetic moment of a circular current element of radius 2×10^{-5} meter and carrying a current of 10^{-17} amp.

11.4. Repeat 11.3 for a circular current element having a radius of 2×10^{-6} meter and carrying the same current.

11.5. Calculate the torques on the circular currents in problems 11.3 and 11.4 in a magnetic field of 10 ampere-turns/meter in vacuum. Assume the axis of the circular current is inclined at an angle of 30° with respect to the magnetic field.

11.6. A given cubic material sample measures 1 cm on a side and contains a total of 10^{18} magnetic dipoles having moments of 0.3×10^{-30} weber-meter. Calculate the magnetic polarization.

11.7. Calculate the magnetic flux density in a material having a polarization of 3×10^{-6} weber/meter^2 when a field intensity of 10 ampere-turns/meter is impressed. Calculate the relative permeability and magnetic susceptibility of the material.

11.8. Repeat problem 11.7 assuming the polarization is

(a) 1×10^{-6} weber/meter^2

(b) 10×10^{-6} weber/meter^2

(c) 100×10^{-6} weber/meter^2

(d) -1×10^{-6} weber/meter^2

Identify each material as ferromagnetic, paramagnetic, or diamagnetic.

11.9. Calculate the numerical value of the electron spin magnetic moment in weber-meters.

11.10. Calculate the total magnetic moment of 1 cc of nickel. You will have to look up the atomic weight of nickel.

11.11. Repeat problem 11.10 for iron.

11.12. Calculate the magnetic moment of a single iron atom. What would be the magnetic moment of 1 cc of iron if all of the individual atomic moments added directly?

11.13. In a thin, rodlike, single-crystal, nickel sample the total fractional change in length through magnetostriction at saturation is 30×10^{-6}. Assume that the sample is 2 cm long and the direction of the magnetization makes an angle of 30° relative to the change in length. Calculate the actual change in length of the rod.

11.14. Compute the change in orbital magnetic moment of the electron in a hydrogen atom when a field of 100 ampere-turns/meter is impressed. What is the electronic susceptibility?

11.15. How does the value calculated in 11.14 compare with the value of the magnetic spin moment?

11.16. A rectangular ferromagnetic device is constructed as shown in figure 11.24 where the lengths of the sides are 5 cm, the top and bottom are 6 cm, with distances measured along the center lines. The sample has a 2 cm^2 cross section and has a relative permeability of 75. Calculate the permeance of the flux path. Calculate the reluctance. Specify units in both cases.

11.17. A coil of 200 turns is wound about the left leg of the device in problem 11.16 and is energized with a current of 2 amp. Assume that the relative permeability of the material is 75 under these conditions. Calculate the magnetic field intensity, flux density, and flux.

11.18. Calculate the self inductance of the coil in problem 11.17. Compute the energy stored in the magnetic field of the coil.

11.19. Three inductors of 1, 3, and 5 henries are connected in series. What is the total inductance of the combination? What is the total inductance if they are connected in parallel?

11.20. A coil of 1400 turns is wound in a single layer, close spaced, on a radius of 2 cm over a length of 230 cm. Calculate the approximate value for the inductance assuming air as the magnetic medium. Describe any approximations you make.

11.21. Two coils are wound about two legs of a piece of ferromagnetic material of the form shown in figure 11.24. Ninety-eight per cent of the flux of each coil links the other coil. What is the coefficient of coupling? If $L_1 = 5$ hy and $L_2 = 3$ hy, calculate M.

$$F = \beta e v$$

$$\beta = \frac{\xi'}{Velocity} \quad (zero \ deflection)$$

balanced field
singly ionized electron

$$\eta e \, \xi' = \eta \, \mathcal{U}g_{nav}.$$

$$* \quad E_g = KT \quad (energy \ to \ break \ a \ covalent \ bond.)$$

$$* f' = \frac{\beta e}{2 \pi m} \quad (cyclotron \ formula)$$

Appendix I

FUNDAMENTAL PHYSICAL CONSTANTS

$M = \dfrac{\text{atomic wt}}{\text{avogadros No.}}$

m = rest mass of an electron

   = 9.107×10^{-31} kilogram

e = charge on an electron

   = 1.602×10^{-19} coulomb

h = Planck's constant

   = 6.624×10^{-34} joule-sec

k = Boltzmann's constant

   = 1.380×10^{-23} joule/°K

R = gas constant

   = 8.314 joule/°K/mole

N = Avogadro's number

   = 6.023×10^{23} per mole

ϵ_0 = dielectric constant of vacuum

   = 8.854×10^{-12} farad/meter

μ_0 = permeability of vacuum

   = $4\pi \times 10^{-7}$ henry/meter

c = velocity of light

   = 2.998×10^8 meters/sec

1 electron-volt = 1.602×10^{-19} joule

(handwritten annotations)

$e^{-\frac{E_g}{2KT}}$

1.38×10^{-23}

$\lambda = \dfrac{hc}{E_g}$

$Ge \quad A = 9.7 \times 10^{15}$

$Si \quad A = 2.8 \times 10^{16}$

Values for c, e, m, h, k, and N from R. T. Birge, "A New Table of Values of the General Physical Constants," *Rev. Mod. Phys.*, Vol. 13, Oct. 1941, pp. 233–239; with permission.

METER-KILOGRAM-SECOND-COULOMB (MKSC) SYSTEM OF UNITS

Basic Units:

d = length in meters
m = mass in kilograms
t = time in seconds
q = charge in coulombs

Derived Units—Mechanical:

v = velocity in meters/sec
a = acceleration in meters/sec^2
F = force in kilogram-meter/sec^2 = newtons
W = energy or work in newton-meter = joule
P = power in joule/sec = watt
p = momentum in kilogram-meter/sec

Derived Units—Electrical:

I = current in coulombs/sec = amperes
V = electric potential in joule/coulomb = volt
E = electric field intensity in newton/coulomb = volt/meter
ψ = electric flux in coulombs
D = electric flux density in coulombs/meter^2
C = capacitance in coulombs/volt = farad
ϵ = dielectric constant in farads/meter
ϕ = magnetic flux in volt-second = webers
B = magnetic flux density in webers/meter^2
H = magnetic field intensity in ampere-turn/meter
L = inductance in volt-second/ampere = henries
μ = permeability in henries/meter
R = resistance in volts/amperes = ohms
G = conductance in 1/ohms = mhos
σ = conductivity in mhos/meter
ρ = resistivity in ohm-meter
P = electrical power in volt-amperes = watts

Appendix III

FERMI LEVEL

The Fermi level denotes the energy level where the probability of finding an electron in a permitted level spaced ΔW below the Fermi level is the same as the probability of finding an unoccupied permitted energy level ΔW above the Fermi level, for small values of ΔW.

INDEX